FLAWS IN THE THEORY
OF EVOLUTION

by

Evan Shute, f.r.c.s.c.

The Temside Press, London, Canada
1961

Copyright 1961 by the Temside Press.

TABLE OF CONTENTS

TABLE OF CONTENTS

INTRODUCTION

Creation versus Evolution, a Primary Dilemma

. . . "to accept as the truth that which is not a truth, or to fail in distinguishing the sense in which a proposition may be true from other senses in which it is not true, is an evil having consequences which are indeed incalculable. There are subjects in which one mistake of this kind will poison all the wells of truth, and affect with fatal error the whole niche of our thoughts."

The Reign of Law—the Duke of Argyle.

"Observe creation mercifully hidden
either in an imaginary Eden,
or buried in some absent-minded spasm
of a self-generated protoplasm."

—Humbert Wolfe.*

PROPOSITION—Evolution faces creation as two alternative theories of the origin of the world of living things. When it is analyzed, the evidence is against mega-evolution. Botanists and bacteriologists must be especially aware of this. The evidence pro and con should be presented for dispassionate analysis once again.

One hundred years after Darwin's publication of the Origin of Species the theory of evolution seems to have won the day as an explanation of the world of life. It is almost universally accepted by educated men as a fact rather than a theory. For example, it can serve as the basis of a series of illustrated articles in Life, a magazine for the American masses, in 1959. He is a brave man, indeed, or at least a very reckless one, who dares to challenge its general validity.

At the same time, some important biologists do challenge its truth, and this heresy seems to be especially common amongst botanists, who persistently fail to find the genealogical connections between the great groupings of plants that the evolutionist must anticipate.

At this point a disconcerting thought could arise in our minds. Perhaps the theory of evolution is only partially valid. It may apply to certain aspects of Nature and not to other aspects. Certainly both friends and foes of the theory would concede there are so many unsolved problems facing the evolutionist that further discussion of them is still in order.

---

*Quoted by permission of Mrs. Ann Wolfe.

Now there are certain major difficulties in the theory which present themselves immediately; for example, the absence of life in the pre-Cambrian rocks, the problems connected with instinct, the absence of demonstrable evolution in bacteria, as well as the very complex phenomena connected with parasitism, social insects, blood groups, speciation, and a host of other puzzles which cry aloud for consideration by some one who can face them afresh, not convinced that evolution is the only answer, the necessary answer and the complete answer. Should we not look more closely at the various facets of this fascinating theme?

Darwin himself forshadowed this approach when he wrote in the Origin: "I am well aware that there is scarcely a single point discussed in this volume on which facts cannot be adduced, often apparently leading to conclusions directly opposite to those at which I have arrived. A fair result could be obtained only by fully stating and balancing the facts on both sides of each question, and this cannot possibly be here done." I fear it has been attempted too rarely since his day.

College textbooks so generally assume the truth of universal evolution that it is difficult for students to find a rational, up-to-date and many-sided treatment of the problems concerned, many not yet solved. Surely it is time that someone made a fresh attempt to marshal the current evidence on both sides in order that students can weigh the truth. I hesitated for years before attempting this treatise, knowing that no one was able to deal authoritatively and exhaustively with this high matter, since it involves a host of facts in geology, bacteriology, parasitology, medicine, genetics, and so on, almost ad infinitum. But one thing that led me to make the attempt was the realization of the almost comparable inadequacy of any other who might try it, and the hope that my effort might arouse helpful comment.

I suspect that the creationist has less mystery to explain away than the wholehearted evolutionist. On the balance of the things that I have both read and discovered for myself I am a creationist, so far as mega-evolution is concerned. By mega-evolution one refers to the origin of kingdoms, phyla, classes and orders, the largest groups in any classification of living things. I concede micro-evolution, of course, which is the origin by evolutionary processes of species, genera, and even families. An increasing number of thoughtful scientists seem to be adopting this view, which I should add is decades old, and far from being original with me.

Anyone approaching this general problem must be cautious, because relevant, detailed knowledge is always inadequate. The case at issue must be tried in a court where the evidence is never all in, where the judge and jury and spectators change with each generation, and where, of late, few have tried to sum up, much less ask for a decision.

Our views alter rapidly in these days. In the last 20 years, for instance, I have seen the rise of antibiotics, whose use has now become a commonplace. Yet I can well recall being taught that such an idea was fallacious on the face of it, for what agent could harm a bacterium that would not be equally harmful to its host? We should remind ourselves that our so-called "laws" are subject to subversion, as when Wang and Lee won the Nobel Prize in Physics in 1958 for a challenge to a widely accepted view or "law"—or when Einstein talked of curved light, or relative time. And the Soviets have recently photographed the rear of the moon!

As Simpson,* the great evolutionist (1), concedes: "As long as everything is not known about life, which undoubtedly means forever, it is necessary to keep other possibilities in mind, and especially to keep before us evidence adduced in support of other theories".

Gregory (2)** knew what he was talking about when he urged "many more researches on the hydra-headed problems of organic evolution," a remark made not in 1859 but in 1955.

Carter (3)*** stated recently that "only now is it just beginning to be possible for the new generation of evolutionists to start a critical evaluation—about evolution" which is "the most spectacular—since the years following the publication of the Origin of Species." In a recent symposium Sonneborn (4)**** comments: "For I know, as you cannot, how pitifully small a fraction we have learned about the complexity, variety and marvels of this 'simple, primitive, stereotyped animal' " (referring to Paramoecium). If a one-celled animal of that sort presents complex problems, as it certainly does, one can see how much remains to be learned about all of that Nature that the theory of Evolution blankets so blithely and recklessly. A striking instance of our growing knowledge is derived from the recent zoological survey of the island of Madagascar (5). It has uncovered 2500 new forms, even new subfamilies, often a 500 per cent increase in known forms, and whole new biogeographical relations, for example leaf-mining drosophilids and a specialized blind soil-fauna. Yet Madagascar has been known and studied for a long time.

We are but children, wondering, bemused children. Let us see ourselves in perspective amidst this maze of concrete and steel and radio-active fallout and placid chlorophyll.

What answers we get to scientific questions, as well as to those of art or politics, are always the answers of our time and kind and place. New archaeological finds, such as Australopithecus or the carbon 14 dating may alter the age of the Neanderthals or the great

---

*Quoted by permission of the Columbia University Press, New York, U.S.A.
**Quoted by permission of the Athlone Press of the University of London, Eng.
***Quoted by permission of Sidgwick and Jackson, Ltd., London, Eng.
****Quoted by permission of the American Association for the Advancement of Science, Washington, U.S.A.

apes, or may confirm the Spinden correlation of Maya dates or date the Inca ruins. We do well to leave some boats on the shore by which we may escape if our theories run short of spears.

But Simpson, whom I have quoted above and hope to quote often, has well said: "The effort to achieve—a synthesis is so manifestly desirable that no apology is in order; the intention will hardly be criticized, whatever is said about its execution—for the purposes of this book, at least, I am not a palaeontologist. I am trying to pursue a science that is beginning to have a good many practitioners but that has no name: the science of four-dimensional biology or of time and life."

In that frame of mind let us address ourselves to a few aspects of our magnificent problem.

I propose to do so as a medical man, following the order of my own curiosity, not necessarily the order of textbooks of biology. This may at least help to explain how my conclusions have developed. Why strive for orderly logic in a field so vast? And if my conclusions are not quite as acceptable to evolutionists as were those of my great predecessors, Keene (6) and Kelly (7), at least I have their authority and prestige for my attempt.

Important references have been appended for those who, I hope, will be stimulated by this book to go beyond it to the best sources of biological information. Many quotations from great evolutionists are given, because no argument is so convincing as one's adversary's when it coincides with one's own views, and the dilemmas of evolution are often best presented by its proponents. At least, they can be trusted to minimize their difficulties and so I can scarcely be charged with exaggerating them.

CHAPTER I

Lifelessness in the Early Rocks: Bursts of Creation, Absence of Ancestors.

"No" said once conveys no sting.
"No" said twice is challenging.
But "No and No and No" encored
Are solely by the deaf ignored.

—Vere Jameson

PROPOSITION—The lower four-fifths of the rock of the earth's crust is lifeless. Then life suddenly appears, is at once general across the earth, and promptly demonstrates most of the types we now know. This is not the evidence the evolutionist wants, and is quite fatal to his claims. This is Creation.

Introduction

The rocks that underlie the basic Cambrian are remarkably lifeless. These rocks are said to constitute about four-fifths of the thickness of the rock crust of the earth. This lifelessness of the earliest rock, of which there is a great predominance, strikes a shattering blow at the theory of evolution, because there should be all sorts of early forms of life in at least the top fractions of this great column of rock. In short, Cambrian forms surely should have ancestors to suit evolutionary theories.

There are a few dubious exceptions to what has been said above, but it is still startling that the exceptions are so few. Colonial forms of blue-green algae may have been found in very old southern Ontario cherts,—an identification still in doubt. Very dubious bacteria have been found, too. "Worm-holes" resembling those now seen in the abysses of the ocean have been reported. Glaessner has reported an early coelenterate or alga from the upper Pre-Cambrian in South Australia (8).

This very important problem has received consideration by Axelrod (9) recently. He points out the puzzle presented by the occurrence of diversified, multicellular, marine invertebrates spread over all the continents in the lower Cambrian rocks,—but their absence in earlier rocks. Early Cambrian fossils include seven of the 11 to 13 great primary groups or phyla into which all animal life has been divided by experts in classification. In other words, in these earliest Cambrian rocks are Porifera, Coelenterates, Brachiopods, Molluscs, Echinoderms, Vermes and Arthropods, and most of the Arthropods found are the highly organized Trilobites, (which already had a complex

5

respiratory system, for example). There are no Protozoa, the "simplest" type of animal, but only members of these 7 "higher" types! Surely by evolutionary theory there must have been simpler forerunners of fossils so advanced. Sections of sedimentary rock over 5000 feet thick have been found in unbroken succession below the earliest Cambrian rock, Axelrod points out. These sediments were eminently suitable for the preservation of such fossils as the evolutionist **must** anticipate,— and yet there are few or no fossils there.

There have been various explanations of this vital lack of fossils. Perhaps any that were there were destroyed by changes in the rocks themselves due to pressure, or heat, or similar physical forces. Or perhaps the earliest fossils had no skeleton, and therefore were difficult to preserve. Perhaps the earliest oceans were acid, and so tended to dissolve the shells of calcareous creatures. Perhaps the earliest layers of rock were deposited in fresh water that had a very low calcium content which did not lend itself to the formation of shell. Perhaps the earliest marine life originated in fresh water and did not reach the oceans until Cambrian times. Perhaps the earliest living forms had no skeletons, and these skeletons did not appear until sluggish forms began to crawl about the sea bottom. But these are all improbable and slightly desperate conjectures, and Axelrod is forced to consider the possibility that the Cambrian fauna had no forerunners. If there had been forerunners, they should have been quite widespread over the world, because the Cambrian fauna in their turn had world wide distribution. This makes it even more difficult to explain their general absence in the fossil record, and evolutionists **must** conclude, as Axelrod has, that evolutionary processes occurred in small localized areas which either have not yet been found or else have been eroded and lost. It can be pointed out, for instance, that one of the most remarkable living persistingly simple forms ("relicts"), Hutchinsonella, was only 3mm. long; perhaps these earliest living animals were so small that they have been easy to overlook.

These despairing suggestions point up the remarkable dilemma of the evolutionist who leans on Palaeontology for its customary support. What greater degree of disproof could Palaeontology provide? Millions of years of "NO" is indeed a resounding "NO"! The book of life has blank pages in the Pre-Cambrian, and yet the bulk of these pages is at least four times as great as all later time added together. How shall the evolutionist explan that there are no entries on these pages, although the conditions were ideal for printing? Perhaps no evidence of life in the Pre-Cambrian is found because no life was there. Creation at the onset of the Cambrian seems to be the only logical alternative. Every other answer is fantastic and unsupported conjecture, whether it is advanced by leading scientists or less educated men. Let us recognize a gargantuan extrapolation when we come across it. Extrapolation is just guessing, remember, no matter who does the guessing.

6

The Antiquity of the Phyla

In the Cambrian period nearly all the phyla of animals now known were already present. Thus at the beginning of the fossil record we see Porifera, Coelenterata, Annelida, Arthropoda, Mollusca, Echinodermata and Molluscoidea. The Chordata date back to the Ordovician, And these great phyla appear suddenly! There is no evidence of any precursors. No new animal phyla have appeared since the Palaeozoic. There may even have been Diatoms, Bacteria and Algae among the earliest plant forms. Is this consistent with the demands of evolution?

The Antiquity of Classes, Orders and Families

In classification the next group below the "phylum" is the "class". If we consider classes the same general picture develops, and is perhaps even more impressive. Apart from Chordates, the evolution of classes had almost finished by the end of the lower Palaeozoic. Is it not startling from the evolutionary point of view that, practically speaking, no new class has arisen for hundreds of millions of years? The Arthropoda and Chordata are the exceptions to this rule, and Arthropods are not real exceptions since the Trilobita and Crustacea appear in the lower Cambrian, the Arachnida in the Silurian, the Insecta and Myriapoda go well back to the Palaeozoic and were not rare in the Carboniferous. Even in the lagging Chordata, all classes but the Birds and Mammals were established well back in the Palaeozoic. Even the Reptiles extend back into the Carboniferous. On the whole, very few if any classes have appeared since the Carboniferous.

Below the class, taxonomists place the "order". Now if we look at orders the story is almost the same. Brough (10) points out that if we consider the aquatic phyla, the Echinodermata, Coelenterata, Porifera and Molluscoidea, add the mainly aquatic Mollusca, and look at the earliest orders of the groups which are known as fossils (all the orders but one, the Aplacophora), the total is 47 orders. Of the 47, 40 were in existence in the lower Palaeozoic, 3 appeared in the Devonian, and 4 in the Mesozoic. In the Coelenterata and Molluscoidea no new orders have arisen since the Ordovician. In the Mollusca all the classes and 8 orders were in existence by the Ordovician. Only 3 orders have appeared since, in the Trias, Jurassic and Cretaceous. Among Echinoderms, all classes had appeared by the middle Ordovician, and 12 of the 13 orders by the end of the Silurian. The 13th appeared early in the Mesozoic. Among Porifera no orders have arisen since the Silurian.

Among Arthropoda the situation is more confused, for apart from Trilobites these are not common fossils. But a number of orders of Crustacea date back to the early Palaeozoic. Of the fossil Arachnids, 7 orders antedate the end of the Carboniferous. Only 2 appear later in

7

the early Tertiary. Some orders of Insecta date back to the Palaeozoic, 16 appeared in the Carboniferous and Permian, 13 orders in the Jurassic and 10 orders in the early Tertiary.

Amongst aquatic vertebrates all classes had appeared by the Devonian, all orders by the early Mesozoic. Among terrestrial vertebrates all classes had appeared by the early Mesozoic and orders arose as late as the Eocene, but none since.

Of the 10 "families" of the order Foraminifera in the Protozoa all are still in existence—yet 9 of these are fossil, 6 being known in the Palaeozoic, 2 from the lower Mesozoic and one from the Upper Mesozoic.

In the Porifera all 5 suborders of the order Lithistida were found in the lower Palaeozoic and all but one of these persist. Of the 29 fossil families of Coelenterates, 14 appear in the Palaeozoic, 12 in the Mesozoic, one in the Tertiary. Among the Echinoderms, excluding the Cryptozonea and Holothuridae, there are 111 fossil families. 51 appeared in the lower Palaeozoic, 22 in the upper Palaeozoic, 25 in the Mesozoic and 5 in the Tertiary. 29 of these 111 families survive.

In the Molluscoidea the families often go back to the Palaeozoic. Among modern Bryozoa 3 families extend from the Palaeozoic, 18 from the Mesozoic and 5 from the Tertiary. Of the 7 modern Brachiopoda all extend to the Palaeozoic and 4 to the Ordovician. Only one undisputed new order of Mollusca originated in the Mesozoic, and that was very early too.

Brough* says, "Natural selection may have come in to play the role seen by geneticists at the present time. It probably dictated the evolution of species and genera, and to a large extent, families. The production of phyla, classes, orders and maybe in some cases families was accomplished in the evolutionary surges when Natural Selection was pushed aside into a minor role." Of course there are people like the writer, who would refer to these "evolutionary surges" as "creative epochs". Otherwise these episodes represent what Brough calls "one of the most baffling and familiar problems to the student of life— the sudden appearance of a highly-developed fauna in the Cambrian." In aquatic animals, he goes on, "post-Palaeozoic evolution was concerned almost entirely with family and lesser systematic units. Since about the end of the Eocene, a period of apparently 50,000,000 years, evolution in both land arthropods and land vertebrates has probably concerned only family and lesser systematic units."

It is not necessary for my argument to dilate on the antiquity of certain genera, although one could. Many modern genera go back to the Ordovician or the Silurian, for example, the Foraminifera Iagena and Rotalia, the Brachiopods Lingula, Crania, Leda, Nucula and

---

*Quoted by permission of the Athlone Press of the University of London, Eng.

Acmaea, the Gastropod Nautilus and the Crustaceans Bairdia, Cytherella and Cypridena. Over 2500 species of the single genus Nautilus have been described from the Cambrian to the present. The land snails date from the Carboniferous. Scorpions were found in the Silurian and some existing species date back to the Carboniferous.

Smith (11)* says: "As our present information stands—the best place to start the evolution of the vertebrates is in the imagination."

Bursts of Creation

As Dewar (12)** long ago pointed out, if the evolutionary theory be true, every great group must have begun small and then very gradually diversified and multiplied. Moreover the fauna and flora of every horizon should merge almost imperceptibly into those above and below it. Hence obvious pedigrees should be generally traceable. Moreover, the early forms should be relatively poorly adapted to their new niches in life or new environments. Unfortunately for the theory, none of these requirements are met by the palaeontological record.

For new classes and orders appear in great variety at their beginnings, often differ markedly from "horizons" just above and below, have pedigrees too brief, demonstrating only small degrees of difference, and often as we trace the ancestries of allied living forms back we find parallelism rather than convergence. This was the striking cause of a recent despairing article by Wood (13) on the parallel evolution of the "related" rabbit and pika.

There are many examples of the variety of organisms as they first appear. The Ammonites (an extinct order of Cephalopod Molluscs) appear in the Devonian in great variety, the fossils spread over no fewer than fifteen families. In the Carboniferous period the class Insecta appears for the first time, its fossils then representing no fewer than twelve orders. In that same Carboniferous appear three of the six orders of the class Amphibia. In the Jura appear twelve new families of Pelycopod Molluscs, fourteen new families of Gastropod Molluscs and twenty new families of Ammonites, as well as eight new orders of Insects. In the Eocene appear twenty-seven new orders of Mammals.

Now this sort of thing is exactly what we would not expect if the doctrine of mega-evolution were true.

Dewar makes a very important point in respect to the carry-over of families and orders from one geologic horizon to the next. What he demonstrates is that there is very, very little such carry-over. Yet such a continuity is basic to evolutionary theory. No continuity—no evolutionary sequences. Then Dewar goes on to say that the "replacement of faunas is not confined to orders and families; it extends to

---

*Quoted by permission of Little, Brown & Co., Boston, U.S.A.
**Quoted by permission of Edwin Arnold (Publishers) Ltd., London, Eng.

genera." He stresses that "it is not possible to arrange a geneaological series of fossils proving that any **species** has in the past undergone sufficient change to transform it into a member of another **family.**" He goes on: "It is not possible to draw up a pedigree showing the descent of any species, living or extinct, from an ancestor belonging to a different order or class. The earliest-known fossils of each class and order are not half-made or half-developed forms, but exhibit, fully developed, all the characteristics of their class or order. Any changes undergone by a great group after it has appeared are comparatively insignificant."

Indeed, the sudden appearence of unrelated major groups in the fossil record is a serious handicap to the evolutionist, one of the best examples being the sudden appearance of the vertebrates in the form of four **orders.**

The Sudden Appearance of Major Types of Structure

Now let me briefly touch on several topics I will discuss at more length in later chapters but which have a direct bearing at this point. I wish to stress at this juncture the sudden appearance of major types of animals and plants and of new and complex organs. This is an important phase of the argument, for it negates evolution, and is also consistent with the utter lifelessness of the first rocks in the earth's crust.

Dewar says: "It is difficult to understand how an aquatic creature could gradually acquire tracheae (air-breathing organs) and legs. It might be though that the acquisition of these would have taxed the powers of an organism to the uttermost. Far from it, primitive insects were not content with being able to run, they must needs fly. As all the earliest fossils known to us possessed wings, these must have grown before the insects split up into orders. The gradual conversion of aquatic organisms into insects representing twelve orders must have occupied many millions of years. If it took place, is it credible that no fossil should have been found of a species intermediate between this hypothetical father of all insects and any of the twelve orders that occur in the Carboniferous, or between it and its aquatic ancestor?

"The Carboniferous insects were certainly less differentiated than those now existing; wingless orders apparently did not then exist, and the known fossils represent twelve orders, while the living insects represent thirty-one, but it is absurd to assert that a differentiation that requires these creatures to be grouped in twelve orders has little depth. A few of these early insects were of greater size than any living ones. In some the wings could not be folded back, in others they could. In some the legs were adapted for jumping, like those of locusts. In one genus the first pair of legs was furnished with a

10

spinning apparatus, indicating that their possessors had habits similar to those of spiders.

"Spiders, like insects, display great diversity on their first appearance. The Carboniferous fossils represent not only most living orders but three extinct orders. These early spiders are fully-formed and exhibit spinnerets similar to those of modern forms. As in the case of insects, no fossils have been discovered linking the early spiders with any other group or species. Presumably they preyed upon insects; therefore, if the evolution doctrine be true, they should not have originated until after the insects had become well established." . . .

To jump to the amphibians (toads, frogs, newts, salamanders), Dewar goes on: "The limbs of every amphibian and terrestrial vertebrate invariably bend at the elbow and wrist or knee and ankle, as the case may be. There is no known fish in which the fin is jointed in this way . . . A vast "amount of change must have taken place in order to convert a fin into a leg. The limbs of the earliest-known amphibia are no more like those of fish than are those of living amphibia. Some of them have five toes, others three. The earliest-known amphibian fossil, Thinopus Antiquus of the Lower Carboniferous, has but three. According to the evolution theory it ought to have five." . . .

The Dibranchiate Molluscs (cuttle-fish and squids) appear suddenly in the Trias. Turtles begin as turtles and have been almost uniformly the same since their beginnings. Yet fossil turtles are very common, and if there were intermediate prior forms they should have been found long ago. Dinosaurs also seem to have always been separate from other reptiles.

The difficulty about birds from the evolutionist's viewpoint is very great. Regarding Archaeopteryx and Archaeornis, the so-called primitive birds, Dewar says: "The characters adduced as evidence of the relationship of these birds to reptiles—the large number of movable vertebrae in the tail, and the teeth—are features that may vary in closely allied forms; thus, some monkeys are tailless while others have long prehensile tails; some whales have teeth, others are toothless. These features, then, count for little against the possession of feathers—essentially avian structures.—That these Jurassic fossils are not links between reptiles and birds in evident from the fact that they (evolutionists) do not even agree on the order of reptiles from which birds evolved . . . At least three reptilian orders have been named in this connection. Nor is this all; no fossil exists intermediate between these Jurassic birds and any other order of the Aves . . . All the Cretaceous birds exhibit teeth structures not found in any living bird. In some cases the teeth are implanted in separate sockets, in others in a common groove. This is not easy to account for on the view that all birds are derived from a common ancestor. One order of the Cretaceous birds—the Hesperornithiformes—seems to have lacked the power of flight. As this group occurs later than Archaeopteryx, which could

11

fly, if the doctrine of evolution be true it would seem that some birds lost the power of flight soon after they had acquired it . . .

"In the earliest layer of the Eocene (Palaeocene) appear suddenly four new orders of placental mammals (those having after-births and so able to keep their young inside their bodies until birth)—the Creodonta, Condylarthra, Amblypoda and Taeniodonta—all of which became extinct long ago. No fossils are known intermediate between any of them and any earlier form . . . Even more surprising to the evolutionist than the apparition of the above groups of mammals must be the great array of new mammals that appear suddenly in the Eocene: Carnivores (Fissipedes), Odd-toed Ungulates, Even-toed Ungulates, Hyracoidea, Edentates, Rodents, Proboscidea, Cetacea (Zeuglodontidae and Toothed Whales), Sea-cows, Primates, Pangolins, Aard-varks and the following orders that have since become extinct: Litopterna, Typotheria, Entelonychia, Astrapotherioidea, Palaeonodontia, Toxodontia, Pyrotheria and Embrithopoda . . . The Chiroptera (bats) have not been included in the above list, as it is not certain whether the deposits in which the earliest-known fossils of this order occur are of the Upper Eocene or Lower Oligocene epoch. In either case the bats appear, fully formed, very shortly after the other groups mentioned above. Bats, being the only mammals that can fly, differ profoundly from all others in skeletal structure. It is scarcely necessary to state that so-called flying squirrels and lemurs cannot fly, nor have they wings. A fur-covered membrane connecting the fore and hind limbs enables them to glide through the air. The structure of this parachute is altogether different from that of the wing of a bat. If bats gradually evolved from an ordinary mammal, the transitional forms cannot possibly have resembled flying squirrels or lemurs. The following are a few of the structural peculiarities of bats: the shoulder-blades and fore limbs are twisted outwards 90 degrees; the upper arm bone is bent into a very elongated S; the bones of the lower arm are much lengthened and curved; the hind limb is twisted outwards 180 degrees, so that the toes point backwards; the fingers are nearly as long as the arm . . . No fossil has been discovered intermediate between a bat and any other animal, despite the high degree of specialization of the former and the fact that they make their appearance at the close of the Eocene—an epoch peculiarly rich in mammalian fossils . . .

"The Pinnipedia are composed of three families: the sea-lions, seals and walruses. These appear simultaneously. Despite their recent appearance no fossil is known that sheds any light on their origin. This is equally true of the whalebone whales . . .

"The monotremes are today represented by the living duck-billed platypus (Ornithorhynchus) and the spiny ant-eater (Echidna). As these are far more lowly animals than the marsupials (kangaroos, opossums, etc.), their appearance long after these is not in accordance with the doctrine of evolution. The evolutionist explains this fact by asserting that the monotremes evolved from an unknown ancestor in an unknown part of the world, and after they had fully evolved, migrated to Australia." . . . He quotes Cuénot, "It is singular that the main stem and petioles (tinier stems) (of the genealogical tree) are always without representatives, that the missing link remains always a missing link." Dewar goes on: "It is most significant that no fossil has been discovered that represents a half-formed type of animal. The earliest-known insects are complete insects . . ."

Dewar is especially notable on flight. He says: "According to the evolutionist wings evolved independently on four occasions, that is in insects, pterodactyls, birds and bats. Although organisms in which the powers of flight are fully developed are not so liable as ordinary animals to become fossilized (on occasions when the latter are buried by landslides or drowned by floods, winged creatures can fly to a place of safety), an animal in the process of acquiring the power of flight is peculiarly liable to meet with fatal accidents. Human experience in aviation demonstrates this. Smith suggests that bats and pterodactyls may have used incipient wings for gliding before they could fly. But no gliders are found, and there should have been enough accidents to them to leave a few bones about. The acquisition of wings by the accumulation of variations or mutations must in each case have taken many thousands of years. For a considerable part of this period the casualties as the result of accidents among the animals so evolving must have been exceedingly numerous. In consequence the deposits laid down during the periods in question should contain many fossils of these incipient flying animals: the Devonian should hold thousands of fossils of what may be termed pro-insects, the Trias a multitude of those of pro-pterosaurs, the Trias and Lower Jura a great many of those of pro-aves, and the Eocene a large number of those of pro-chiroptera. It is submitted that these pro-creatures exist only in the imagination of evolutionists" . . .

Very much more could be said in this same general field and many more examples given, but enough evidence has been brought forward here to indicate that the lifelessness of the Pre-Cambrian strata is a startling challenge to the evolutionist, that the sudden appearance of most of the phyla of animals now in existence in the earliest Cambrian layers is not explainable on the basis of evolutionary theory, and that a broad survey of the characters of early forms presents a picture much different from what the evolutionist would anticipate.

Plants tell the same Story

Seward* (14) points out how "lamentably incomplete" the geological record of plants still remains. Many another modern botanist emphasizes the same point. It is curious that this plaint should persist

---

*Quoted by permission of the University Press, Cambridge, England.

undiminished since Darwin's and Huxley's day, despite all the evolutionary sleuthing and exploration since. This complaint, of course, always presupposes (as no scientist should) that when and if further palaeontological evidence appears it will confirm the evolutionary theories already proposed. This is a tremendous and totally unscientific extrapolation, and it should always be remembered that it is such. Evolutionists continually beg this vital point.

Seward points out, for example, that in the great section in the Arizona Grand Canyon there are no records in the strata between the Cambrian and Carboniferous except for two small Devonian patches. This sort of discontinuity is often seen over large areas of the earth's surface. In developing the geological evidence this writer mentions that perhaps the earth once had its poles in other parts—an opinion unwelcome to astronomers. Or one can accept Wegener's theory of continental drift—"or, alternatively, we may adopt the view that too high a value has been placed on plants, as 'thermometers of the ages'." What this really means, it would seem, is that the geological problems raised by palaeobotany are so great that a botanist must question the evolutionary sequence of plant forms!

Other major problems are the probable lack of contemporaneity across the earth of comparable strata and flora—millions of years may divide them. Fossil identity, too, may be illusory, due to incomplete knowledge of a fossil plant's structure and especially of its reproductive organs. "It is clear that we cannot hope to do more than trace in broken outlines the history of the rise and fall of plant dynasties." How tenuous the basis of plant palaeontology has become to support the massive superstructure of mega-evolution!

He goes on: "Geology tells us nothing of the origin of life." Then he stresses the well-known and startling contrasts between the Cambrian rocks packed with living forms and their lifeless predecessors. Yet one-fifth of the whole land surface is of Pre-Cambrian rocks, and therefore easily accessible to study. Seward refers to "the realm of sheer speculation and the hopeless endeavour to trace the plant and animal worlds to their common starting point . . . We cannot measure the rate of the earlier stages of evolution, nor can we accept as proof of the existence of plants much of the evidence that has been adduced, and not infrequently presented with a confidence worthy of a better cause." It should be added that these sentences come after a thorough discussion of Pre-Cambrian relics!

One could mention here just one feature in the evolution of plants, the puzzling development of those primitive plants, the Algae. Here is a crucial problem, and yet little can be conjectured about it. It is certain that names have been given too freely to impressions in shale and other rocks which may be ascribable to plants or animals,—or neither. For example the fossil imprints of early Algae and of Graptolites (animal) are indistinguishable.

14

To sum up, in the Devonian period a varied and complex vegetation spread over the world; we know little of its antecedents. But those missing pages are crucial to the evolutionist.

Ancient Plant Complexity

As has been intimated in respect to animals, some early plants also were very complicated structures, such as the stem of Palaeopitys Milleri, or of the genus Cladoxylon, another Devonian form, the latter having a stem containing several woody strands like some existing tropical climbers. A Middle Devonian tree like Dadoxylon was so differentiated that it left little to choose between its anatomical complexity and that of living araucarias. The Palaeozoic lycopods, in their seed-(like)-bearing organs had acquired a much greater degree of specialization than we find in any surviving Lycopodiales. The Pteridosperms of the later Palaeozoic had an amazing range of design in the leaflets and reproductive organs. One of its families, the Medullosa, had a stem whose structure was uncommonly complex - perhaps more diverse than that of any existing plants. The Calamites in size and complex plan were superior to the modern Equisetum.

Absolutely nothing but speculation governs our ideas of the origin of the Pteridosperms, and their vague connections to ferns or seed-bearers.

Many extinct forms had a greater range of design than is illustrated by any surviving members of the same stock, for example the Jurassic genus Klukia.

The Carboniferous Lepidodendrons were far more specialized than their modern forms. Many Palaeozoic stems were much more complex than our stereotyped modern forms, for example Medullosa, Calamites, Lepidodendra.

More on this head will appear in a later chapter (XVIII).

Paleozoology vs. Palaeobotany

Seward remarks: "Both fossil plants and the remains of fresh-water and marine molluscs have been used as guides to geological horizons. These two classes of records do not always tell the same story; the animal fossils may indicate boundary-lines at certain levels in a pile of strata inconsistent with the evidence of the plants: for our purpose plants are the most valuable guides." Elsewhere in his book he reiterates this point—but then he is a botanist.

He also points out that palaeobotanical records are often illegible, and many should never have been read at all. "It is notorious that many of the published lists of Tertiary plants are misleading and untrustworthy . . ."

Nothing is known of the origin of the Mesozoic Cycadophytes, "nor by what steps, if any, their progeny led to the cycads of the present day." Hence the development of the term Cycadophyte, indeed. These old trees had epidermal cells and stomata in the leaves much like those of modern cycads, leaf form and structure and habit of stems nearly identical, but very different reproductive organs. Seward goes on:

"The oldest Dicotyledons which clearly reveal their relationship with flowering plants are old only in a geological sense and astonishingly modern in their anatomical features." Hence he infers, as an evolutionist must, a prior evolutionary history of several geological aeons before the recognizable forms appeared!! But where are they? Similarly "our knowledge of the early history of Monocotyledons is very meagre and of little value as a trustworthy guide to the course of evolution." Moreover there is no light on the ancestry of the existing blue-green Algae, although they are found as early as the Tertiary. Fossils do not help to settle the relative antiquity of Monocotyledons and Dicotyledons. The flowering plants "appeared as a new creation."

Seward (opposite p. 524) gives a map which shows the sudden and unrelated origins of plants,—no branching tree of life is postulated here. Indeed, botanists in general have discarded the whole idea of a phylogenetic tree, and refer to the parallelisms they find as a "bundle of faggots". Yet where is the theory of evolution without that necessary ancestral "tree of life"?

Seward concludes: "The problem of evolution cannot be solved by a study of the plant-world in its present state; nor can we expect to discover a solution from the records of the rocks; the fragmentary relics of the past enable us with more confidence to make guesses at the truth; they supply facts which convince us that all authority must go for nothing' . . . Since the publication of the Origin of Species the progress that has been made is rather in the accumulation of additional and more trustworthy data than in a closer approach to a solution . . . The theoretically primitive type eludes our grasp; our faith postulates its existence but the type fails to materialize . . . We may fail to discover in the tattered pages of the history book of the plant world facts that enable us to construct geneologies which carry conviction." . . .

Darrah* (15) observes that "The refuge of every doubter is in the incompleteness of the fossil record, but this is a gross exaggeration." As he reviews the posited ancestry of the Angiosperms in detail he points out how we often relate hypothetical ancestors to presumed primitive plants, but "We do not know what is primitive or what is advanced, nor what is generalized nor what is modified by reduction.

---

*Quoted by permission of Appleton-Century-Crofts Inc. New York, U.S.A.

Palaeobotanists have no answer for these questions." Perhaps 70 per cent of plant evolution antedates the Devonian, yet almost all of our plant fossils follow that time. So little is known of Cambrian, Ordovician and Silurian plants that a survey of them scarcely occupies a page. Darrah discusses the possible traces of the earliest algae, fungi, and so on, in great detail, in his chapter 26, which should be read by those interested. The fungi are very ancient, yet probably all are referable to the 39 families of existing Fungi. There is no good theory of the origin of seeds, nor can palaeobotany yield an interpretation of evolution within the Angiosperms. We will say more of this in Chapter XVIII.

Summary

It is clear that the solid ground the evolutionist seeks in the earliest pages of palaeontology is not to be found there. Indeed, his theory could easily sink into that wide morass of ignorance and theory interspersed with surprising (and often unwelcome) islands of fact. Mega-evolution is a shaky conjecture indeed.

17

CHAPTER II

Mechanistic Theories of the Origin of Life

I felt the river clutching at my skin,
As I plunged into it and thought how thin
The membranes fencing liver, brain and blood.
I laughed—I was such bold, immortal mud!

—Vere Jameson.

The flint is struck from flint, the good from God,
How else can goodness wrap such bone as ours?

—Vere Jameson*

PROPOSITION—The biochemical probabilities of the spontaneous origin of life are so infinitesimally small that life obviously could not have suddenly started up on its own. It must have been created.

Introduction

Where, when and how did life originate? This is one of the major problems for any evolutionist, theologian, or philosopher. The man in the street is just as curious for the answer.

It is quite logical for the evolutionist to believe in the spontaneous origin of life upon earth, because as he traces all living things back to simpler and simpler forms he come inevitably to the place where he wonders how the **first** simple forms appeared. Since natural causes alone have been sufficient for answers up to that point, he is apt to assume that natural forces alone could have been responsible for the initial step, without the intervention of any outside source of energy or any outside will. The most optimistic modern scientist still feels that there is very little possibilty of creating life in any laboratory, but he likes to think that he has come closer than his predecessors to creating some of the necessary substrates of life.

Even the organic molecules that we know—the tiniest portions of living tissues, have a bewildering complexity. We must postulate in any theory of the spontaneous origin of life the development of such complicated molecules **synchronously or in proper series, in tremendous variety, in proper proportion and in just the right arrangement,** because structure here is just as important as composition. Perhaps constructing an electronic brain would be simple by comparison with the problem that we have here set ourselves in this very small dimension. Mathematically such a problem is maximally improbable on the face of it, and yet there is always a mathematical

---

*Quoted by permission of the Ryerson Press, Toronto, Canada.

chance, and in this one instance we have **enormous** time in which to work and to wait for that one chance. If one waits long enough, what may not happen, asks such an evolutionist as Wald (16).

A difficulty that presents itself at the outset is the important place of **enzymes** in the synthesis of any living material; since enzymes are complex proteins in themselves they are an added complication. Enzymes, however, are not absolutely essential, perhaps, since they control the **rate** of reaction and very little else. If we have enough time, we do not have to care about rates. But **time is also a limiting factor** in our equation, because any reactions favourable to the development of the living cell must occur at **the** time and place when its perpetuation is favoured and, more essential still, its amalgamation with other simultaneously developing living substances is possible and probable. Perhaps under primitive conditions in the universe there was not the same widespread breakdown of matter that there is now. There may have been adjacent molecules which could aggregate. Now what brings order to such cell complexes, because order is an essential item here. Indeed, such order is eventually demanded as will produce self-repair and a self-constructing machine. Perhaps this order need not be imposed from outside on our primitive material, because some degree of order may be implicit in molecules themselves. This has been shown, for example, in the dissociated molecules of muscle fibre, or of cartilage, even of kidney.

However, if by some obscure chance a number of molecules once aggregated to form a primal tissue, that tissue was still far from being a living thing. This tissue could live only by consuming adjacent molecules by fermentation in order to acquire energy, the energy that it needed to grow and reproduce. At this crucial stage the tissue or cell was compelled to develop the process of **photosynthesis, just before it ate away any substrate** it had been fortunate enough to accumulate. If it could do this, it could live henceforth on the energy of sunlight to form its own organic molecules. Such a process would liberate new cells or tissues from dependence upon any accumulation of organic matter and fermentation to produce any energy they might require. For **fermentation produces poisonous waste products** and our tender early cells must already have been killed by them, unless by this time through photosynthesis they had produced oxygen and had **learned the secret of respiration,** which does not produce a lethal waste as fermentation does. The first respiration produced a surplus for the first time. It engineered the organism at a profit by which it gained something. It made organisms self-sustaining. Moreover with the appearance of oxygen from cell metabolism an ozone layer formed in the atmosphere to protect early life from the lethal rays of the sun. The theorist makes no calculation at this juncture as to how many early cells were needed to produce such a layer deeply covering the earth, perhaps because it is a supremely awkward piece of mathematics!

There have recently been studies aimed at producing amino-acids, the units of protein, by artificial methods. Electrical discharges in mixtures of water, methane, ammonia and hydrogen have produced such amino-acids as glycine, alpha-alanine and beta-alanine. Thus it appears that some of the building-blocks of proteins **could** have been formed by lightning out of the earth's first atmosphere—**if the apparatus were as large as the ocean and the experiment had gone on a million years** in place of a week. Be it noted, such organic synthesis could have occurred only when the atmosphere of the earth was "reducing", and contained ammonia. Many other problems present themselves to the chemist, as Miller and Urey (17) point out, namely the origin of the necessary porphyrins, the development of optic activity and many **others** of major difficulty. The evolutionist must not be allowed to sidestep these, for these insuperable **difficulties** are much better qualified to be called "science" than the elaborate hypotheses of coincidental magic touched on above.

Helium beams emanating from a cyclotron have reduced mixtures of carbon dioxide and water to formic acid and formaldehyde. Thus, by means of lightning acting on primeval gases, it could be assumed that the simplest organic matter **could** have been formed to provide a **substrate** for life. However, such agents as light and radiation also tend to break down such substances as these when they are formed. Enzymes present a dilemma here, too, as has been pointed out above. **Enzymes are necessary** for the synthesis of protein, and yet they themselves are protein. What synthesizes them? The problem is nearly insoluble logically, and resembles the old problem whether egg or chick came first. Logic also demands an ever-increasing number of new and specific enzymes for the synthesis of each new protein molecule. Indeed, it has been said on this account that it is probably easier for an organism to produce a whole new protein than a first new small molecule. To produce that molecule one or more new enzymic proteins would be required in any case in order to catalyse the reactions. Crick (18)* points out: "The complete amino-acid formula for insulin in five species of animals has been worked out. Only two are the same (the pig and the whale). It can be argued that these sequences are the most delicate expression possible of the phenotype (inherited bodily structure) of an organism and vast amounts of evolutionary information may be hidden away within them." (the close relations between pigs and whales, for example!) . . . "As in even a small bacterial cell there are probably a **thousand different kinds** of protein, each containing some **hundreds of amino acids** in its rigidly determined sequence, the amount of hereditary information required for **sequentialization** (of these amino acids) is quite considerable." I hope the magnitude of the bland assumptions of the modern mechanist is obvious to every reader. To emphasize this I have italicized some words as we went along.

---

*Quoted by permission of the Company of Biologists, Ltd., Cambridge, England.

It must be pointed out, too, that it is the whole cell which reproduces, and not a mere additive pile of viruses, genes, proteins or nucleic acids. Evolutionists must assume that at some time during the earliest geological history catalytically active molecules were reproduced without the need for cell structure. However, it is also true that so far as we have been able to ascertain, proteins are synthesized only by intact cells. We run into a blank wall at this point.

Moreover, all these theories beg the introduction of life into suitable protein substrates. We could give the evolutionary theorist far more than he asks for, namely a perfect body, just killed by electrocution in prison, a body that already has all its organs and tissues, even lungs that were breathing 30 seconds ago, blood still fluid and a heart barely stilled. Giving life to this should be easier than giving it to a single inanimate cell or virus. Resuscitation of a heart that has stopped only seconds before merely involves reanimation of the short-period rhythmicity inherent in this unique muscle, the only muscle having this property. This is not adding life to non-life. Our resuscitation merely picks up a rhythm by physical stimuli before the muscle has forgotten its long, unique habit. But if we let only a few minutes pass even this cannot be done. This clearly points up the theorist's difficulty, which he is apt to ignore blithely in a long, chemical discussion of primal molecules and their pseudo-adventures. "Life" is the problem—not merely the inert tissue life animates. The evolutionist must not be permitted to talk all around the point.

Recent studies upon DNA (desoxyribonucleic acid) indicate that it is the substance that, from the stronghold of the nucleus, determines heredity and governs all cells and therefore all life. DNA molecules probably carry the coded information which determines whether a fertilized egg shall grow into a whale or an acorn. DNA can penetrate certain bacteria, changing them permanently into a new strain. Many viruses are packets of DNA wrapped in a coat of protein. When a virus infects a cell, it leaves its wrapping outside. The DNA enters the cell and takes charge of its activities, issuing chemical orders as if it owned the cell. Its orders are simple: "Stop everything and form more virus particles packed with DNA." The cell obeys helplessly, turns its contents into such virus particles, bursts and dies.

The wonderful achievements of DNA have suggested to some scientists that the first living things were crude versions of DNA, which floated in the primeval ocean and seized on adjacent organic molecules until they were ready to divide. This would be true growth, say the geneticists, and evolution would soon improve the original breed. DNA would eventually wrap itself in cells and retire to their nuclei to give orders. Cells would later band together into multicelled animals, but they would not escape the commands of the DNA within them. Samuel Butler wrote: "A hen is only an egg's way of making another egg." Geneticists tend to make this remark more universal:

21

"All plants, and animals," they suggest, "are DNA's way of making more DNA."

This sort of reasoning seeems scientific, rational and understandable. Actually, of course , it deals with overwhelming difficulties. These are handled glibly here in scientific jargon. Almost all the stages postulated above are unimaginably difficult or inexpressibly unlikely.

There is one evolutionary by-product of recent studies on nucleic acids, however, and that is that we now have conceived a lower stage still in the evolutionary scale. Bendich et al (19)* say: "In view of the fact that the free nucleic acids are active both in bacterial transformation, in producing viral progeny when applied to leaves of the tobacco plant, and in producing Eastern equine encephalomyelitis in mice, it is proposed that these substances should be accorded taxonomic recognition along with the viruses and the fully competent cells. Viewed in this manner, a least common denominator for all members of the extended evolutionary scale is nucleic acid . . . In the event that these or other preparations of DNA can be resolved further into discrete molecules endowed with specific genetic activity, a further evolutionary subclassification might be possible." In other words, we should speak of all life as evolving not from cells but from mere nucleic acids, long before cells were thought of. The problem now becomes a very difficult one indeed. Can a nucleic acid **"live"** independently? It would be a hardy evolutionist and a hardier chemist who would say yes.

Beadle (20), in his Nobel Prize oration in 1959, touched on another major difficulty of the evolutionist, the appearance of biologically important compounds which must be synthesized by steps, the intermediate phases having no useful purpose. The simultaneous appearance of several independent enzymes demanded by such steps would be highly improbable, of course. He says that the end product must have been present somewhere first, then it was synthesized in reverse, one step at a time, since each such step made one less exogenous product needful! There seeems to be no alternative to such a theory. And yet it makes enormous demands on credibility, from the presence **already** of the end product to be **evolved,** to the back-stepping phases of its synthesis. Why the need for synthesis now, when it was already there—by Creation? And where did each new enzyme for each new step appear from? Why all this to do what had already been done?

De Nouy Speaks Next

De Nouy (21)** has analysed the statistical probabilities of the spontaneous generation of life on earth. He begins by saying, "It is

---

*Quoted by permission of the Company of Biologists, Ltd., Cambridge, England.
**Quoted by permission of Longmans, Green & Co., Inc., New York.

impossible because of the tremendous complexity of the question to lay down the basis for (such) a calculation." He cites Professor Guye who has tried this—for an imaginary protein molecule of considerable dissymmetry (0.9) (The elementary molecules of living organisms show considerable dissymmetry, maximum dissymmetry being represented by 1.0—where their constituent parts are completely separate and heterogeneous) and whose component atoms equal 2,000, supposedly having a molecular weight of only 20,000 (whereas a **simple** protein like egg albumin has a molecular weight of 34,500). There are to be only two kinds of atoms in this molecule, whereas there are always at least four, carbon, hydrogen, nitrogen, oxygen, plus either copper, iron, or sulphur, and such in a living molecule. He was deliberately giving his problem an easy setting, as you see. The mathematical probability that a configuration of dissymmetry 0.9 could appear under these arbitrary simplified conditions by pure chance is 2.02×10^{-321} or $2.02 \times \dfrac{1}{10^{321}}$.

"The volume of substance necessary for such a probability to take place is beyond all imagination. It would be that of a sphere with a radius so great that light would take 10^{82} years to cover this distance. The volume is incomparably greater than that of the whole universe including the farthest galaxies, whose light takes only 2×10^6 (two million) years to reach us. In brief, we would have to imagine a volume more than one sextillion, sextillion, sextillion times greater than the Einsteinian universe.

"The probability for a **single** molecule of high dissymmetry to be formed by the action of chance and normal thermic agitation remains practically nil. Indeed, if we suppose 500 trillion shakings per second (5×10^{14}), which corresponds to the order of magnitude of light frequencies (wave lengths comprised between 0.4 and 0.8 microns), we find that the time needed to form, on an average, one such molecule (degree of dissymmetry 0.9) in a material volume equal to that of our terrestrial globe is about 10^{243} billions of years (1 followed by 243 zeros).

"But we must not forget that the earth has only existed for two billion years and that life appeared about one billion years ago, as soon as the earth had cooled (1×10^9 years).

"We thus find ourselves in the case of the player who does not have at his disposal the time necessary to throw his die often enough to have **one single chance** of obtaining his series, but instead of a period three or four hundred times too short, we are faced with an interval which is more than 10^{243} times too short.

"On the other hand, we can always bring out the fact that, no matter how slight the chance, it nevertheless exists, and that there is no proof that the rare configuration will only appear at the end of

23

billions and billions of centuries. It can happen right at the start, in the first seconds. Not only is this in perfect accord with the calculus, but it can be admitted that the phenomenon occurred twice, and even three times in succession and then practically never again. However, if this happened and we maintained our confidence in the calculus of probabilities it would be equivalent to admitting a miracle, and the result would be: ONE SINGLE MOLECULE, or at most two or three.

". . . Now, one molecule is of no use. Hundreds of millions of identical ones are necessary. We would need much greater figures to 'explain' the appearance of a series of similar molecules, the improbability increasing considerably, as we have seen, for each new molecule (compound probability), and for each series of identical throws. . ."

"Events which, even when we admit very numerous experiments, reactions, or shakings per second, need an infinitely longer time than the estimated duration of the earth in order to have one chance, on an average, to manifest themselves can, it would seem, be considered as impossible in the human sense.

". . . We are brought to the conclusion that, actually, it is totally impossible to account scientifically for all phenomena pertaining to Life.

"We are faced by a hiatus in our knowledge. There is a gap between living and non-living matter which we have not been able to bridge . . . We can hope that (it) will be bridged by science some day, but at present this is nothing but wishful thinking."

De Nouy calls attention to several of the extraordinary gaps in basic evolutionary theories of the continuity of animal life as it extends upward from the simplest types. One of these has to do with the chemistry of blood pigments.

". . . The active base, the nutritive liquid of animals, is in the blood, and that of the superior animals contains a fundamental substance, the red pigment called haemoglobin, which transports oxygen to the cells so as to oxydize or burn the refuse. The molecule of haemoglobin is very large and highly complicated; its structure varies from one species to another (mean molecular weight: 69,000).

"Chemically, this hemoglobin is fairly close to the circulatory pigment of plants and algae, chlorophyll (molecular weight: 904). There is, therefore, a relationship; but whereas hemoglobin is characterized by the presence of one atom of iron in its molecule, chlorophyll, which is much simpler, is built around an atom of magnesium. To complicate the problem further, the blood of certain arthropods and mollusks, inferior animals which preceded superior animals, contains a pigment with a molecular weight varying, according to species, between 400,000 and 6.700,000 and containing an atom of copper instead of iron or magnesium. (Certain snails, for instance).

"How was the chemical transition from one to the other accomplished? Honestly speaking, it is impossible to conceive it, and yet the hypothesis of a sudden appearance is not satisfactory. . ."

Summary

Surely, all these considerations illustrate the complexity of the problems and difficulties faced by the evolutionist and anyone who thinks that Life arose of itself and ever since has developed on its own. One must remember at this juncture how many of these evolutionary suggestions used as arguments above are based upon the most tenuous possibilities,—not probabilities, just possibilities,—and how step after impossible step is begged in the course of these polemics, which are really more in the nature of intellectual exercises than science. Because scientists enjoy playing such a game of chess, the game does not become truth. It is still just a crossword puzzle, or a problem like that of a sonneteer who undertakes to discuss the dictionary thoroughly in fourteen lines, which must end in certain specified rhymes. A long succession of elaborate postulates, such as we have listed in this chapter, and which are necessary, mind you, if an evolutionist is to be consistent in his survey of all of life, including its origins, is still science fiction.

CHAPTER III

Bacteria, Viruses, Fungi and Such

Some are venomous,
Some are not.
Their small round bodies
Flesh begot
When it was shamed out
Of Eden grot.

—Vere Jameson.

PROPOSITION—There is no evidence that bacteria, fungi, viruses and comparable forms have evolved further since life began, or are evolving beyond the level of strains now. Yet here are the simplest forms, the most readily observed, with a speed of manipulation which sidesteps the element of time the evolutionist always calls to his aid. In the most ideal place to study evolution the phenomenon is not found —and, indeed, its discussion is carefully avoided.

Introduction

When one sets himself the task of studying life, and especially life as it varies during the generations, it is logical to turn to its smallest and simplest forms, to types which multiply rapidly under conditions capable of strict control and the most intimate scrutiny, and to types whose history and descriptions have long been thoroughly and accurately recorded. Naturally the bacteria, molds, fungi must be the life forms best able to meet such demands. The viruses, though recognized recently, fit in this group on other grounds.

And here one runs into one of the major difficulties of evolutionary theory, if not its greatest dilemma. If all life stems from one multipotential cell, how remarkable that one cell was, to contain in embryo the oak and the rose, the man and the spirochaete, Jesus and the dinosaur, all lumped together! Of all staggering conceptions to enter the mind of man, only those of God and starry space compare with this one. It is little wonder that so many biologists talk of multiple and various (polyphyletic) origins—but that merely moves the problem on a bit, to the difficulty of first evolving several such cells.

It is to be noted that in his Philosophie Zoologique in 1809 Lamarck urged the study of the smallest objects in Nature to discover her "laws, methods and progress".

More recently, Muller (22)* has said: "even the bacteria have protoplasm about as complicated as that of higher organisms, and . . .

---

*Quoted by permission of the Princeton University Press, Princeton, U.S.A.

therefore a great many more biochemical complications had to develop in the time between the origin of the first genes and that of bacteria than in the whole time elapsing from that stage to the present." Has this thought not made things almost incredibly difficult for the evolutionist?

Definitions and Descriptions—History

Bacteria are microscopic single-celled organisms of simple and fairly constant shape which are stopped by porcelain filters,—as viruses are not—and which have been described by Cameron (23) as "pockets" of enzymes which will grow if given the proper chemical substrates. Indeed, the specificity of their biochemical activities allows them to be described in terms of their enzymes and enzyme reactions. Non-parasitic bacteria are known, and many can be cultured, of course, outside an animal body.

Viruses are very difficult or impossible to define. They are enormously variable. Cameron says they are probably polyphyletic in origin. They pass through the filters which arrest bacteria and therefore are much smaller. They are often parasites on bacteria (bacteriophage). Certainly they are always and exclusively parasitic. Almost none seem to have enzyme systems. None have metabolic processes, says Stanley (24). They can multiply rapidly, but only in the presence of live cells. Hybrid types are known, due to the "recombination" of different parental strains.

Plant viruses have been isolated, and even crystallized, but most animal viruses have not. Indeed, only poliomyelitis and Coxsackie animal viruses have yet been crystallized in the latter group. Plant viruses contain RNA rather than DNA. How shall heredity act on them when genes contain only DNA? Perhaps the DNA in the nucleus helps. Or else the plant virus transmits by non-genetic methods, no relationship existing between plant virus and animal virus mechanisms. Indeed, the concept of an infectious nucleic acid, RNA, is now arising, in at least the smaller animal viruses, such as poliovirus and encephalomyocarditis virus.

Fungi are hard to define, too. Are they plants lacking chlorophyll and secondarily parasitic or saprophytic, or were they always saprophytic and colourless? Are they related to algae? There is really no evidence that they ever had chlorophyll, and any relation to algae is a pure assumption. Some cannot form cellulose, although all plants can. They reproduce by spores. They were first classified about 1822.

Bacteria have been under close observation for an incredible number of generations, although not a lengthy span of years. Leeuwenhoek first recognized them in 1676 and Muller studied them in 1765. The red colonies of bacillus prodigiosus were named Serrotia Marcescens by Bizio in 1819. Robert Koch studied anthrax bacilli in 1876 and the tubercle bacillus shortly thereafter. Nearly all the common bacteria pathogenic to humans had been described by 1900. Now this means that our organized knowledge of bacteria goes back 60 years or a little more. Considering how these germs multiply inside a few hours this represents many more generations than days, all carefully scrutinizable. Indeed, Thimann (25) tells us that one bacterial cell under conditions ideal for reproduction could in 36 hours cover the whole earth with a layer of bacteria one foot deep. Now the evolutionist always demands many generations for his slow processes. Here are life processes readily studied under controlled laboratory conditions, accessible to the closest kind of inspection, where any change would be obvious at once—and supplying all the observable generations the most time-avid evolutionist could demand. And yet perhaps no bacterium has ever been seen to jump the species line spontaneously. Many new strains have been produced by mutation, notably since the introduction of antibiotics, but only dubious new species, certainly no new genus. What a major and conclusive set-back for the evolutionist!

Nicol (26), speaking of viruses, asks if virus crystals are living or dead. It all depends on the point of view, he adds, and the absolute answer may never come. He describes the virus as like the visualization of an abstract border-line, since it is at that border itself.

Thimann observes that for viruses to grow the living host must cooperate. The virus is not strictly self-reproducing, but as Muller would say, it is "self-determining in its reproduction." It organizes the host's anzymes to enslave them. No virus preparation has its own respiration, as was mentioned.

Oginsky and Umbreit (27)* say: "The virus is not alive per se; it exhibits no metabolism, no reproduction, no growth" . . . its 'living' attributes are due only to its host. The cell reproduces the virus, the virus does not reproduce itself.

The recent infection of Australian and European rabbits with myxoma virus has shown that new strains of virus—as well as resistant strains of rabbits—have cut the rabbit mortality down from 79 per cent to 30 per cent since 1950. This is the evolution of strains, however—neither of new viruses nor new rabbits (28).

Age of Bacteria and other Simple Forms

Fossils of bacteria have been found in the Pre-Cambrian ores of Lake Superior, in rock from the Jurassic and Cretaceous of Great Britain, and in certain coals.

Walcott found that some calcareous algae of the pre-Cambrian rocks contained bacterial rods, vaguely like the nitrifying bacteria of soils. Raymond reports that the oldest actual records of the presence

---

*Quoted by permission of W. H. Freeman & Co., San Francisco, U.S.A.

of bacteria are furnished by certain late Devonian ostracoderm plates in which the loss of the original structure appears to be due to the action of such organisms.

Cameron says there is a growing opinion that bacteria are more closely related to the yeasts than to the blue-green algae. Jarwetz et al* (29) say: "The origins of the rickettsiae, the viruses, the algal divisions, and of the bacteria are completely obscure; the protozoa are believed to have had a polyphyletic origin in the algae, and in turn to have given rise to the fungi and the slime molds. The blue-green algae and the bacteria have many similarities and so may be assumed to have evolved from a common ancestor." Here the evolutionist must rest his case, on these vague analogies, in the most vital and most readily analyzable area of his argument, an area much better documented than the fossils he usually makes so much of. What shall he do with very large bacteria, like Caryophanon, the Achromatiaceae and Lineola, or the order of stalked bacteria, or the Pleuropneumonia group? He is admittedly at sea here. Yet the origin of these forms lies at the crux of his argument.

Lichens do not fossilize readily and we can tell little of their geologic age. They are claimed to have developed recently from the sac fungi, Ascomycetes. But although the algal component exists independently in Nature, the lichenized fungi never do and cannot be preserved in independent culture (30).

Several "interspecific" bacterial hybrids have been produced in the laboratory, (never found in Nature, by the way). The first was between cells displaying the O antigen of Salmonella typhosa and the H antigen of Salmonella typhimurium; now hybrids between Escherichia coli and many Shigella species, also between Salmonella Typhimurium and S. paratyphi B, S. abortus-equine and S. Strasbourg (31). Where only such rare hybrids have been found in a whole class of animals, imagine the chance of a new genus arising—and the fact is, in the millions of generations of bacteria that have been studied, none has.

Bacterial Mutation

Mutations (sudden alterations in a species) are common in bacteria. They can be induced by nutritional changes in the substrate, the medium on which they are being grown, as, for instance, by taking nicotinamide out of the latter. In some cases a mutation develops which causes the loss of an enzyme involved in the biosynthesis of a necessary compound. Chemical agents, such as antibiotics, readily induce mutations, as do changes in temperature, radiation, even competition between cell cultures. Lactose-fermenting organisms could be adaptive to the appearance of milk-sugar (lactose) in the environment, which would in turn

---

*Quoted by permission of Lange Medical Publications, Los Angeles, U.S.A.

be related to the development of (nursing) mammals on the earth. But it appears that these mutations can develop or be preformed before any contact with lactose develops. They are either created and pre-adapted, or pre-adapted by chance, obviously.

"Preformation" is well seen in mutations against antibiotics. These mutants arise independently of exposure to the drug, Jarwetz says, and the antibiotic only serves to "select" them. These mutants may also develop resistance to other drugs to which they have not yet been exposed. But always these are strains or varieties, not new species. They seem to be just like other bacteria less resistant—they merely act differently in one regard, their reaction to an antiobiotic. The most troublesome of these are the gonococci and staphylococci which currently plague physicians all over the world. Curiously enough, organisms have now developed which grow only in the presence of antibiotics, such as certain strains of streptomycin,—and these mutations can reverse themselves occasionally!

Not only are morphological mutations found, but biochemical mutations are common in bacteria and molds. In these, specific genes seem to control the specific enzyme needed to catalyze chemical reactions at each step. However, the "one-gene-one enzyme" hypothesis is not completely valid. Nor are genes and enzymes identical, nor are genes just enzyme inhibitors. Braun (32)* comments: "It is important to note that analyses of several specific gene-controlled biosynthetic pathways in different organisms, for example, Drosophila, Neurospora, and Bacteria, have revealed the occurrence of identical sequences of biosynthetic reactions. This demonstrates that there is a close relationship between all living things, both in the evolutionary sense and from the standpoint of the generality of biosynthetic and genetic processes." Of course, the similarity is genuine—but there is no necessary evidence of genetic relationship in this observation. Both elephants and mosquitoes have stomachs, but are otherwise not close relatives. This is another instance of "convergence", and nothing more biologically profound than that, I believe.

Biochemistry

Biochemical adaptations have been well studied in bacteria, and are certainly as vital to any discussion of the theory of evolution as morphological changes. Outside of bacteriological texts like Braun's or Thimann's, little is said of them, however. It is really amazing how few of the data of modern science were even glimpsed when the evolutionary theory was promulgated. Why biology and like sciences should have been confined to that strait-jacket since would be hard to comprehend were it not for the mental convenience of such a simple world concept and the materialistic bias so common among scientists.

---

*Quoted by permission of the author and his publishers, W. B. Saunders Co., Philadelphia, U.S.A.

Burkholder (33) points out the puzzle raised by the presence of antibiotics in lichens, algae, bracket fungi, toadstools, Gorgonian corals, conifers, onions, mountain ash. How did these substances evolve in these different plants—in response to need? If molds and trees produce similar antiobiotics, do the hosts have a similar ancestry of genes and enzymes? The evolutionist should ponder this dilemma.

Mutations in General

Most mutations are lethal or at least disadvantageous. But evolutionists have to say that the unhappy mutations we get in the laboratory are those already eliminated in the history of the species—which is just a speculation, of course, since no one can know what mutations have already been eliminated! Another example of evolutionists hiding behind a plausible but sketchy explanation is the proposition they advance that mutations obviously disadvantageous originally may later prove valuable when the environment changes, for example streptomycin-resistant mutants later meeting with that antiobiotic. But still these are only new strains, not new species. Finally, a gene unfavourable in one genic environment can prove valuable in other gene companies—here, again, we deal with strain variation only. Mutation rates are such that only one cell in 10,000 to one in 10 billions mutates, depending on the environment, the gene involved, or the presence of such mutagenic agents as x-rays, ultraviolet rays or nitrogen mustard.

Taxonomy and its Difficulties

Braun says: "Currently used schemes of bacterial classification are helpful determinative keys but do not represent natural classification systems based upon the biological relationship between species. Certain easily detected character differences have been chosen to separate 'species', 'genera' and 'tribes', even though such differences may frequently be brought about by a single mutational step, as for example, the difference between the tribes Eschericheae and Proteae and between the species Micrococcus (Staphyloccus) aureus and Micrococcus (Staphylococcus) albus in the classification of Bergey's Manual. Similarly, many of the so-called species of Salmonella merely represent mutants from the genetic viewpoint and the same applies to certain Clostridium and Pseudomonas species, which, though frequently considered as distinctly different from each other, prove to be nothing but relatively stable variants of the same species. The bacterial species thus has little in common with the taxonomic species in higher organisms with recognized sexuality, where species have been defined as 'groups of actually or potentially interbreeding natural populations, which are reproductively isolated from other such groups'. It is possible that increasing recognition of sexual mechanisms in bacteria may eventually permit a similar approach to more natural taxonomy in this

31

group. In the meantime the present descriptive classification of bacteria can be vastly improved if it is more generally recognized that what is currently described as the 'typical' representative of a species merely represents a particular mutant which happens to be predominant under the conditions of laboratory cultivation" . . .

. . . "Ideally, a description of a bacterial species should include its total potential mutational range. If one compared such mutational spectra of individual species, it would become evident that the mutational range of species overlap, resulting in the often confusing observations that the progeny of the species may display characteristics of another species, or even of species currently classified as belonging to different genera. For example, some R mutants of Pneumococcus are indistinguishable from certain strains of Streptococcus viridans. Agrobacterium radiobacter (Alkaligenes radiobacter) and Agrobacterium tumefaciens (Phytomonas tumefaciens) lack serologic similarity when their M types are tested, but show antigenic identity between their S types. The antigenic gulf usually existing between the nonhemolytic diphtheroids and the hemolytic streptoccocci has been bridged by variants of the latter, establishing an antigenic continuity between what have been traditionally regarded as distant genera. Such overlapping of the mutational ranges of diverse species does not mean that there is a continuous genotypic spectrum connecting all bacteria. In other words, the potential genotypic and phenotypic range of each species, that is the potential mutations of a given biotype, are normally limited, **else we should have been able to observe drastic evolutionary changes in laboratory studies with bacteria. Despite the rapid rate of propagation and the enormous size of attainable populations, changes within initially homogeneous bacterial populations apparently do not progress beyond certain boundaries under experimental conditions."**—This last point is worthy of notice, for it tells very strongly against evolutionary theory.

Thimann says that streptomycin resistant strains may acquire new enzyme systems and become virtually new species. At least they are now as new and different as the difference between other known bacterial species. This merely emphasizes, of course, how unclear we are as to what constitutes a bacterial species.

All that this means, really, is that mutants have been erected artificially into species, either for convenience sake, or before the tendency to variant mutations was recognized by bacteriologists, for example in staphylococcus aureus and albus—or before the mutant antigens were recognized, for example in the agrobacterins above. The striking point to make is—no genuine evolution in bacteria in countless generations. Probably no evolution in viruses in countless generations, although they have been much harder to scrutinize. The same can probably be said of fungi as well.

Thimann* remarks: "The naming of bacteria is a matter for endless discussion . . . it is not clear what constitutes species . . . Modern geneticists recognize enough 'strains' of B. coli to staff a whole family of the older taxonomic type, with sub-divisions into dozens of genera and species . . . If the border line of a species is difficult to draw, that of a genus is equally so. Hence the bacteria are constantly changing."

Cannon (34) has a very cogent criticism to offer when he points out that there probably are more living forms without chromosomes than with them. The former can therefore carry no genes and could not evolve according to Neo-Darwinian theory. Perhaps bacteria have sex, but what can this mean in organisms which do not have nuclei? Only in a narrower field of observation than is generally recognized can the geneticist contribute usefully to evolutionary theory, it would seem.

Summary

The general conclusion of all this must be that in the ideal situation for the study of evolution—in the simplest known living forms, bacteria, for example, and viruses, in the forms that can be best controlled under definite laboratory conditions, and those where reproduction is fastest so that a phenomenal number of generations can be studied within a short time, in a field where there has been close and agonized scrutiny for at least sixty or seventy years,—no evidence of evolution can be seen. This might be because we have been unable to set up proper taxonomic boundaries. It might well be that the taxonomic classes that we have made for the larger multicellular animals and plants have no relationship to those which should be developed for the creatures which this chapter discusses. In any case classification is probably merely systematic shorthand for the puzzled human observer. But say it how we will, the fact remains. No mega-evolution has been perceived amongst bacteria and viruses under conditions ideally suited for such mega-evolution to occur and be detected. New strains there may be; new varieties there may be; even new hybrids there may be. But mega-evolution,—definitely no. (See Editorial in Canadian Medical Association Journal, April 16, 1960, p. 838). Is it any wonder that textbooks on evolution say very little about bacteria and viruses?

---

*Quoted by permission of the MacMillan Co. of New York, U.S.A.

CHAPTER IV

Evolution and the Embryo; the Testimony of the Unborn

A logarithm no one understands;
An exponential curve a master drew;
Progression infinite, no terms defined;
Life's idiotic prefix."

—Vere Jameson*

PROPOSITION—The embryo does not recapitulate, notably in plants, parasites, stationary forms, moths and butterflies. Any resemblances there are between other embryos are superficial and crude, are not demonstrable by truly scientific analysis, do not show evolutionary relationships, and, as a result, the "biogenetic law" is now generally discredited.

Introduction

Every embryo plant or animal develops from a single cell to the adult form in a matter of weeks or months, and in doing so goes through many intermediate stages and complicated bodily alterations. These stages are somewhat similar in all mammals, whatever the mammal concerned. Based upon this latter phenomenon, Haeckel in 1866 enunciated the law of Recapitulation or the Biogenetic Law, which is still quoted in every college textbook on Evolution or Biology, although de Beer calls its influence on embryology "regrettable". In 1909 Sedgewick pointed out its fallacies. Only naive or poorly informed evolutionists still cite it. It says, briefly, that the ontogeny of all creatures recapitulates their phylogeny, or, in other words, that the individual in his embryonic development comes up through the history of his race, "climbing his ancestral tree." It is a facile and comprehensible view, and it seems the most obvious demonstration of the truth of evolution. As soon as it was enunciated, and ever since, all sorts of phylogenetic trees sprang up in the thin soil of this theory from a few seeds of fact. De Beer and Swinton (35)** say "In spite of the exposure of the theory of recapitulation, its effects continue to linger in nooks and crannies of zoology." It is of interest that Muller had come to the very reverse conclusion (1864) before Haeckel, and indeed had based phylogeny on the ontogeny, as de Beer and others would do again.

Is there any Recapitulation in the Plant World?

Most plant development is fairly stereotyped and does not introduce new and distinctive features. Moreover, it appears that the embryo-

*Quoted by permission of the Ryerson Press, Toronto, Canada.
**Quoted by permission of the Athlone Press, the University of London, Eng.

logy of whole families of plants is unknown, and that in others our knowledge is only fragmentary. One can see that there is very little to gain from a survey of the plant world toward establishing the Biogenetic Law. Surely, it is an extraordinary law which has so many blanks left in its book of evidence.

Sinnot and Wilson (36) tell us, however, that seedling cacti possess leaves that the mature plants lose. Again, the genus Acacia of the Legume family has many species with typical compound leaves. In other related species the leaves of the adult plants are merely flattened petioles, callled phyllodes. In the first few seedling leaves of such species, however, the typical foliage leaves appear—as if this were the persistence of an ancestral trait. In eucalyptus trees the leaves usually hang limply, but the first leaves of the seedling trees are still horizontal, as in other members of this family.

Perhaps such examples are not ancestral memories at all, but due to a juggling of plant hormone balance at early stages of development, before the plant has settled on its mature type. It has been found, for example, that gibberelins can produce "juvenile" leaves in Hedera and hasten their disappearance in Eucalyptus (37)! It may suggest that the adult degenerates from the general generic type the embryo begins to trace out.

De Beer and Swinton emphasize the same point, viz., that the Biogenetic Law, which claims that young leaves of the descendant represent adult leaves of the ancestor, cannot be true "in view of the frequency with which young foliage leaves are found to be more specialized than those formed at later stages." This is notably true of conifers.

Other Major Difficulties

What parasitic insect or worm can have a recapitulatory ontogeny? Its development is a series of degradations, not of developmental processes. Likewise the egg-bursters of insects, the caruncles of vertebrates which help the embryo hatch, as well as the nauplius of Crustacea and the trochosphere of Annelids and Molluscs cannot represent ancestral adult forms. De Beer* (38) mentions as other examples the spiral cleavage of the fertilized egg in certain flat worms, annelids, molluscs and Nemertina. Where items such as foetal membranes could not possibly have ancestral significance Haeckel postulated that here we had "intercalations" (to be passed over in our considerations). Yet the whole history of mammals could never have happened without these foetal membranes!

Moths and butterflies, of course, especially those with mimicking larvae, admittedly do not "recapitulate", and a chrysalis is a totally new

---

*Quoted by permission of the Clarendon Press, Oxford, England.

35

invention no primitive pre-insect "ancestor" ever thought of. Many frogs, too, have no tadpole stage but hatch directly into adult frogs. This is very inconsiderate, for this "law" loses meaning if inconstant even inside a single genus. The ichthyophys of the Amphibian class has gills only in the egg and never has any trace of legs. It probably had never heard of the Biogenetic Law it should follow. The shells of Ammonites are commonly cited as examples of this Law, showing a change from straight or arcuate forms to close-coiled forms as in the ontogeny of a modern Nautilus. But Palaeontology does not support this view, for only one genus, Bacterites, had a straight shell, and it lived in the Devonian together with close-coiled forms, says Dewar Indeed, all three types of shell may be seen in the same family.

Passing mention may be made here of forms that forgot to evolve, for example the Amoeba and other simple Protozoa and the one-celled plants. Here the phylum itself has not altered, the result being that the individual's life history is exactly that of his remotest ancestor's. For example, Lull says that Orbulina and Globigerina, of the Protozoa, date back at least to the Ordovician. Among Brachiopods, Lingula and Crania are practically unchanged since the Ordovician. Nautilus goes back to the Tertiary, as was mentioned in an earlier chapter. The lung fish Ceratodus has a modern genus in Australian rivers, but goes back to the Triassic. The Port Jackson shark, Cestracion, has persisted since the Jurassic and even has family relatives in the lower Carboniferous. The modern tuatera of New Zealand is a Permian type, and the sole survivor of a whole order of reptiles. Why did evolution pass by these and other such forms while it altered all other life? More of this in a later chapter. Here we should point out, however, that these cases are the only perfect examples of this "Law of Recapitulation", but appear only where no "evolution" has been or can be claimed. What a dilemma for the evolutionist!

Indeed, exceptions to it are so common that the law must be abandoned, says J. M. Smith (39).

The freshwater variety of Palaemonetes varians differs widely in ontogeny from the seawater variety. Which recapitulates? There are birds whose young are helpless for weeks or whose young can at once fend for themselves. Which recapitulates? De Beer and others call these novelties of early maturity "caenogenetic". Are they not merely differences in rates and types of individual development about whose hormonal or enzymatic mechanisms we must admit complete ignorance?

The mamalian liver develops as a compact mass of cells permeated by bile canaliculi, subsequently vascularized. This can never be traced to any possible phylogeny, says de Beer, but takes an entirely new route. The lung, likewise, now forms respiratory epithelium last, rather than first, as evolutionary phylogenists would expect. In the human it starts as a dense mass of mesenchyme into which lung-buds grow, followed by bloodvessels. Similarly there is no relation between the ontogeny and phylogeny in the pharynx, thyroid and thymus in man—nor for the changes in retroversion of the head of the tibia or displacement of the bladder in man. So, too, for the shape of the embryonic head in dogs, cats and pigs,—very unlike that of their so-called "ancestral" adults. The neural tube arises by two different means in chordates, as is true of the lateral line canals in fishes. Which is phylogenetic?

Dewar has listed some of the general facts fatal to the Law of Recapitulation:

(a) It obviously does not apply to plants.

(b) The embryos of closely allied species may follow very different courses. The common crayfish emerges from the egg as a crayfish, but its allied form, the crustacean Peneus, hatches out as a Nauplius larva, passing through other larval stages before it becomes adult. Sea-crabs usually emerge as larvae, but freshwater crabs emerge as adults or they would be swept away and lost. Which recapitulates?

Again, the order of a phylogeny often is not followed in ontogeny.

Carter (41) says the Haeckel's doctrine can be rejected because we realize that evolution is not to any significant degree due merely to the addition of stages at its end with all the beginnings in common.

Commonly Quoted Examples

However, the validity of the "Law" is said to be illustrated by such facts as the arches appearing in the early embryos of vertebrates; these have been compared to the "gill arches" of fish, are regularly called "gill arches" in biology texts, and are obviously designed to teach us that the human or cow embryo goes through a fish stage which is its memory of an "ancestral" fish. At the other end of the tiny embryo is the tail which is unduly long and clearly reminds us of tailed ancestors. What other value or purpose can it have if it is not to humble proud man? The human embryo has three phases in the manufacture of its kidney, an early structure resembling the pronephros of the lamprey, an intermediate form resembling the mesonephros of the fish, and finally the human metanephros. Here is surely a clear "recapitulation" of "ancestral" types. Not only does the human embryo recall its ancestral anatomy, but also its ancestral habits. As soon as it is born it can support its weight by clinging to a bar, and one of the best-known illustrations in any book on Evolution is a picture of this copied from book to book since Drummond reported the experiment and Romanes published a figure of it. The infant actually flexes its thighs and turns its feet inward as it would if it were going

37

to climb a tree. What better proof of man's anthropoid ancestry could there be?

The Story of all Embryonic Cell Masses

Let us proceed to analyse these evidences and others like them.

Every embryo begins as one fertilized cell. This cell, and the clump of cells into which it divides to form first a blastula, then a gastrula, of necessity must all resemble one another closely. Any embryo may therefore resemble embryos of early or vaguely similar contemporary forms. One could interject here that we only rarely know anything of the ontogeny of primeval creatures, unless in gastropods and ammonites. But, to go on, similar embryos are **not** identical, first appearances to the contrary, for **every** cell in the cell mass is characteristic of its **own** species, and never can develop into a tissue of any other species, whatever casual appearances might at first glance suggest. There may be some initial uncertainty about polarity, as Child showed. After that is settled, the parts differentiate **qualitatively,** the human fertilized ovum, for example, being able to produce a man in 56 generations. It is kindergarten science to confuse appearances with realities, the gross features with the facts revealed under the microscope. Savants should be more accurate. Indeed, this error would never have been made nor quoted had it not been found to supply such convenient and graphic evidence of evolution.

The developing embryo goes on to develop a body more and more like its adult form. All along the way it looks like other embryos making their own parallel trips toward adulthood—but it is always itself and nothing else. Here is no genealogical tree, but the same old bunch of faggots, as separate at the bottom as at the top. Looked at from 1,000,000 years later, or from 100 feet away, one embryo may vaguely resemble the embryo of another mammal. But scientists should look closer. Hertwig (1880) did, as did T. H. Huxley (1898), and they promptly voiced their doubts. Modern scholars look at facts of chromosomes and organogenesis,—and these say that each embryo is always of its own kind and no other.

The Branchial Arches

But, you say, those gill arches! Was man ever fish-like? De Beer states categorically: "The gill pouches of embryo reptiles, birds and mammals do not resemble the gill slits of the adult fish." In a fish or other gill-breather, the arches mature, divided by real clefts. The gills grow on the arches and are supplied by divided bloodvessels, to produce a breathing mechanism analogous to our lungs. But in the embryo of a reptile, bird or mammal, the arches are not separated by clefts, the bloodvessels of the arches do not divide, and any vague resemblance to true gill arches ends there. Hence these "gill arches" should never be called that. They are early stages of much different organs than gills, precursers of portions of the ear, the hyoid and thyroid gland, the thymus gland, the parathyroids and the pharyngeal tonsil, palatine and lingual tonsils. In mammals these arches are always headed in this direction, never toward gills. However, in Elasmo-branchs the mandibular arch forms the adult jaw, the recapitulationist being forced to conclude that this means that some early pre-fish vertebrate lost the mouth it had developed as in other like forms, felt the need of another, and gradually (for evolutionists demand time) replaced it with a modified gill arch! It is of interest that the fifth and sixth arches disappear in amphibians, reptiles and birds. Man and other mammals perhaps do not have the fifth vascular arch. Perhaps they forgot it was their duty to recapitulate their fishy ancestry more accurately. Moreover, in no fish known do all the so-called gill arches give rise to gills! They have a developmental rather than an anatomical function to perform. Perhaps to some extent they control the arteries that lie between them, Smith suggests.

Why does the snake "repeat" its pharyngeal pouches and not its limbs? Because the former are essential. There were aeons in which these unused pouches, like the legs, could have undergone complete atrophy. But the evolutionist has to say that after millions of years of uselessness in simpler vertebrates the pouches again became essential for the development of the mammalian epiglottis and thyroid cartilage. Dewar says: "Had not the history of these two arches been different from that of every other useless organ, mammals could not have evolved." Branchial fistulae in the human do occur if slits between the visceral arches develop, but these are rare pathological features in-compatible with human health. Drummond records families where a second ear has developed from an arch lower than the usual second, a fact readily explainable by modern tissue induction experiments—and scarcely an indubitable reference to an ancestral four-eared form. The latter is never postulated by the evolutionist, for some reason! Right here one should raise an important question. There may be better ways of forming a mammalian ear and the neck cartilages than to use pharyngeal pouches, but who can propose it? Until we can suggest a better alternative we can scarcely criticize the mode used by the Creator.

The Human Tail

Now that tail, you say! Darwin laid stress on this when he discussed rudiments. A footnote in the Origin refers to a human foetus, exhibited to naturalists by Fleischmann in 1840 at a meeting in Erlangen, which had a free tail containing vertebral bodies, something that is very rare. Arey (40)* mentions one "reported to have become 9 inches long at 12 years. Most of these tails are soft and fleshy." Ballantyne (41)** says: "No modern instance has been reported of a

---

*Quoted by permission of W. B. Saunders Co., Philadelphia and Dr. L. B. Arey.
**Quoted by permission of W. Green & Son Ltd., Edinburgh, Scotland.

39

human tail containing more than the usual number of coccygeal vertebrae, namely 3 to 5, and even of them there are very few . . . of soft tails several specimens have been reported." Obviously these are not mammalian type tails which contain bones. In the embryo of about the fifth week and 14 mm. length there are 7 coccygeal vertebrae. From the third such vertebra onward the tail projects beyond the trunk. Later the 7 vertebrae fuse to 3 or 5. "No evidence can be extracted from them to support the view that they are atavistic revivals of the animal tail of a far-back ancestor," concludes Ballantyne.

The tail in the human embryo is well developed from the 5th to the 8th week, and has corresponding muscles. Later these muscles atrophy and the vertebrae fuse into what is called the coccyx or tail bone, as has been just mentioned. Now the overall appearance of a "tailed" embryo is due to the disproportionate development of various parts of the foetal skeleton. The head is always too large, the neck and hind limbs much too short for our adult concept of proper bodily proportion. At an early phase of development the tail end of the spinal column looks disproportionately long compared to the neck or the adjacent legs or lumbo-sacral portions of the spine. The tail bones fuse to form a useful coccyx which serves as the point of origin of some of the smaller muscles in the pelvic floor. Take it away, and patients complain; indeed the operation for its removal has time and again fallen into disrepute, only to be revived by some naive surgeon who really believes what the biologists have told him about this useless "rudiment".

However, I will concede that a human baby's tail is "atavistic' in origin, suggesting arboreal ancestral forms (monkey), if everyone else concedes that the little embryo's small legs and gigantic head also are reminiscent of the same small-headed, long-legged monkeys! I'll grant one end of that creature if the evolutionists concede the other,—but they will scarcely assent to such a deal. Until that time it is obvious that disproportionate growth along the spinal gradient during embryonic development explains the pseudo "tail". A similar developmental gradient makes the embryonic elephant's mandible protrude and later recede.

The Kidney

The kidney? Arey remarks: "Nowhere can be found a better illustration of the principle of recapitulation." Well, the early embryo needs a kidney of simple type, nothing like as complex as the marvellous filtration and refiltering plant that adults require. Accordingly it develops a simple type far forward, near the head end. This is a nephridial system such as is used by other small creatures, but one that is retained by them because they have remained simple. The nephridia can drain the body cavity and pour fluid out of two excretory ducts as in lampreys and Amphioxus; but in man this organ possibly remains quite functionless. Then the embryo grows, and needs a better mechanism. Economically it retains its pronephric duct as the Wolffian duct, the rest degenerating at the 4th week of embryonic life. If the development of this duct is blocked, be it noted, the mesonephros and metanephros never develop because a stimulus they demand is now lacking. This demonstrates that so-called ancestral (?) structure is really an inductor, or stimulant tissue. The embryo grows this second set of nephridia behind the first one; this is called a mesonephros, resembling that of amphibians and recent fish. It has functional internal glomeruli, which grow to meet tubules. By the tenth week, however, every one of these tubules is broken, and most of this structure degenerates by the 16th week. In the female it degenerates almost completely, but in the male a few tubules remain and drain into the end of the Wolffian duct (vas deferens). There are aglomerular and glomerular types of fish kidneys, and now Homer Smith regards the latter as being the earlier and originating in fresh water, not in the sea! Which of these widely different types of fish kidney do humans "recapitulate", the earlier (thereby forgetting the later type)? Why did we choose the early glomerular type and not the other?

Following the traditional phylogeny considered above, the evolutionist must demand that the Malpighiian corpuscles must always connect with the ureter,—for selection by usefulness would call for this. But in our ontogeny the metanephros has two quite different and independent origins for its ureteral buds and glomerular corpuscles.

Only man divides the kidney substance into pyramids; he has about nine papillae. Other primates, for example, have one great pyramid and papilla. The human cortex may be lobulated to cover its pyramids, but this lobulation disappears in early childhood. It resembles the normal adult lobulation of reptiles, birds, and such mammals as the whale, bear and ox—man in this respect being more like the whale than the ape!

Thus in the kidney we have one of the most complex of all adult organs arising in stages, the most perfect being developed only when needed and obviously better placed far back in the abdominal cavity than as far forward at it appears in the tiniest embryo. Homer Smith says: "the vertebrate nephron could not by any conceivable stretch of the imagination be derived from Amphioxus's nephridial complex", all the nephridia in the latter being ectodermal rather than mesodermal in origin, and confined to the pharynx or head. Here is another example of a close look upsetting a theory built on crude anatomical similarities. Arey points out that the pronephros seems to be induced by the notchord, and later the mesonephric tubules by the adjacent pronephric duct. Finally, unless there is a ureteric bud the metanephrogenic tissue cannot cap it to form the final kidney itself.

Nitrogen is excreted by adult invertebrates as ammonia, by fish as urea, and by birds as uric acid. The chick embryo produces urea by the arginine-arginase system and the adult fish by the ornithine cycle! Needham cites many such sequences, as De Beer relates. The latter goes on: "There is apparently a natural order in which things can be done, a necessitation which affects all ontogenies alike. Repetition of such sequences is evidence, therefore, not of any influence of phylogeny on ontogeny, but of the limitations of physiochemical possibilities in the transition from the simple to the more complex."

The Heart

What about the heart? In every vertebrate embryo a simple heart appears early. Of course, that is all that is needed so early. Two parallel tubes coalesce to form a pumping chamber of two parts, an auricle and ventricle. It happens, by coincidence, that this type also is adequate for a fish. In further growth the heart divides into three or four chambers, resembling superficially the heart of a reptile, or a bird, or a mammal, all of which need different types of heart for various types of life. Early in development the ventral aorta sends several arches dorsally and then each vessel bends back to supply the tail of the embryo. Then the anterior branches fuse and other great vessels, such as the aorta, develop from the fourth aortic arch. In reptiles two aortae persist, only the right in birds and only the left in mammals. Occasionally in man the right replaces the left, which is awkward for the evolutionist who does not believe that man descended from birds.

Carter deals with a major difficulty that the evolutionary embryologist **must** face, the complex structure of a heart before it can **begin** to function. Its early stages could have had no selective value, surely. Yet he says such complexity was obviously demanded and so "would be evolved". Surely this sort of thinking in a circle does not advance the argument.

The Athletic Newborn Human Infant

Finally, that newborn baby hanging from a limb, a limb which never bends (in the illustrations), and often has leaves on one end to make the simian-in-tree innuendo even clearer. This picture has been faithfully copied decade after decade, and no one seems to suspect Drummond's original observations (1897) on the seventy babies he studied. But I have, and say that here is another "scientific" hoax, as silly as Piltdown. Newborns cannot suspend their bodies. Any limb of a tree that their tiny hands could grasp must needs be very slender; It would certainly bend if so thin. The whole thing is just a specious fable. It is odd that it should wait so long for an obstetrician to expose it as a myth. The feet turned inward, as so often may be seen in the newborn, are twisted thus as a space-saving device attending the universal flexion the child assumes in utero. They revert to adult posture in a day or so—but the foetal posture is never atavistic in any

42

sense. Moreover, the baby's leg has a muscle peculiar to man, called the peroneus tertius, which helps to hold him erect on his leg. Certainly here is no reminder of the ape.

Miscellaneous Puzzles

The embryos of modern flightless birds, the Ratites, do not show the archaeopteryx stage, although the embryos of flying birds do show tails with a row of rectrix rudiments on each side. By the evolutionary view this puts the latter **much** closer to their ancestor. Are they? De Beer says that this means that the **latter** resemble the unknown archaeopteryx embryo!!—which is an odd sort of evolutionist argument, retreating into the unknown and unknowable.

In the human embryo there is proportionately much more brain than skull. Does this mean that this was our ancestral state? If so, we are really 'fallen" away to bone!

Bill (42) describes the embryology of the human rectum, with especial reference to the problem of "imperforate anus", and tells us that the blind rectal pouch inside the embryo migrates down the perineum, seeking the occluding cloacal membrane, until it reaches the latter, which then disintegrates. As this process is going on, the external sphincter muscles, which are going to grip it at its lower end and hold it closed when desired, are, with their nerve supply, developed independently at the normal position for the anus. This surely must be either pre-adaptation at its best, or great rectal foresight,—but the evolutionist chooses to call it chance favoured by selection! Perhaps it is Creation!

As an illustration if the tortuous mazes of evolutionist thought as it bears upon Medicine, I could quote a great neurologist (43) in a recent Lancet in which he was discussing the circulation of the human brain. He noted the observation that mammals show three main types of arrangement of these vessels, one shared by man and the horse, one represented by the cat, one by cattle and swine! What this tells us of human phylogeny is a little startling. The same phylogenetic confusion applies to the anastomoses of intracranial and extracranial circulation at the eye and orbit, where the sea-lion, tiger and civets all differ, but the marmot resembles man! Here is "ancestors" chaos— but the author still insists it is phylogenetic, for the calibre of the internal carotid artery increases from lemurs to monkeys to apes to man! The dog's cerebral circulation is unlike that of the human, fortunately, and must even respond differently to vasoconstrictor nervous impulses. Then he cites the giraffe which has a specialized shunt mechanism which adjusts the brain flow to postural changes. But at this stage in the argument this has become an example of evolutionary "adaptation" since there can and must be no question of ancestral inheritances in any animal known to us!

Adult man retains the embryonic cranial flexure characteristic of all developing mammals, and hence **must** walk erect. But this cannot be neoteny, as has been claimed,—the sudden maturation of a form retaining juvenile characteristics,—because man has almost the longest gestation, and cannot be claimed to suffer a premature expulsion! This flexion places the foramen magnum far back as in ape embryos, flattens the face and hence permits the binocular vision so useful to man. Man does not need heavy brow ridges to buttress the upper jaw against the brutal ape type of mandible.

White skin has been ascribed to a neoteny in white men and apes, but no one seems to have dwelt on the corollary of this, which makes the negro the more completely developed! Conversely, human lanugo is said to be a retardation, though less retarded than the human dentition, the retardation of the latter being needless, too, as the chin is so large. The ovaries are said not to be retarded anatomically, but retarded hormonally. The slightly protruding jaws of the human infant are designed for sucking, surely, and need not be apelike survivals. Which conditions are recapitulatory? Obviously all cannot be at the same time.

Even twinning has been regarded as a litter number man had largely discarded to permit bigger single young to develop! These evolutionists have not seen how well twins thrive. Nor have they shown that twinning or triplets were common in Peking man! Evolutionists have called the finger and toe webs of the human embryo frog-life. How else can one put forth digits from the hand? They talk of the separation of the great toe at birth—which is rarely true, but is often used as a reminder of our arboreal ancestry by such writers.

Anticipation

The widespread phenomenon called "anticipation", the formation of a structure in anticipation of its use, is difficult for the evolutionist studying ontogenies to explain. For example, the haemoglobin suitable for extra-uterine life in the sheep begins to form before birth, although the human foetus is not so foresighted and makes it only at birth, and the stupid chick waits until six weeks later. Yet in man this process can occur at birth only by biochemical processes already laid down beforehand. Teleological? The evolutionist must infer that this occurs in the sheep and it is so well developed at birth because it probably has telescoped some of its extra-uterine life into the womb!—but the chick, equally adequate at birth to fend for itself, cannot have its blood picture so explained! De Beer concludes: "In a sense, of course, the problem of anticipation is that of all embryology during the prefunctional period, when organs are formed seemingly teleologically . . . It would be more than rash to conclude that all cases can be explained as the one above" (sheep) . . .

Cross Purposes

Those embryologists who make phylogenies sometimes work at embarrassing cross purposes with paleontologists, as in the Foraminifera series ranging in increasing complexity and geneologically from Nubecularia to Spiroculina—which the paleontologists insist must read the other way! It really is unfortunate when evolutionists get their fossil phylogeny methods mixed! For years Lingula was shown to have an ontogeny exactly recapitulating the adult stages of the "older" genera, Paterina and Obolella—until it was unfortunately found that Lingula was earlier that its two ancestral genera, and another good fossil series went out the paleontologists' window. This indicates how artificial fossil phylogenies can be, even where one has such good data as Brachiopod shells to work with.

Homology

The whole germ layer theory is basic to studies on embryologic homologies. Studies on asexual reproduction, regeneration and experimental embryology prove that other germ layers can replace the usual layers in organ formation. But evolutionists cling to homology for, as de Beer says, "It is the only concept which related the structure of organisms through their phylogenetic histories". More recent knowledge of the germ layers upsets most of the old homology. For example, muscles do not always rise from mesoderm; cartilage and bone can rise from ectoderm as well as mesoderm. In the chick the bloodvessels, connective tissues, cartilage and bone are formed from wandering cells, not from any primal layer at all. Many organs in the lower animals can apparently make their choice of the tissue layers from which they are to develop. Some organisms seem to be able to make organs out of any material available. Indeed, the germ layer may occupy different regions in the blastula of various creatures. One can say that embryonic "processes are homologous" because "contrary to the theory of recapitulation, variations of evolutionary significance can and do arise at the earliest stages of development." (de Beer) This, of course, traces "evolutionary" changes back so far that they antedate morphology and almost antedate histology, getting far, far back into biochemical and genetic "processes", hence takes the argument far back behind the evidence on which the theory of "recapitulation" was based; it obviously makes tissue homologies rude and unnecessary. It reduces "evolution" to a proposition that is difficult or impossible to demonstrate, at least by means of embryology. Indeed, Herbst and Lindahl exposed the eggs of sea urchins to lithium salts and sodium thiocyanide and this respectively "entodermized" and "ectodermized" the larvae! After experiments such as this the germ layer theory seems really to have disintegrated. It remains a problem of embryonic anatomy, not, as the evolutionist would have it, a "problem of the production of the anatomy of the adult" (de Beer). Its "ghost", he goes on, "has a descriptive and limited didactic value", and helps systematize descriptions of many animals. Hence its mendacious preservation in college textbooks.

45

False Recapitulations

False "recapitulations" must be numerous. For example, the late embryo of the dugong has molar teeth with flattened "grinding" upper surfaces. These could not have been worn down before birth, as any similar appearance in the adult would suggest. The flattening develops by an altogether dissimilar process, i.e. by clastic cells brought in by the bloodvessels peculiar to dugong teeth'. When the young ostrich hatches it has callosities it needs and some (on its ankles) that it does not. Other callosities develop later as required. Which does it acquire by inheritance? And if all are inherited, why the useless inheritance, and why an incomplete inheritance? This looks like recapitulation until one thinks—but then scientists are supposed to think before leaping to evolutionary conclusions. Does the ligamentum teres in the human hip joint recall that of the ostrich chick? What other resemblances to the ostrich have we, apart from the two eyes and two legs we share?

Allee (44)* tells how Peripatus, which is "undoubtedly an arthropod, begins embryologically like an annelid worm." This "continues until there is a row of segmentally arranged bodies, in each one of which appears a cavity just as a coelom appears in each developing annelid segment. From this point onward, however, the development is like that of arthropod. Rudiments of appendages appear, the growing annelid-like coelom degenerates into the arthopod form in which the coelum is practically suppressed, and there is an enlargement of blood space. Tracheae appear as ingrowths from the ectoderm and simple eyes are formed as in the insect larvae." By recapitulatory law here is complete confusion surely. Either this means that the embryo foreshadows both widely different types of adult forms or neither. Let the evolutionist decide.

"Recapitulation" has been a "strait-jacket", de Beer admits, J. S. Huxley says there is a difference between the descriptive historical method and the correct analytic methods of study of living organisms. This means, in short, that there is a gap between evolutionary theory and the facts! De Beer says "clearly phylogeny does not explain ontogeny at all". Vice versa is also true.

Wald (45)** has recently written of the metamorphosis of the retinal pigments and even of nitrogen excretion and such in amphibians. He calls these changes "the most striking instances we known of recapitulation", for it is "biochemical recapitulation". But then he goes on to jeopardize his case by mentioning the fact that many forms, for example the common spotted newt and the sea lamprey, have a secondary metamorphosis as well which is the exact reversal of the first. The secondary changes are thus "antirecapitulatory"! Any

---

*Quoted by permission of the University of Chicago Press, Chicago, U.S.A.
**Quoted by permission of the American Association for the Advancement of Science, Washington, U.S.A.

evidence of biochemical recapitulation in chicks or other land verte-brates is very hard to uncover, Wald indicates.

Evolutionists have long leaned very heavily upon the evidence of embryology. The "Law of Recapitulation" is still quoted in every college textbook even though every expert who writes such a text must know how fallacious it is. This is one of my principle objections to the theory of mega-evolution. It has been bolstered up from the first and is still erected upon illusion and just plain falsification. It seems to me that it is a poor theory which **must** have that kind of support,—and I believe that mega-evolution **must** have that kind of support if it is to survive as a plausible doctrine.

Summary

The general effect of such an analysis as the above is to prove that Nature has overleaped the bounds within which any evolutionary law like Haeckel's would try to corral her. The diversity of embryologic patterns is almost inconceivable, certainly indescribable under any general rule we yet know. A "law" that excludes all plants and whole phyla of animals is no "law" but a sieve, which a multitude of facts and habits drift through.

The alternative explanation is preferable. The Creator made living forms as He chose, in infinite diversity, often with comparable plans, often diverging from them, as a Supreme Artist playing with so plastic a thing as life could be expected to do, for His glory and for His purposes, which are often hidden from us.

The Biogenetic Law is not a law, and few if any modern biologists believe it. It is widely quoted merely because it is so usable for evolu-tionary argument. For example MacBride could say that this ancestral record, as it is retained in embryonic development, gives us the only means known of re-tracing the history of life to its beginnings and of completing the inadequate record of the fossils.

It is based on crude conjecture, not upon scientific fact. For example it was promulgated before chromosome numbers were con-sidered. It has too many exceptions. (For example, all plant life, all lepidoptera, all parasites.) It is only valid in the forms that have persisted unchanged from primeval time, since these have no altering phylogeny!

The facts can be better explained otherwise; for example, the gill pouches, tail, kidney, or the grasp of the human hand! A host of facts can be adduced which cannot be explained by recapitulation.

Larval and mature forms are so dissimilar in many creatures that they fall completely outside this "law", as do many of the principal organs of man. "Anticipation" cannot be explained by this "law".

Artificial phylogenies constantly fall foul of palaeontological phylogenies. False "recapitulations" are numerous.

Embryologic homologies are based on the germ layer theory, but the latter no longer is tenable, and has now been replaced by the theory of homologous "processes" rather than the key histological differentiations the old views were based upon.

There is no evolutionary principle involved in the general development of the embryo beyond that which necessarily accompanies the growth of the complex from the simple. Enormous diversities of pattern can be found, following no discernible general rule, certainly reflecting no phylogenetic history.

CHAPTER V

VESTIGIAL ORGANS AND RUDIMENTS

How can I doubt that He
Framing earth to His mood,
Mad counterpoint above,
Moves in such ecstasy,
Throws in discords for good,
Strange harmony must love?

—*Vere Jameson.

PROPOSITION—Rudimentary organs and structures are common. They are usually not useless, and this has often been shown. They often have biochemical values during development, and are not to be judged on adult anatomical structure only. Structures on the way out are not what the evolutionist needs, but structures on the way in. These he finds harder to discover. Their rarity could be fatal to evolutionary theory, which is essentially the story of structures coming into being.

Introduction

Are rudimentary organs a clear evidence of our ancestral relationship to animals in whom they were fully developed and useful? Was man made in God's image, presumably perfect, or in the image of animals? That is the crux of this discussion, and emphasizes its importance.

Charles Darwin realized this, and said: "to take any other view (than community of descent of man and the animals) is to admit that our own structure, and that of all the animals around us, is a mere snare laid to entrap our judgement."

Professor Packard (46)** more recently said: "To those who believe in special creation the presence of vestigial organs has proved a stumbling block—an insuperable obstacle". Man, he says, is a repository of relics of his past "whose significance can be truly understood only if they are viewed from the standpoint of the evolutionist."

Dewar points out, however, that "If the evolution doctrine was merely that many types have degenerated since they were created or originated, then the presence of vestigial organs would afford strong support for it. What the doctrine demands is not vestigial, but nascent organs, and the latter appear to be non-existent. Such a state of affairs seems to strike at the root of the evolution doctrine." The only example of presumed nascent organs that the evolutionist can propose, and

*Quoted by permission of the Ryerson Press, Toronto, Canada.
**Quoted by permission of the MacMillan Co., New York, U.S.A.

that Dewar knew of, are the simple filamentary limbs of the mud-fish, lepidosiren, and the small independent slip of the rectus femoris muscle seen in some birds.

Recently evolutionists have pointed to the fin of the Coelacanth as an example of a incipient limb in a fish of very ancient date. Millot and Anthony (47) have just upset this argument, however, for they find nothing in such a fin to compare with the radius, ulna, tibia or fibula (bones of the limbs), and the ball and socket joints of the fins are the reverse of those seen in limbs, the socket being on the fin and the apophysis on the pectoral girdle!

Historical Note and Original Examples

Charles Darwin, both in "The Origin of Species" and "The Descent of Man" stressed the value of rudimentary organs as evidence of evolution. He mentioned male breasts, the "bastard-wing" in birds, the single lobe of the lung in snakes, bits of pelvis and limb bones in some snakes, teeth in foetal whales and in the upper jaws of foetal calves, traces of teeth in the beaks of certain embryonic birds, useless wings in flightless birds, and soldered wing-cases hiding wings in some beetles, rudimentary teats in cattle, blind eyes in cave animals, the swim bladders of certain fish, rudimentary petals and pistils in flowers, and so on.

He went on to talk of nascent organs, that is organs on the way in, just as rudiments are organs on the way out. These incipient structures, he admitted, were hard to detect. For example, he was uncertain if the peguin's wing was rudimentary or nascent—and there is still no reason to conclude that it is developing. The mammary glands of the platypus or the ovigerous frena of some cirripedes (barnacles) were other instances that occurred to him. He could name no others, apparently, and was very unsure of these. This is very strange. for "evolving" Nature should be literally crowded with myriads of organs and structures on the way in. The fact that this is not demonstrable is one of the really strong arguments against evolution.

Rudimentary organs or parts are common in domesticated birds, as Darwin points out. He mentioned tail stumps in birds without tails, vestigial ears in birds (that have no external ears, of course), bits of horns in hornless cattle, the state of the whole flower in the cauliflower, the rudiments detectable in monsters. He concludes in the "Origin" by saying that "rudimentary organs may be compared with the letters in a word, still retained in the spelling, but become useless in the pronounciation, but which serve as a clue in seeking for its derivation."

In the "Descent", Darwin adverts to this evidence. He ascribes rudiments to the inheritance of disuse, an explanation no biologist could now support, but adds that the last stages of decay are hard to

50

explain since there could be no positive value in their final suppression. He cites the panniculus (superficial fascia) of the skin and scalp, the ear muscles ,indeed the whole external ear in man and apes ("Darwin's tubercle" on the helix especially), the semilunar fold of the eye (in monkeys and man) which recalls the nictitating membrane in birds, some reptiles, amphibians, and sharks, where it is a third eyelid, our defective sense of smell, our hair, especially the foetal lanugo, and the course of the hair tracts on the forearms, the last molar tooth, the appendix, the supracondyloid foramen of the humerus which occasionally transmits a great nerve, the coccyx, and the prostatic vesicula.

Other Examples of Rudimentary Organs

As the fish Xiphophorus is bred in captivity the adults decrease in size. The sword-like extension of the tail, however, reduces in size even faster than the body until finally there is still a tail—but no spear on it.

Many reductions occur in Nature, for example the adult oyster loses its foot. The abdominal limbs in the insects Compodea, lapyx and Machilis, which begin to appear, soon stop growing and remain small. The slow-worm, Angius, has small limbs like a lizard in its embryonic stages, but these disappear in the adult. In such snakes as Glauconia, Python or Boa only traces of limbs appear. The notochord-like structure in early embryonic reptiles, birds and mammals becomes the vertebral column. Whales and their relatives have no nictitating membrane over the eye. The young ostrich has 3 toes, the adult having generally only two—although some adult birds have three toes. The chelonian (turtle family), Emys lutaria, has intercostal muscles in the embryo which disappear in the adult. The pronephros persists in some adult fish but is lost in others.

Thomson (48) mentions the tiny vestigial gill in the spiracle of the skate, an opening in the mouth replacing the first gill-cleft. The comb of this gill is too small to aid in respiration. The hairs on the whale's upper lip are richly innervated tactile structures—but Thomson says they are reminders of the hairy coat all mammals—and the whale's ancestor—once had! Frogs and other amphibians have multicellular skin glands, but so do lungfish, unlike other fish. The lungfish also has an incomplete septum in the auricle of the heart, resembling amphibians which have only one ventricle but two auricles.

In short, nascent organs are difficult or impossible to find—just as animal and plant breeders probably cannot produce a new genus by the introduction of new characters. But vestigial structures are common, as breeders also have found.

As non-vestigial structures that have often been called rudiments Dewar mentions the organ of Rosenmuller in female mammals, the male breast, the right ovary and oviduct of birds, the hidden bony tail in man, the muscles of our ear, and the semilunar fold in the human eye. All these are due to common features of embryonic development, and are correlated with essential structures during that development, although they are not useful in the adult. One could add Darwin's point in the ear, a reminder of the common features of all mammalian ears. Unusual structures which are vestigial, although probably still serving a purpose, are the pelvic and occasional hind limbs of whales and sea-cows, and the claws and bones beside the vent in pythons, the rudimentary spurs of female birds—many of which indicate that organs do not disappear by disuse or they would long ago have disappeared completely.

Now certain organs may not be needed as the environment changes—going into caves perhaps, or living on an island where flight is impossible—or as an animal's diet or habits alter. Such truly vestigial structures, says Dewar, are the splint bones of the horse, the lateral toes of deer and other artiodactyls, teeth in the foetuses of toothless whales, the eyes of cave animals and fish, wing structures in flightless insects, wings of flightless birds, and the human appendix. Yet Thomson says the young forms of the blind Proteus (salamander) of the Dalmatian caves can become able to see if raised in red light! And Davis (49) points out that the cave fishes of Yucatan belong to four separate families, each one showing weakened vision but a compensatory development of touch and other senses, breeding habits adapted to the dark.

Many snakes have only the right lung, the left being vestigial. The right ovary and oviduct are vestigial in birds.

Some 180 structures have been listed as vestiges by ambitious biologists. Indeed, Drummond could name 70 many years ago.

Vestigial stamens, petals and sepals, stipules and leaf blades, and various functionless internal structures are common in plants.

Geographical Phenomena and Vestiges

Scott (50) tells of the world-wide family of rails. Many insular species which cannot fly are seen on islands which seem never to have been connected with any mainland. Such loss of flight involves great structural modifications, which cause such birds to be assigned to new species or even new genera. In the Galapagos there is a flightless cormorant which still fishes in the sea. Penguins live on islands in the seas. The recently extinct flightless dodo was a large pigeon living on Mauritius. Another flightless pigeon, also extinct, was the solitaire of the Isle of Bourbon. The moas and the little kiwi have been seen only in New Zealand. Amongst flightless birds only strong runners, like the rhea or ostrich, live on the continents. In the Kerguelen Islands are many flightless insects. Obviously, all these flightless species could never have reached the islands as they now are. It would seem clear that flight-capacities have been lost by these creatures because they were needed no longer—but such a degenerative process remains a complete mystery—and losing a structure once adapted to a peculiar mode of life is quite a different kettle of fish from developing one able to cope with a needful activity. In this regard Wallace (51) noted that in Madeira he found at least three European species of insects which were wingless but otherwise identical. Since it is a stormy area those species in Madeira which do have wings often have larger wings than their European allies. The only difficulty here is the genus Acalles, which is always wingless, and which is abundant in all the Atlantic islands but is also seen as such in Southern Europe—although a related genus occasionally has wings. How did it reach the island?

The owl-parrot or kakapoe of New Zealand is a nocturnal, burrowing parrot, feeding on roots, berries, occassionally on lizards. It climbs but does not fly, although it has fully developed wings. It seems to have forgotten how to use its flying muscles! Here is a **habit** which has become a rudiment!

Cave mammals, the bats, the white-footed mouse, and cave-birds such as owls or the "oil-bird", Steatornis caripensis, show no atrophy of the eyes. On the other hand there are blind crickets in caves, and blind crayfish. Four types of cave salamanders exist in North America, two with normal eyes and two with degenerate eyes. Typhlotriton spelaeus has normal eyes as a larva. The eyes of Typhlomolge rathbuni are covered with skin and have no muscles. In Europe there is a blind salamander, Proteus anguinus (slightly sensitive to light, however). Cave fish are often blind, for example catfish and the Amblyopsidae, where 8 species have degenerate eyes and 5 mere vestiges. Many degenerations involve only certain members of one genus, as in blind lizards or catfish. In the Mammoth Cave is a small fish, Typhlichthys subterraneus, where eyes appear in the young but become useless and partly overgrown in the adult. The blind fish of Mammoth Cave, Amblyopsis spelaeus, has (alternative) terminal buds on its head, giving it a prodigious tactile or directional sense. The organs of digestion and locomotion in cave fish may also become degenerated. No good evolutionary theories for the degeneration of such creatures have been proposed, for the obvious tendency is Lamarckian, and Lamarck's views we must not admit.

Gene Controlling Factors

Gypsy moths can be developed so slowly in response to "slow" genes that they may not form reproductive organs before the genes controlling segmentation divide the abdomen. The result is segmental repetition of the reproductive glands, as in worms, and not in adult moths.—Here is a 'primitive'' character reproduced by differences in gene acceleration! Similarly winged caterpillars are explained—surely not as phylogenetic atavisms. Their impulse to wing development

53

merely strikes too soon. An inhibiting factor in the front half of the Echinoderm larva, Antodeon, can be cut away, letting the back part reproduce two body centers. This is not atavism, although like one. It is a case of escape from a suppressing factor. The bands on snail shells may or may not have time to appear if their speed of development is retarded. Wigglesworth (52) found a development-suppressing hormone in the corpora allata of the heads of certain insects that metamorphose. Removing it induced tiny worms to become midget moths—rudimentary moths, one could say. This illustrates the wonders of hormonal control of development.

All embryos of the higher vertebrates show the rudiments that may later give rise to limbs—whether these are to be a human hand, a dog's pad, a seal's flipper, or a bat's wing. This is how such embryos are made. Certain genes controlling limb development are no doubt related to, or conditioned by, genes stimulating the growth of other vertebrate features. All tend to develop in parallel, although the impulse may die out early in any one direction, particularly a useless direction. Thus, if all mammals originally have 5-toed feet, guinea pigs seem to have lost 2 of the primal toes and dogs the big toe. By artificial recombination of certain growth genes these digits can be restored. On the other hand, loss of digits can be due to suppressive genes. Certain lizards, for example, thus fail to produce certain phalanges of the digits. Such genes occasionally fail to suppress the 2nd and 4th toes of horses. An extra splint bone can occur in horses, not by atavism but by subdivision of the 3rd digit, something very different (negative allometry).

Puzzles

Cetacea (whales) and Sirenia (sea cows) have tiny pelvis bones and occasionally tiny bones homologous with the femur and tibia of land animals. These finding are all the more difficult to explain by evolutionists since no fossils intermediate between land animals and the Cetacea or Sirenia are known. Surely there should be transitional stages in a gap between related forms that is so enormous. The pelvis of the male sea-cow or manatee differs greatly from that of the female, indicating that sex factors probably play a major role in the development of these "rudiments". The size of the pelvis in Cetaceans has not altered from the early Eocene, be it noted. Any **gradual** transformation of a land animal into a whale or sea-cow is inconceivable. How could the tail have changed into a propellor moving **up and down** during the time the hind limbs were becoming slowly more and more useless and while the pelvis remained large? Yet it must have happened twice, evolutionists insist, in the Cetacea and Sirenia! Some Cetacea, such as the aquatic Gangetic dolphin, show no traces of either pelvis or hind limbs— and this is the best adapted aquatic form. The Right Whale has the hind limbs best developed. Only the whales, not the **less** aquatic Sirenia, have hind limb remnants! The pelvis, by the way, is horizontal in whales and vertical in sea-cows, something very odd for a useless vestige! The real reason for this must be that the sea-cows have short backs and whales long backs, and therefore their tail muscles need different types of bony origin.

'What is inexplicable," says Dewar, "is how an ordinary leg could be **gradually** transformed into the wing of a bat and thousands of successive generations of organisms could hold their own in the struggle for existence while the tranformation was being effected." This raises the problem common to all nascent structures, of course—usefulness during immaturity.

What about the male breast and supernumerary nipples in the female? These are now known to be hormonally conditioned; the latter are not relics of a row of teats, because occasionally seen on the thighs as well,—where they can even be functional! A three-toed horse suits the reminiscent evolutionist well, of course,—but he never talks of the six-toed man, for that does not. What an awkward ancestor that would be! Darwin even referred to the fact that a medial teat in the human could be matched by certain bats'. This was a truly marvellous example of a long leap in despairing argument! Originally all human gonads appear to be female. Male changes develop early (where intended, of course), but female relics may persist, as in the above example.

The electric organ of the skate is hard to account for, as its discharge is so feeble. Why have it at all? On the other hand, how can one explain the development of the powerful electric battery of the electric eel and the torpedo, which could have had no usefulness in the undeveloped state?

The pineal or "third" eye is supposed to have been lost three times—yet it was a useful eye in the back of the head, and surely should never have become lost. It must always have had evolutionary value. The pineal gland still may be a useful hormonal structure. Indeed, workers at Yale have recently isolated from it the hormone, melatonin, which decreases pigmentation in dark skin in frogs. Meantime, we know that this gland had no "eye" function in elasmobranch and teleost fishes! One theory is that it mediated stimuli to the chromatphore-expanding hormone of the pituitary, which hormone even develops in birds and mammals that have no chromatophores. In these animals its (hormonal) function is not clear, but perhaps it is vestigial! Imagine a vestigial hormone! The human pineal gland was recently reported by W. B. Quay (53) to have a high metabolic activity probably related to lipid metabolism. It it not more reasonable to withhold judgment here, remembering that the thyroid gland was long counted among the useless "rudiments"? Now we realize, of course, that even a tadpole cannot become a frog without thyroid stimulation. A man with thyroid hypoplasia is a cretin, only half a man.

H. Smith suggests that the aglomerular conditions of most marine fishes reflects a **degeneration** of glomeruli, implying a fresh water and glomerular origin of the salt-water fishes as recent as the Caenozoic. This throws the evolution of fish into a tailspin, but indicates the blind alleys into which new knowledge can force a theory.

In the embryonic nostril of man is a pore called Jacobson's organ, placed at the position of an accessory organ of smell in many mammals and other vertebrates. These last have a branch from the olfactory nerve running to it, although man does not. It may be a true embryonic vestige in man.

T. H. Morgan commented long ago that eyeless fruit flies could arise at one mutation in the laboratory—not by the slow changes that Darwin postulated for cave animals. Similarly wingless insects can also arise at one step, not only by isolation on desert islands when all their winged relatives were blown out to sea.

All adult vertebrates possess haemoglobin as a blood pigment, and it is carried by the red blood cells—with one exception. Three species of fish of the family Chaenichthyidae, have neither pigment nor red blood cells. These fish with colourless blood live in the waters of South Georgia Island. They live on what oxygen can be dissolved in their blood plasma, and usually live in very cold water—as low as $107°C$. (54). Is this rudimentary blood?

The caterpillars of the Swallow-tailed moth, the Brindled-Beauty and the Peppered-moths, have had the number of their legs reduced to leave only those near the tail. These grasp a twig and permit the rest of the body to stand out at an angle, resembling a branch. This posture can be held for hours, and is a helpful adaption. But how explain the reduction of legs coincident with a change of habit, either being useless without the other? Pycraft (55)* well says: "It passes the wit of man to discover the agency by which living bodies can obliterate all semblance of their original form and come to assume a likeness to inanimate objects"—(a twig, in this case).

Poulton (56) tells us that that "simplified" creature, the platypus, has no teeth, but instead has hard plates for crushing its food. Have they ever had teeth? Yes. Infantile teeth cut the gum, are used for a time by the young animal, then fall out and are replaced by the horny plates which invade their sockets. This writer also tells of the female of the vapourer moth which has only rudimentary wings. But in the chrysalis these wings lie inside wing cases much too large, although still reduced. In other moths the wing cases as a rule are obviously too small and the wing must be pleated to be totally enclosed.

The appendix is an abdominal tonsil, set at the junction between the small bowel's fermentation and the large bowel's putrefaction,

---

*Quoted by permission of the Hutchinson Publishing Group, London, England.

which should be as vital a point to guard against bacterial assault as that other sentry box, the pharyngeal tonsils. It may serve as a quiet sentinel all our lives, or it may become septic and even form an abscess —but who has not heard of quinsy in the other tonsils? We think the latter are valuable. Why call the appendix a useless rudiment? The ape, by the way, has a large appendix but monkeys and cats have lost theirs. Does this imply that man is more primitive than the monkey and cat in this respect—since our appendix still persists?

Foetal hair (lanugo) seems to be vestigial, for it is lost at birth and yet resembles the foetal hair of most mammals. However, here we argue from ignorance. It could be useful for keeping the vernix caseosa in place, and the vernix provides insulation in utero and lubrication at delivery.

The "useless" nictitating membrane in the human and anthropoid eye may be useful in directing lubricating tears down the nasolacrimal duct.

"Vestiges" in Domesticated Species

Darwin pointed to the atrophy of wings in the domestic duck and the drooping ears of dogs, the atrophy of the oil gland in fantail pigeons, even a reduction in the number of ribs in some pigeon breeds —all of these changes **within a species** being produced by domestication. Here is the artificial production of vestiges by selective breeding, for mutations out can occur as well as mutations in, indeed are much the commoner, since mutations usually are degenerative. But still these stay within species limits, and such variations **hint** at the production of major degenerate rudiments but do not tell how they occur. They are mere shadows of the real thing.

Vestigial characters in domestic species can characterize varieties, because mutants can be selected which progressively reduce certain features such as beak or tail or colour or song or habits of flight. But these vestigial structures never set up a new species, merely a strain. They do not concern what are called "specific characters".

Explanations

It would seem, therefore, that rudimentary or vestigial organs do occur in man and animals, probably due to the presence or absence of coordinated stimuli common to all similar structures of flesh by a process called allometry; these stimuli we all share as products of one Designer interested in economy of plan and habit. These structures may atrophy to various degrees, or may serve other useful or lesser purposes in animals in whom they would seem "rudimentary" at first glance. We should know more about embryonic hormonal and enzyme stimuli on proximate organogenesis before we pass final judgment here.

As has been said, it is obvious that degeneration has occurred in many types of animals and organs. This would be easy to explain if acquired characters could be inherited, and so disuse could be passed on to descendants. However, probably no modern biologist would concede that this is the case. If the actual loss of structures could be helpful, as of mammae in the male or the right oviduct in birds or the third molar in man or the tail of the tadpole or the left lung of snakes, one could understand the loss developing because of helpful and favoured mutations, perhaps. But an **active** advantage to the creature losing an organ or structure is only rarely conceivable. Usually it is just the useless or probably useless structure that tends to disappear. Why do not useless structures vanish completely, as has the cat's presumed appendix? Why do male mammals still have breasts, however small, and humans have a coccyx? There has been time enough to lose them. Dobzhansky (57) points out that the human body shares a "developmental **system**" with other mammals, not just individual organs, Traces of the system produce traces of organs or "vestiges". In fact we may finally come to see development as a biochemical process rather than a series of morphological changes or homologies.

As has been pointed out above, it is striking that organs on the way in are so hard or impossible to find when organs on the way out are relatively common. Can evolution be only in the direction of loss and degeneration,—as is the general rule in mutation?

The notochord may be necessary for the development of the vertebrae that replace it. Certainly Spemann et al have proved it is indispensable in inducing the overlying ectoderm to differentiate into the neural tube. Many a so-called rudiment may be a necessary "organizer" of this sort. Thus we cannot have a tympanic cavity, tonsils, thymus or parathyroid glands in amniotes without preliminary pharyngeal pouches. Repetition of "ancestral" characters occurs because animals often share common developmental genes, not inevitably inherited, but genes they can share as well as they can share such morphological elements as shell or fur or backbones or feet with five toes.

Embryologically, part of the pituitary gland in the brain is built up by a process originating from the pharynx, but no trace of this remains in the adult except in the Coelacanth (genus Latimeria). There a vascular tube persists as a connection between the pharynx and the gland—in a form 200,000,000 years older than the dinosaur. But the brain of this fish is the smallest of the vertebrate brains in proportion, being only 1/15000 of the weight of the body. In short, the oldest vertebrate has persisted with the least brain! And it has that character of the fossil Crossopterygii, fins on an articulated stem. As has been mentioned before, evolutionists say this is the precursor of the tetrapod limb. Therefore they assigned the most advanced step towards limbs amongst all limbless forms to a creature whose brain is smallest and whose pituitary gland, the key instrument of the whole endocrine symphony, is the most primitive! What a problem in incongruity they make for themselves!

Natural forces tend to work in habitual grooves, and to form organs and structures en bloc. They can be short-circuited when the genes or hormones or enzymes controlling growth fall short because they have no discernible goal, and probably meet none of the coincident and mutually exciting stimuli and organizers which contributed allometric growth demands. We are familiar with the concept of lethal genes which can harm or exterminate the organism. What we must oftener think of is genes which can suppress or extirpate only that part of it which is in their peculiar care, such as the digits of guinea pigs or dogs. Vestiges could scarcely appear gradually, and we know of none that have. They must have always depended upon the gene complex which now has reversed itself and permits them merely to put a foot in the morphological door before slamming it shut.

A gene may cease to act on one character and take over another. Thus in poultry a gene controlling a crest of feathers also produces cerebral hernia, characters having no homology. Independent and parallel mutations of genes may produce identical but not homologous characters. Genes can even deputize for each other, as in Drosophila eyes. Genes can be different but can mimic. Similarly the homology between neural tubes in chordates is probably basically an homology between the gut-roofs underlying the neural tubes and conditioning them. Homologies may involve not only corresponding tissue layers, but inductors as well. Thus the eye lens of Rana esculenta is determined by the gradient of the whole embryo, but in Rana fusca it is induced by the optic cup. The chordate gut is homologous throughout, but comes from very different embryonic sources. Homologous structures can arise from different segments of the body. In the newt the arm arises from segments 9 to 11, in man from 13 to 18. Thus "homologies" are not evidence of ancestral relationship. They are largely accidental—or artificial!

Perhaps a general rule applies to the correlated or allometric development of nearly all rudiments; 3rd molars develop because 1st and 2nd molars develop, and all grow en bloc; the appendix develops because the ileo-caecal junction develops; the ear muscles develop because the ear develops along a plan shared by many similar creatures, and they develop en bloc. Vestigial stings appear in "stingless" bees because the latter are so tiny that allometry has made the stings unusable. Why should it be necessary for a Creator to develop a different plan for each species (although in general He has)—and one different in **every** detail? Why not make use of similar modes where and as long as they serve His purpose? I would think of homology as being an indication of design rather than of common descent or familial relationship.

Vestiges do reflect the general community of design of similar types of living forms—but then there is no reason to take the Designer to task for His economies, once the primal scheme has been found "good".

Then, too, there are structures called "vestigial" on slim or no evidence, such as the paler stripes on the rump of Burchell's zebra. No one knows whether these stripes were ever darker, nor why **alternate** bands should be lighter in colour than others still very dark, nor why the "shadow stripes" should be only on the rear. Why focus on the pale stripes and not on the dark ones—but evolutionists clutch at everything, even going far beyond the margins of their factual knowledge.

There is no doubt at all that the human body (like many other bodies) contains so-called vestigial structures, rudiments of structure which are useful in grossly similar forms but which may have limited if any use in us. This merely emphasizes, not that we are close cousins of these similar animal forms, but that there is a certain economy in Creation, probably biochemical economy or enzyme economy or hormone economy, which acts upon germ layers which are going to produce homologous structures, which activates these tissues en bloc so that similarities develop in the mature structure although the totality of the tissues or organs so produced may not be immediately helpful to the **adult** animals. There is no real reason why the Creator should have been forced to produce a different scheme in basic hormone or enzyme or tissue layers for each genus on the earth, certainly no reason to compel Him to have a unique scheme for each species. I doubt if He was and is so foolish. Rudimentary organs we certainly possess. It is equally certain that they are no proof of evolution.

Summary

Rudimentary or vestigial organs are found in Nature in abundance, especially in artificial breeds of animals. However, nascent organs, organs under construction, rarely or never can be found. This is a very powerful argument against evolution.

Such reduction or atrophy of parts or organs has many known and some unknown causes. It can, for example, be due to gene imbalance or alteration, suppressive genes or the loss of these, allometric correlation with decreasing size, the loss of embryonic characters or hormones, or the presence or absence of organizers. But primarily it would seem that Nature has a plan or design for each great group of creatures, and starts to follow that plan in many or all, but may stop short as desired at any stage, depending on the later uselessness or need of the organ in question.

Certain organs become useless as the environment changes. The stimulus for their perfected development seems to cease and development lags. How environment can react thus no one has explained, although it could be due to impaired nutrition or defective oxygen supply. Living forms are in constant flux, a process we call mutation. Mutations usually are small changes and are nearly always deteriorations.

Many vestigial organs are improperly labelled as such. With increasing knowledge many are accordingly stricken off the list. Many turn out to be essential organizers of other structures which remain useful. Many are due to negative allometric correlations.

Evolutionary, **slow** processes can never explain the gradual loss of a structure, especially the **final** stages of its disappearance.

CHAPTER VI

Parasitism and its Variants as Related to Evolution

I've vaguely heard about coral isles
And cannibal chiefs and crocodiles,
But I, like them, never ask to tea
People who do not agree with me.

—Vere Jameson.

PROPOSITION—The complexity, variety and perfection of parasitic adaptation, particularly where animals and plants become interdependent, or where a parasite demands several hosts, defy evolutionary explanation.

Introduction

It has long been of interest to naturalists that animals lived in associations of various kinds, ranging from the bacteria of the human body, to the societies of termites and ants, to the pilot-fish accompanying sharks, to the rhinoceros bird warning the stupid rhinoceros of an approaching danger. Did such relationships evolve? Are parasites degenerate? What does all this mean?

The field under consideration is of vast dimensions, as we soon see. Animal associations may be of many types, the principal sorts being parasitic, commensal (eating at the same table) and symbiotic (living together for mutual help). Examples of the first are the tapeworm or the ichneumon fly. Commensal creatures may benefit each other by their association, for example the hermit crab and a hydroid, or the association of gnus, ostriches and zebras in Africa. Symbiotic creatures live together more intimately, for example the lichens, which are compound plants made of fungi and algae, (and actually thus form "species", whose algal component can live alone but whose fungal component cannot), or human bowel bacteria which synthesize the vitamin K man needs for survival. Perhaps communalism can be included under our general discussion, because so often associated with the above, examples being the termite and a hundred different kinds of insects labelled termitophiles (termite lovers), or the bumble-bee and its guest Psithyrus, or the 5000 species of ants that are all communal.

Antiquity

Gastropods such as the Capulidae parasitized echinoderms back in the Devonian—for many fossil Platyceras have been found attached to crinoids. These parasites have not altered appreciably in aeons. Galls appear on fossil echinoderms, for example the sea urchin Collyriates dorsalis infested by a parasite probably close to Pionodesmotes. Parasitism by Myxostomaria is also ancient. It still infests Crinoids similarly. Rhynia, fossil plants in the red sandstone of the Scottish Devonian, have stems with tubercular segments showing structures attributed to a symbiotic fungus! One must conclude that parasitism is very ancient.

Degree of Change

Parasites often degenerate remarkably, perhaps retaining only reproductive and alimentary organs. They may show hermaphroditic characters. The adult forms may degenerate so thoroughly that no taxonomist can possibly classify them unless he can find their earliest forms and detect larval affiliations that the adults would never suggest. Thus the adult crab parasite, Sacculina, becomes nothing but a system of rootlets invading the whole crab; however, the larva resembles barnacle larvae, first of the Nauplius type, then a Cyprid. Systematists use this information for tagging the creature.

One group of Protozoa, the Sporozoa, is composed of parasites only, says Lull (58),—and then he goes on to speculate on how many of these may be examples of convergence. Convergence confuses the whole picture and probably has introduced many errors into taxonomy.

Many parasites infect two or more hosts in turn, for example the plasmodium of malaria which infects the Anopheles mosquito and man. Then there is the roundworm, Trichina spiralis, which can infect the rat, dog, cat and pig. When we eat uncooked pork in which it lies encysted we get trichinosis. It has been estimated, says Lull, that a diseased man can contain 100,000,000 trichinae—equal to the population of the United States in 1915. There is a flat worm, the liver fluke, which inhabits the liver and bile-ducts of the sheep, deer, and certain other grazing animals. It is discharged into ponds or on moist ground. It then infects the pond snail or even a Helix, then leaves it as a larva to lie in wait for sheep. Roundworms of the genus Porocaecum develop in seals, then infect fish eating their faeces. Seals eat the fish and in the seal's stomach the worms eat the fish eaten by their host, and mature. In each host the parasite lives and looks differently, by the most complex adaptations.

Kershaw (59) points out that the true evolving entity is not the parasite but the parasite-host-vector complex. Behaviour rather than structure is critical. Thus filaria may differ only in their adaptations to the habits of their vectors, or even, as in onchocerciasis, in the locus of attack on the host. Parasitism may be controlled by such a subtle item as variations in species-specific substances in the body, such as the surface mucus of freshwater snails; this can even be strain-specific. Mattingly (at the same Symposium) pointed out that human and simian malaria is carried only by anopheles, and bird malaria by culex mosquitoes, but human filariasis is carried by both.

Remarkable Adaptations of Association

The remora swims beside the shark, to which its sucker holds it as if it were magnetised. The pilot fish swims just ahead of the shark, separately. What an intimate adaptation! A fish of the genus Trachichthys (or Amphiprion) always resides among the tentacles of a sea anemone. When the anemone closes up the fish becomes temporarily locked up inside the anemone's digestive tract. Of course, the latter's nematocysts are very poisonous; this implies that the fish has developed an immunity against them. Presumably the fish eats some of the anemone's food and itself is not digested! If not protected by the anemone the fish is in turn eaten by its predators. How could such a protective biochemical and social adaptation develop **gradually** or even by sudden mutation, as evolution demands? Many such associations are seen in the sea, notably in coral reefs. For example, in Madagascar Geary found a crab living permanently at the mouth of a holothurian and entrapped in its mouth when the tentacles were retracted. Fishes of the genus Fierasfer enter the cloaca (rectum) of holothurians, and dart out to feed. If not protected thus, they are killed by other fish. Many crustaceans shelter within the mantle cavity of bivalves. Igoceras patulocrinus cements its shell to the tegmen (skin) of certain crinoids near the anus to feed on the excreta!

Thimann points out that many species of Protozoa are identical in soils from all over the world, including Arctic soils and tropical soils, even on unworked Pacific islets. How can this be explained by the apostles of change?

The pagurid (crab), Epagurus prideauxi, always lives in a shell too small to contain it. The anemone Adamsia moulds itself to attach to this shell and cover the crab, thus allowing it a freedom of movement it could never attain otherwise. However, the anemone sits on the crab shell in such a position as to steal much of the crab's prey. If the crab is removed the anemone soon dies, even if fed. The crab Melia carries its anemone in its half-closed anterior claws. It snatches food from the anemone. Even a fragment of anemone is picked up by reflex action by the crab. The great parasitologist, Caullery, (60)* says: "these associations involve complicated reflexes which are the culmination of long-standing adaptations just as are morphological specializations." I'd say "yes" to that. But it is impossible to imagine such commensalism arising by degrees. The same applies equally to all the intricate morphological and biochemical adaptations we know, of course.

The flatworm, Convoluta rescoffensis, has a larva which swallows green flagellates until these colour the worm green. If it does not become infected thus the worm remains colourless and dies. When full grown it eats a few, then later all of its flagellates, then dies of

---

*Quoted by permission of Sidgwick and Jackson Ltd., London, England.

starvation. Here the symbiosis is only temporary and apparent. Really the planarian is a predator on the flagellate. The former has no excretory system and needs the flagellates to break up its nitrogen products of metabolism which otherwise would accumulate in it and kill it.

The polychaete annelid, Ichthyotomus sanguinarius, attaches itself to the fins of Myrus by a scissor-like pair of stylets. These separate when relaxed and have to be contracted to free the worm! How could this complex structure have evolved piecemeal? Caullery concedes this evolutionary dilemma: "The mechanism by which this structure was achieved is mysterious; we can hardly invoke a Lamarckian explanation; these stylets ane non-living structures, they have their definitive form from the beginning and the way they work cannot influence their structure; the animal must make use of them as they are; on the other hand, we cannot reasonably accept as a matter of pure chance the sudden achievement of a piece of apparatus which is so complicated and also well suited for attachment. The problem will remain obscure until the discovery of related forms possessing the analogous organ but one that is less differentiated. But at present we have no knowledge of such a case apart from Schmarda's species. And this simple example shows how most of the morphological problems concerning adaptation to parasitism present themselves."—An anti-evolutionist could almost end his case here, could he not? **Mega-evolution is really a philosophy dating from the days of biological ignorance; it was a philosophic synthesis built up in a biological kindergarden.**

Parasites of similar habits, such as blood-sucking leeches, ticks, the larvae of oestrid flies, Ancylostomum duoenale and the parasitic annelid, Ichthyotomus, all possess anticoagulants to keep any ingested blood in liquid state. Here are different groups of animals converging on a similar and **very complicated** biochemical mechanism, one that we can scarcely unravel even now! Other facts of the same nature must be discoverable in the future in the digestion of parasites. Caullery discusses anticoagulant organs in blood suckers and admits we have not the data to decide on any hypothesis of explanation—as is true of many "facts of evolution". Then he goes on to postulate the gradual development of anticoagulant powers, something I simply cannot imagine! He concludes by denying the ability of mutations to explain such phenomena.

In the Cryptoniscidae, during the incubation of the young the mother no longer has a mouth or alimentary canal and only a few ventral nerve ganglia. However, this degenerated animal continues to contract rhythmically in order to ensure the respiration of the developing embryos! How could such a maternally protective habit evolve? It staggers the imagination, surely.

To return to Sacculina: Its migration inside the crab it parasitizes follows a regular course from wherever it starts to its customary abdominal site. When it settles there a **new differentation** occurs,

65

constituting a **new** internal Sacculina! This new creature melts the crab's shell externally till it escapes and becomes external. Then Caullery can say: "The processes which constitute the development of the internal Sacculina (dedifferentiation and migration, then new differentiation) can only be the result of a progressive evolution . . with a succession of stages in the past which still remain entirely unknown to us." What flights of fancy evolution subsumes!

Imagine the evolutionary origin of a parasite like Haemocera danae! Its nauplius **lacks a digestive tube** and the third pair of appendages is only a pair of hooks. But it finds an annelid, Salmacina, penetrates its skin, moults, and is reduced to an undifferentiated cellular mass. Then it makes its amoeboid way into the longitudinal vessel of the annelid, develops a chitinous cuticle and two long filaments at the front end which act as absorptive organs. Next, it moults and differentiates further, leaves the host as a fully developed adult which does not feed but breeds and dies. This is all truly remarkable, so Caullery says: "Here again we know of no other stage in the achievement of so specialized an adaption; it must nevertheless result from a long evolutionary process." And this parasite is not an isolated example! Was there ever so definite an instance of the inadequacy of evolutionary theory?

The "death-watch" beetle bores in wood, books and such. "At the beginning of the digestive part of the food-canal of the larval death-watch there are two minute pockets which are crammed with yeast-plants. These work in the unpromising wood pulp, and there is a little brewery inside the larval death-watch. Careful examination showed—that there were no yeast plants in the eggs, yet they were always present in the grubs. The solution to this puzzle is almost incredible. Associated with the egg-laying apparatus in the female there are two minute reservoirs opening to the exterior, and these are full of yeast plants. When an egg is laid, some yeast plants are expelled along with it, and they adhere to the rough surface of the egg-shell. When the beetle-grub is ready to hatch out, it nibbles at the egg-shell, and thus its food becomes infected with yeast-plants." Indeed, a partnership between yeasts and insects has been found in scores of cases! How could such an intricate mechanical and nutritional relationship ever evolve piecemeal!

All lichens are formed by an associated fungus and alga. The former can begin to develop but cannot continue without the latter. Many lichens propagate only by special organs called socridia, masses of alga surrounded by hyphae. The associations are generally strict, although the same alga can form different lichens with different fungi. What a remarkable association between widely different types of plants!

Some Outstanding Puzzles

Caullery says of insect parasites: "How does the parasite recognize the presence of the larva or egg on which it will deposit its eggs and where its progeny will find favourable conditions for development? What factor, for example, reveals to the Ichneumonidae or Braconidae the presence of a wood-eating larva under the bark on a branch or trunk? But nevertheless the hymenopteron knows how to find the exact point where, by drilling with its ovipositor, it will deposit its egg, **barely touching** the larva that it cannot see but wishes to parasitize. Thus Thalessa lunator reaches the larva of Sirex gigas, deep in wood, And so . . . does the braconid Sycosoter lavagnei drill through a branch of the fig tree to lay its eggs on the larva of a scolytid, Hypoborus ficus, which lives in the wood." Mistakes are made . . . but how do these parasitic insects succeed so regularly and so well? What a remarkable process! A dipterous fly, Systropus corropoides, shares the cocoon of Sibine bonaerensis, then leaves it, as does the pupa, by developing a sharp point on the head and screwing its way out. How could such a mechanism evolve in stages?

Thomson says the heather flourishes because it lives with a fungus, which penetrates through and through the heather, from root to stem, into every leaf, even into the flower and seed. The prothalli of the club mosses often can develop only in intimate association with a fungus.

The witchweed, a corn parasite, has seeds that can lie dormant in the soil for 20 years and still survive. The seed waits until the root of a host plant comes near, then it sends out a strand to seize that root, dissolves the host cells, invades the vascular system of the host, and flourishes. However, it can be made to invade the resistant roots of soybeans, peanuts and sunflowers, where it dies. These decoy plants can thus be used to kill it.

The fact that a parasite is tied to its host restricts opportunities for the sexes to meet. Hence many are hermaphroditic, or become so after a unisexual phase, or may even show sex reversal. There may be extreme sexual dimorphism, with the tiny male living in permanent association upon a huge female. In some free-living abyssal fishes of the family Ceratioidea the dwarf male lives as a permanent parasite on the female. How explain this on an evolutionary basis? Not only that, but the partners fuse their vascular systems and tissues, although the male has retained his gills and breathes independently. Were it not for this arrangement boy might never meet girl in the abysses of the dark sea.

Specificity

So specific are many parasites for certain species that the former can be given specific rank just on that basis, even when identical in every other way.

Can this specificity be evolutionary? Parasitologists might assent. But then there is a problem like the tongue-worms, Pentastomes, found in such "archaic" reptiles as crocodiles, turtles and varanid lizards— but also attacking modern birds—though only gulls and terns! And a second genus is found in carnivores!

The human louse, Pediculus humanus, has two common forms in man, infesting the head and clothes. These strains interbreed, but the hybrids are often sterile and differ by a number of characters. The louse of the chimpanzee belongs to a morphologically different species, and the louse of old world monkeys to a separate genus. But all new world monkeys, supposedly the monkeys least related to man, carry the human genus, Pediculus! A second species of human louse may have close relatives only on the gorilla and the lemur of Madagascar. How explain all this on an evolutionary basis? Did South American men infest New World monkeys, but Old World anthropoids keep their own lice while becoming men—or did man evolve separately in the New and Old World?

Galls on plants are formed by nematodes, acarines and almost all orders of insects. Each attacks a specific part of the plant, whether root, stem or bud. Often only a specific plant is attacked, moreover. Morphologically similar species (?) may be classed in different races by the specificity of their gall formations. "The morphology, structure, dimensions and colour of the galls are as strictly determined as in normal organs," says Caullery. Pontenia attacking willows inoculates them with its ovipositor with very delicate precision, so that only certain cells of the willow react. Imagine all this precision developing in stages!

Certain fungi surround tree roots, forming Mycorrhizae. They probably live off the root tissues, but they also act as rootlets for the root. Probably most trees and larger plants have such symbiotic nutritive arrangements.

Luminescence in many animals is due to parasitic symbionts, for example plankton, luminous insects such as the cucujo, various abyssal fishes. In fish the light organs may even involve lenses and reflectors, which can be in many different parts of the body. In Java a fish, Equila splendens, has a luminescent ring at the entrance to the stomach, furnished with a reflector ,and the adjacent ducts are crammed with bacteria. Was this evolved for use? A luminous fluid crammed with bacteria occupies the luminescent mandible of a Japanese fish, Monocentras japonicus.

Final Considerations

Considering all the adaptations involved in reproduction amongst parasites Caullery observes "the mind is much attracted towards a teleological explanation". On any other basis "the problem is to know how they have been achieved." But he rejects the teleological (creationist) explanation "a priori". One wonders how a scientist (seeker of truth) can be cavalier about this crucial point. Caullery goes on to offer two very weak alternatives, namely pre-adaptation, or some unique property of the egg and its environment. He compares these changes to those modifications induced in tissue cultures by changing environmental conditions. All this explains what?

Of the symbiosis of plants and the Metazoa, Caullery says, "we find adaptations whose origin poses, as is always the case, problems of extreme difficulty. What has brought about the establishment and permanence of these assocations which have become characteristic of the organism concerned, and are as precise and stable in their final structure and morphogenesis as the other elements concerned in the structure of the species". The evolutionist has increasing troubles as he learns more biology. The facts do not fit his theory. Caullery goes on: "The symbionts in each species are clearly defined; even the number of mycetocytes is fixed. There are some insects . . . which possess two or even several species of symbionts. The respective proportion of these species is constant, the number of mycetocytes corresponding to each of them being fixed. The host organism appears as a precise regulating mechanism of symbiosis, capable in certain cases of eliminating the symbionts at a definite time by expulsion or by lysis." How wonderful!

Summary

In conclusion the complexity of the world of parasites defies description or classification. It is subtle, complex and intricate beyond belief. Its facts must stagger the evolutionist who, be it noted, knew very little about parasitology when the theory was formulated. This is another instance of the evolutionist speaking too soon.

CHAPTER VII

Wasps, Ants, Bees

But for my choice I'd be a bee,
Pollen garter at my knee,
Scorn of acres in my wings,
Queens to suit my marryings,
Busy in tranquility
With summer's cloth set just for me.

—Vere Jameson

PROPOSITION—The lives of the social insects defy evolutionary explanation. These insects arose suddenly, de novo—apparently by creation.

Antiquity

Wheeler (61)* points out that a small number of ant species have been found in Eocene deposits—but a greater number have been found in Baltic amber of Lower Oligocene age, from Miocene shales in Europe and the United States, and in Sicilian amber. The fossil ants usually belong to extinct species, but most belong to existing genera, and "none of the species is more primitive in structure and habits than many now existing. Indeed, many of them are quite as highly specialized as the most specialized existing forms. We are therefore unable to detect any significant evolution of the ants as a whole during the millions of years of Tertiary time." In the Lower Oligocene at least six of the seven existing subfamilies and many modern genera were established. What is still more interesting is that the amber shows even the plant lice the ants tended and a few characteristic ant guests (Paussidae) and parasites (mites). They "had parasitic mites attached to their legs in the very same peculiar positions as in our living species." Some species are practically indistinguishable from modern species. Indeed, a typical modern kind of ant from the Green River Eocene has now been described. Social bees, wasps and termites are also found in the Baltic amber.

All this might seem to indicate that there has been no notable evolution of the group, but only a gradual extinction of species among a very considerable number that were suddenly created and distributed over the globe. But Wheeler goes on quickly: "Such a conclusion is unwarranted. We are bound to assume, on the contrary, that the significant vespoid or wasp-like forms among which the ants had their origin must have lived before Tertiary time"—which indicates how the evolutionist is driven to extrapolate a history for which there

---

*Quoted by permission of Constable and Co. Ltd., London, England.

is not a particle of evidence. As Wheeler indicates, all the 6000 species, subspecies and varieties of ants are social, whereas most of the wasps and bees are still solitary. This means that the ants have evolved further, from "an earlier date in geological time." Here is an example of another dilemma. There is no evidence for such priority of evolution of social forms, but the evolutionist is convinced that societal organization is superior to and therefore must arise after and from solitary forms—although he sees the latter all around him in Nature leading perfectly adapted solitary lives, even among wasps and bees; such a situation clearly indicates competitive contemporaneity of both ancestral and descendant types in our own day! What logic!

Termites are old, too. A genus now confined to Northern Australia had representatives in the Eocene and Miocene, and other genera appear in the Baltic amber.

General Note

The literature is impossible to study exhaustively, of course. For example, in 1922 there were 20,000 titles on the honey bee alone in one library at Washington. There are about 10,000 species of bees described.

Ants and termites have domesticated other animals too. Social organizations analogous to ours "have arisen at least 24 different times in five orders of insects."

Commensalism in Beetles

Silvanid beetles occur in the hollow leaf-petioles of a tree called Tachigolia paniculata. They gnaw grooves inside the stem. Then small mealy-bugs enter the stems, settle in these grooves, and suck the plant juices. Both the larvae of the beetles and their adults stroke the mealy-bugs and feed on the honey-dew their backs exude. Several may assault the same mealy-bug, the stronger butting the others out of the way. As the tree grows, ants enter, oust the beetles, and adopt the bugs!

Ambrosia beetles excavate galleries in trees and grow larvae, which in their turn are very solicitous of the eggs and the very tender young of the same parents. Each species grows a pure culture of its own peculiar fungus, which the mother beetle has brought from her last home in a basket on her head, or in her stomach.

Wasp Instincts

Wheeler says only 800 wasp species are clearly social—but only 5 percent have been well studied. Human ignorance of insects alone is so great that one wonders how a theory thought out a century ago can be made to cover the new facts constantly being brought to light, but still largely unknown.

Solitary wasps prey on other insects, usually a specific species, genus or family—even on a particular sex. Thus the common wasp, Aphilanthops frigidus, preys only on queen ants. The wasp stings its prey reflexly as soon as the latter has been seized and touches the wasp's sternum. The stinging goes on till the prey lies inert. The sting can be so antiseptic as to preserve the prey for weeks or months. Wheeler* (62) ascribes this sort of thing to "recall experience" and ensuing "condensation" in individual behaviour—thus there is nothing supernatural about instinct, and the neodarwinians and mutationists are equally at fault, he claims. However, "racial experience" and "condensation" are abstract, unprovable theories, a scientific misuse of otherwise rational words; such terms are far harder to understand than teleological explanations.

Ant and Other Commensalism

Wasmann, in 1895, is said to have estimated that there was commensal life in 1246 species of ants, 993 of beetles, 184 of other insects, 60 of arachnids and 9 of Crustaceans. Commensal insects are usually permanently located in the nests of particular species. Indeed, there are ants like Formica sanguinea which capture and cherish a parasite (Lomechusa) even to the exclusion of their own young,—and yet this insect eventually kills off the ant colony which has raised it. The evolutionist has a puzzle here since he demands that usefullness assist change. In other ant hills the larvae of Claviger are raised, by Lasius, for example, but Claviger does not harm its host. The larva of the fly, Metopina pachycondylae, forms a collar about the ant larva (Pachycondyla vorax) and protrudes its mouth to snatch morsels offered the host ant larva. The ant keeps it clean in return! Ants seek and capture caterpillars of the Lycaenidae, which exude a secretion from their abdominal glands. The caterpillars even protrude the opening of these glands as structures to be sucked! The ants herd these caterpillars in flocks. Imagine caterpillars learning to cooperate with their captors thus by evolutionary processes! The ants that rear and milk aphids are classics. These ants even pasture their captives.

Some insects are structurally modified for their commensal life. Some beetles, for example, develop huge abdomens by fat hypertrophy. Caullery thinks this could be due to hereditary overfeeding!

Thomson tells of the tailor ant, Polyrhachis, whose grubs make a nest of leaves by spinning silk threads. The caterpillar of the moth, Wurthia, lives in the same nest and helps spin these threads, although these ants fiercely repel other intruders. Sometimes such a caterpillar rides about in an ant's pupa-case. If the ants move, the little caterpillar clings to cocoons, or larvae, or egg clumps, and develops anew in the new nest. It eats many ant-grubs in growing up—but its cocoons

---

*Quoted by permission of the MacMillan Co., of New York, U.S.A.

incorporated in the wall of the ant nest make the latter appreciably stronger! The ants could devour the caterpillars at any time, but do not. The caterpillars seem quite helpless outside the ant's nest.

Caterpillars of another moth, Batrachidia, live in the nest of another kind of Polyrhachis ant and strengthen the wall with their spinning, while eating ant grubs. The ants tolerate no other caterpillars. The caterpillars of another species of Batrachidia live in commensal relations with a South African spider.

Polyergus rufescens, the Amazon ant, is a good warrior. It carries off the pupae of species like Formica fusca and Formica nufibarbis. But its mandibles have lost their masticating edge and its workers cannot even feed themselves; they depend on their slaves for survival. Imagine this development taking place **gradually** by evolutionary processes. Admittedly, "the truth is certainly less simple" than the theories of explanation offered to date.

Ants harbour more than 2000 species of ant guests, insects, spiders, mites, millipedes and even land crustaceans, For example, the fly, Metopina pachycondylae, lays its eggs on the larva of a Ponerine ant, the larva of the fly stealing food from the ant larva by the peculiar method mentioned above. When the ant pupates it encloses the fly larva in its silken cocoon, in which the fly goes to the safe posterior end and pupates. The ant hatches first,—then the fly escapes through the hole made by its host. The ant larva is unharmed by its parasite throughout. Here is almost perfect commensalism.

The mites of the genus Antennophorus attach themselves **symmetrically** on the body of a host ant so as to balance the burden they produce. There they steal food from the ant's mouth, or stroke it to make it regurgitate, or reach out to steal from passing ants! Imagine so perfect a scheme evolving slowly! In New England the Lasius ants tend plant-lice and mealy-bugs on the roots of trees. There are Antennophorus mites in the group, too, and when the ants milk honeydew from lice or bugs, the mites beg the ants for it and are given some because they ape the antennary movements of hungry ants with their long, hairy forelegs!

Many ants tend and preserve a great variety of beetles whose aromatic secretions are enjoyed by the ants. The beetles, and their larvae too, solicit food from the ants by stroking them. Many of these beetles later eat the ant larvae as well. However, the ants and beetle larvae need to be buried to pupate. Only the ant pupae should be unearthed later—if beetle pupae are brought up they die. The solicitous ants unearth **all** they find, as their own brood requires—thus unwittingly revenging themselves on many beetle larvae for killing off ant larvae! Here is an automatic equilibrium in Nature!

Ants and Plants

More amazing still are the myrmecophilous plants, which have hollow swellings or hollow spines or other such adaptations to shelter ants. They supply food to the ants. The latter protect the plants from animals that attack their foliage. These ant practices were long used as arguments for natural selection,—but now it appears that the ants exploit the tree although the tree does not need the ant. The ants die if the tree is felled.

The Attiine ants grow fungi for their young. Each species of these ants grows its own particular fungus and tolerates no other. **Such fungi are not found elsewhere in Nature.** How did the ants first acquire the habit and how did they develop what Wheeler calls "such consummate skill" in its culture? The queen takes a good meal of fungus before her marriage flight, and when she settles, gardens is carefully, **even breaking up some of her eggs in order to fertilize it.**

Ant Allies

Certain brigand ants construct nests near or on the nest mounds of travelling ants of the genus Pogonomyrinex. Thief ants may build nests whose galleries connect with those of their prey but are too large for the latter to enter. The genus Carebara has a queen several thousand times as large as her workers. On her nuptial flight the latter attach themselves symmetrically to her legs, are thus carried to her new nest, and there tend her first brood.

In British Guiana two ant species live together—a small black Crematogaster and a large brown Camponotus. The former occupies the superficial part of the common nest-mound and rushes out to repel minor intruders. A more serious assault on the nest brings out the larger and more vicious Camponotus from deeper in the mound, the little black ants being mere skirmishers for the latter. The two species live and breed absolutely separately! In New England Leptothorax workers penetrate Myrmica galleries, and ride the Myrmica workers while petting the latter and now and then taking some regurgitated food from the Myrmica. But the Leptothorax permits no Myrmicas to intrude into its own galleries.

Ant Slaves

Some predator ants kidnap and adopt the young of other species, the latter growing up to be hostile to their own species, Formica sanguinea being a good example of this. But some subspecies of sanguinea do not do this, or later forget to do it! How shall the evolutionist explain this? Here is an instinct in all its variants inside a single ant species! And here one might comment that many closely allied bird, fish and other **species** have slightly different but essential instincts—about food plants, for example. The instinct has evolved pari passu with the morphological change, which is **most** remarkable—or a mindful Creator has found a new combination by turning the wards in the nuclear lock somewhat differently.

An Ant Enemy

A parasitic bug haunts the paths of one ant species, Dolichodorus bituberculatus. It shows its trichomes to this ant, but no other, and exudes a paralysing substance from them that the ant loves. The ant eats it and so becomes paralysed. The bug now sucks it dry and leaves it lifeless. **The nymph and adults of the bugs work alike** in luring ants of this species to their destruction. Imagine the evolution of such a process!

An Unusual Wasp Marriage

Several females of the wasp Scleroderma may cooperate in paralysing the same beetle larva and then may lay their eggs on it cooperatively. The males as soon as they emerge burrow their way into the cocoons of the females and fecundate them while they are still pupae! Imagine this habit evolving step by step!

The Hunting Wasp

The hunting wasps operate in the hottest months and, of course, cannot leave a pile of as many as 20 putrefying caterpillars for their young. Hence the wasps paralyse the caterpillars but leave them alive for the sake of the fragile egg they lay on each. These wasps hunt only one class of insects. To paralyse a beetle the wasp may do so in one stab. With other prey the ganglia may be separated widely and need several stabs. But the Ammophila preys on caterpillars having 13 segments and therefore having 13 separate ganglia to be stung separately. What an anatomist! The base of the brain is delicately bitten also, perhaps 20 times, since the wasp must not bite too hard and so kill the caterpillar. (The palsy is sometimes imperfect, even at that). Crompton (63) points out that one of the most wonderful things about the hunting wasp is that it provides just the right amount of food for its young. Too little food and the grub would starve. Too many caterpillars and the putrefying bodies would poison the nursery. But if it has provided two crickets and you take one away, it provides two more, making three, and therefore the larva does not survive. The paralysed grasshopper prey may eat (if fed) and live as long as 40 days, Fabre (64) found.

There is a big larva of the Cetonia beetle which has legs but elects to travel on its back! When in danger it doubles up tightly. However this larva has its controlling ganglion in one spot, under the neck. Here the wasp can reach it—the only spot it could reach. How anatomically unfortunate for the grub and lucky for the wasp. How did the wasp choose this particular grub? When it lays an egg on this grub its larva must not kill the grub too soon. It must mind its manners and carefully dodge all vital organs as long as it can. It does this by eating in a fixed direction. If taken up and planted elsewhere it eats improperly, kills the grub, and dies itself. The paralysed grub ordinarily can live about nine months. Imagine all these supremely accurate anatomical and soundly timed physiological devices developing piece-meal or by mutations according to evolutionary theory!

The wasps Odynerus and Eumenes hang their egg on a thread from the roof of their cells, and place 2 or 3 caterpillars directly under it—then about 20 farther away. When the egg splits the tiny larva hangs down and carefully nibbles at one caterpillar beneath. The grub wiggles—so the wasp larva retreats, returns, retreats, till it eats more, grows, and the caterpillar has vanished. After it has eaten the three under it, it drops from its thread and eats the other caterpillars farther off.

A drone fly, Volucella inanis, says Crompton, is a scavenger of the cells of the wasp Pegomyia. Her larvae wriggle over the combs, ignored by the wasp nurses, squeeze in and out of the cells past their occupants and are safe—other similar maggots one introduces are killed! Evolution?

A Wasp Enemy

The beetle, Rhipiphorus paradoxus, is a very wise parasite. Its larva waits on a post till a wasp comes by. They the beetle larva leaps on it and is carried to the wasp's nest, where it eats into the body of a wasp grub. But it avoids harming important parts of the grub, grows bigger, then bores its way out of the grub without killing it. As it does so it plugs the hole it has made in the grub's body with its own moulted skin. Then it attaches itself to the grub and carefully sucks its juices—just enough, and no more. The grub finally spins a cocoon around both, whereupon the beetle larva eats its host, metamorphoses in the cocoon that is now the coffin of its host, and emerges as a beetle. What timing and technique and dexterity for an evolutionist to explain!

New Wasps

In 1958 two genera of parasitic wasps were found (65) in subtropical America, wasps whose eggs are laid inside caterpillars and whose young carefully eat the fats and fluids of the bodies of their hosts without injury to vital structures. The hosts may continue to thrive, at least till the mature wasp larva breaks out. So much remains to be learned about the world of living things that it is still unwise to shackle it too soon to a tight theory like evolution.

76

A Note on Spiders

A spider lives inside the pitcher-plant of Malaya, taking first choice of the plant's game, but discarding its rejects and offal into the pool of the plant. The spider even immerses in the dreadful fluid below it when in danger, often for minutes at a time. In doing so its spiracles are protected by hairs which hold a film of air. When it emerges it wipes dry its hard chitinous coat. How could this amazing habit and delicately adapted structure evolve?

The Ichneumon fly lays its egg in a saddle-like depression on a temporarily paralysed spider's back. This is the only place where the spider host cannot reach it. The grub feeds on its host while the spider eats, mates and even lays. At just the right moment the grub kills the spider, eats it, grows big and pupates. Other Ichneumons lay in a cocoonful of spider eggs; timing is very essential here, for if the spider eggs hatch first their young eat the ichneumon's eggs.

The radii of a spider's web are spaced so regularly they do not differ by an angle of more than one or two degrees.

Termites

Many termites grow fungi, too. Termites may nest in the nests of other termites and steal their food or fungi. The species never intermix colonies, however. Infusoria occur in many species of termites, probably helping the latter to digest wood.

Termites disintegrate dead plant matter, dry grasses, but are a great menace to all wooden structures, houses, even books. Wheeler says they are "the subtlest enemies of the historian and archaeologist" because they have eaten so many books.

Summary

The social insects, spiders and termites are amongst the most wonderful creatures on the earth. Their societies have often been compared to that of man, but perhaps human groups suffer by the comparison. How habits and instincts of their complexity, involving such subtle interdependence, have evolved piece-meal and by intermediate stages or by mutations passes ordinary understanding. Now when evolutionists discuss the social insects they tend to classify them into arbitrary stages of development, the solitary insect preceding the social type, and so forth. There is no evidence that such a sequence ever existed in palaeontological history, and no evidence that there ever was a precursor of any such social type as the wasp or bee. Indeed, social instincts have no value, surely, until they are **completely** social. Let the evolutionist continue to pore over this difficulty.

CHAPTER VIII

Blood Groups

The terrible anonymity of name
Shared with the fools and rogues wet with your blood
Within the misalliance of their veins.

—Vere Jameson*

PROPOSITION—The blood groups have long been used to demon-strate the affinity of man and apes. They do not do so—nor do they demonstrate the affinities of human races, even of adjacent tribes. We have outgrown this argument.

Introduction

I said initially that I did not propose to follow the classical approach to Evolution but would deal with various items in relation to the theory as they strike a medical man. Hence the long jump at this stage from ants to blood groups.

The attitude of the evolutionist as of 1909 could be illustrated by Thomson's quotation from Schwalbe. The latter was referring to a rabbit anti-serum, which this animal forms against human blood after the latter is injected into the rabbit, and its precipitin reactions with other primate bloods: "The reaction to the blood of the lower Eastern monkeys is weaker, that to the western monkeys weaker still; indeed, in this last case there is only a slight clouding after a considerable time, and no actual precipitate. The blood of the Lemuridae (so-called half-monkeys) gives no reaction, or an extremely weak one; that of the other mammals none whatever. We have in this not only a proof of the literal blood-relationship between man and apes, but the degree of relationship with the different main groups of apes can be determined beyond possibility of mistake."**

By contrast look at J. Maynard Smith's book on Evolution, per-haps the most recent discussion in English. He has a good deal to say of human blood groups,—but not a word to say of any animal relation-ships. What has produced the change in polemic?

Dewar has a fine chapter on this topic, written 30 years ago, it is true, which helps to explain the true picture. He reverts to Nuttall's original data (1904) and quotes his table of results on precipitin reactions.

---

*Quoted by permission of the Ryerson Press, Toronto, Canada
**Quoted by permission of the Yale University Press, New Haven, U.S.A.

Anti-Human Serum Reactions

	No Reaction	Faint Reaction	Med. Clouding	Marked Clouding	Full Reaction
97 primates:					
34 Human (4 races)	—	—	3(8%)	7(21%)	24(71%)
8 Anthropoid Apes (3 species)	—	—	—	—	8
36 Old World Monkeys (26 species)	3	—	26(72%)	3(8%)	4(10%)
13 New World Monkeys (9 species)	3	2(15%)	5(38%)	3(23%)	—
4 Marmosets (3 species)	2	1	1	—	—
2 Lemurs	2	—	—	—	—
29 Bats	26	3(10%)	—	—	—
15 Insectivora	13	2(13%)	—	—	—
97 Carnivores	70	13(13%)	14(14%)	—	—
65 Rodents	53	7(11%)	5(7%)	—	—
70 Ungulates	40	19(27%)	11(16%)	—	—
3 Cetacea	—	3(100%)	—	—	—
13 Edentates	12	1(7%)	—	—	—
26 Marsupials	25	1(4%)	—	—	—
1 Monotremes	1	—	—	—	—
320 Birds	319	1(3%)	—	—	—
49 Reptiles	49	—	—	—	—
14 Amphibians	14	—	—	—	—
19 Fish	19	—	—	—	—
7 Crustaceans	7	—	—	—	—

"When commenting upon the results embodied in the above table, Nuttall lays great stress on the fact that the maximum reaction occurs only amongst the Humans, Anthropoids and Old World Monkeys. He considers this to prove the close blood relationship of these three groups. If so, it proves that some of the human beings experimented on were less closely related than the anthropoid apes to their fellowmen, since all anthropoids but only 71 per cent of humans show full reaction to anti-human serum. Moreover, three of the humans exhibit closer relationship to some Old World and New World monkeys than they do to some of their fellow-men; Indeed, some of them are as nearly related to carnivores, rodents and ungulates as to their own kind. This, as Euclid would say, is absurd.

"These anti-serum reactions regarded as tests of kinship teem with similar absurdities. They show that some whales are more nearly related to man than some monkeys are." . . .

One has only to read the pages of any book on blood group studies, Gates (66) for example, to realize the vast confusion in blood group studies carried out on the races of man, which sometimes differ among themselves more than they differ from other primates. The lack of inference derivable from human blood agglutination studies should apply equally well to primate relationships and differences generally.

The gorilla, orang-utang and gibbon have blood groups A and B but not O, and the chimpanzee has an A agglutinogen, probably identical with human A, and also O, but no type B and consequently, of course, no AB. It may be that gorillas have two kinds of B. Hooton (67)* attempted to explain this by a community of blood groups amongst human beings and anthropoid apes, the human inheriting these from ape-like precursors. However, he had to concede that there must have been an evolutionary mutation of such agglutinogens independently in various human stocks and in the several apes. He pointed out an outstanding example of the puzzles of the problem by citing the blood groups of the long isolated Ona and Yahgan tribes living immediately adjacent to each other on Tierra del Fuego.

Group	Investigator	No. tested	O	A	B	AB
Ona	Rabin	18	94.4	5.6	0	0
Yahgan	Rabin	33	9.0	0	91.0	0

He remarked that "it would seem that the present distribution of the blood groups does not greatly illuminate the prehistoric migrations of man, if it is necessary to start with a wholly gratuitous assumption of the blood group composition of earliest man and then throw the onus of subsequent changes almost entirely upon hypothetical isolations of small groups and the vagaries of chance." . . .

It is possible to draw up a table—and, indeed, Hooton has done so,—which shows that peoples physically and racially about as unlike as they could possibly be may possess an almost identical blood group distribution, such pairs of people being Eskimos and Australian aborigines, Negrito pygmies and Russians, South Africans and Melanesians, Californians and Tunisian whites, Buriats and Negro Bambarras. It is quite evident that blood groups are inherited quite independently of racial relationships. Hooton goes on to say, "In human serology, as far as present data serve us, there is not even any consistent mutual association of the various antigen series that have been discovered; the O, A, and B groups; the M and N types; the Rh-positive and Rh-negative systems; the P-positive and P-negative systems to be inherited independently . . . We have absolutely no clue as to the relationship (of serological races) with taxonomic morphological races in primitive human times, nor, for that matter, any indication that the mathematically possible serological combinations ever existed as 'pure' serological races . . . We can hardly discard the ordinary anthropological criteria of race in favour of serology.

---

*Quoted by permission of G. P .Putnam's Sons, New York, U.S.A.

The reconstruction of primitive races and prehistoric migrations that are based upon serology (at least as respects the standard blood groups) are even more speculative and implausible than those that result from the study of skulls and bones . . . We shall continue to call a gorilla a gorilla and a chimpanzee a chimpanzee, even if they belong to the same blood group . . . No physical anthropologist can afford to dismiss the data of serology as irrelevant, merely because it does not jibe with conventional anthropometric technique . . ." Using blood groups to establish genetic relationships between man and other primates is like claiming a genetic relationship between man and the octopus or man and the cow because their eyes are so similar. In the octopus and cow this phenomenon is called convergence!

Weitz (68) tells of the troublesome cross-reactions in precipitin tests, for example the positive reaction when anti-horse serum was tested with rhinoceros antigen; no reaction was produced when ox antigen was tested against an eland anti-serum; a good reaction was obtainable when goat antigen was tested against the anti-serum of Thomson's gazelle and the hartebeast, even against the duiker—this last group belonging to a different family! He found that a chimpanzee inoculated intramuscularly with human serum produced a specific anti-serum (of low titre) active only against human antigen, but inactive against chimpanzee or other primate antigens!

This confusion is seen even in a tiny single-celled protozoan like Paramoecium, against which one can produce antigens in rabbits. But these serotypes can change over within a single line of descent—as many as 14 different serotypes have been found within a single such line, indeed. Moreover, such changes are reversible. Different strains of the same variety can show different serotypes, and more are continually being found as more strains are studied, says Sonneborn (4).

Mourant (69) discusses the blood group findings in various species in detail. Cattle and horses have in their saliva, either, both or neither of the antigens A and B; these are indistingushable from those of human saliva. Many rabbits have in their serum and tissues an antigen nearly indistinguishable from human A. The deer-mouse has a group of species giving strong agglutinations with human anti-A and anti-B sera—and a group giving weak or no reactions! Most dogs have a specific agglutinin for human A cells. Red blood cells of numerous mammalian species contain B_2 but they never contain B_1—although the sera of such animals may contain anti-B_1.

Very much more could be said about animal and human blood groups, but it is evident that all the polymorphism in the genes controlling blood groups could be due to random fluctuation. Any similarities that appear are just as apt to be due to change or convergence as to inheritance.

Mourant* concludes: "It will have been noticed that little use has been made of our knowledge of the blood groups of the primates in the formulation of suggestions as to how the main distribution of the human blood groups arose. This is because we know relatively little of primate blood groups and also little of primate and human population genetics. We need to know much more about the distribution of antigens related to the human blood-group antigens in a wide variety of primate species, - - -. "

It would seem, therefore, that the older evolutionary arguments derived from blood type similarities seem to have gone out the window as more has been learned about them. Now they have been made even more difficulty by the finding of anti-A and anti-B human haemagglutinins in plants. Are we related to such a non-leguminous plant as Hyptis swaveolens or some of the species of Euonymes of the family Celastraceae (70)? When your friend refers to you as "old bean" perhaps he means it!

Perhaps one could comment here very briefly on an analogous type of puzzle that arises in respect to sex chromosomes (71). Very odd relationships can be deduced from them—the idea, for example, that genealogically salamanders resemble sauropsids (birds and reptiles) while frogs resemble mammals. Similarly the opossum is exceptional among mammals in its similarity to reptiles, and the frog very like the Eutheria (placental mammals) while unlike the toad and salamander. Now surely sex chromosomes should have been more considerate than blood groups in indicating to us clearly what the relationships between animals is. They prove to be no more helpful. The evolutionist really has troubles.

Then there is still another puzzle recently introduced by students of tissue enzymes (72). The heart enzyme (lactic dehydrogenase) of the salamander is quite different from that of the frog, and such flatfish as the flounder, sole and halibut react distinctly differently from this enzyme found in other vertebrates. The heart lactic dehydrogenase of the dogfish is more like that of the grass frog and the lamb than it resembles that of the herring, flounder or sole. The herring enzyme seems to be in a class by itself.

If these enzyme studies throw light on individual ontogeny it is a slightly confused light, too. For example, the heart muscle lactic dehydrogenase and that of dark muscle are much alike in the mackerel, trout, herring, butterfish, scup, dogfish and chicken, but in the sea robin and salamander the enzymes from the light and dark muscles are alike and different from the heart enzyme.

On the other hand, if we study malic dehydrogenases, human muscle reacts much like that of the horseshoe crab, although clam and halibut muscles show great differences.

---

*Quoted by permission of Blackwell Scientific Publications Ltd., Oxford, England.

Thus a classification of animal relationships based on their tissue enzymes may be as unhelpful as any of the types of studies mentioned earlier in this chapter, although of perhaps equal validity. This must have the up-to-date evolutionist very confused, I am sure.

Summary

It is abundantly clear that the blood groups have now shown such marked and often theoretically unexplainable variations among the races of man that it is asking too much to utilize their distribution in sera and tissues to provide evolutionary clues below the human level. Such attempts either prove too much, such as our similarity to rodents and whales, or that humans differ more from one another than from chimpanzees, or that gorillas are much more distant from us than chimpanzees and orangs, or that we share blood groups with plants, or that the most topsy-turvy relationships exist throughout the world of mammals and birds. Since serology cannot be used to explain the relationships of human races, since that would integrate widely different and disparate nations, they can scarcely tell us more reliably of our relations to other animals, even primates.

Certainly evolutionists are much less certain of this schedule of argument than they were 50 or even 25 years ago. They tend to leave it open for further exploration or to pass it by completely. Let us do the latter, since at the moment its relevance to our discussion is far from obvious.

CHAPTER IX

Evolution and Visual Beauty

"Yellow birds guard Huexotzinco among the waters,
Among the flowery waters, the golden waters,
The emerald waters, at the junction of the waters
which the blue duck rules
Moving her spangled tail."

—Ancient Nahuatl poetry
translated by D. G. Brinton

PROPOSITION—Beauty is so widespread in the world of life, so complex, so thoroughly adjusted to need, that it defies evolutionary explanation.

Introduction

If the natural world developed by the evolutionary mode out of single protozoan cells or viruses or such, which could have had no beauty because they were so minute, simple and colourless, then the appearance of visual beauty in our present world demands an explanation. Did it evolve by itself and of itself? Since so much of such visual beauty appears to be quite needless, except for the aesthetic gratification of man (and God?), how shall such useless, and yet widespread and complex visual beauty, be explained? I contend that evolution completely fails to explain either its origin or development or perfection. Let us analyse the visual beauty of animate nature with this problem in mind.

What is Colour?

What is colour in animals? It is due only in part to pigment. For example, the peacock or humming-bird owe their splendor less to pigment than to a peculiar and subtle modification of the horny surface of their feathers,—which could scarcely be useful. Blue is usually due to a pigment, but in butterflies, birds and the mandrill the blue is structural, and green is due to a combination of pigment and structure much as has been mentioned. Green is pigmentary, however, in marine worms, corals and sea anemones. The iridescence of mother-of-pearl is solely due to an unuseful modification of the structure of the shell. But the dark brown and black pigments of hair and feathers are melanins derived from (red) haemoglobin, as is the blue of birds' eggs. The yellow pigment of some butterflies is a derivative of uric acid, and guaninin which gives fishes their pearly lustre is another waste product! Carotin in plants and the red colour of salmon are due to lipochromes, fat- soluble pigments. Red is always due to pigment, and is most brilliant in the deepest abysses of the sea!

84

Then there is the "powder" sack of certain feathers in herons, some hawks and many parrots. This powder gives "bloom" to the feathers, but why is a mystery. What is still more mysterious is that many if not all pigeons also have "powdered" plumage, but no "powder-down" feathers.

What controls the destination of pigments—the blue that does not colour a bird put paints its egg? Why is turacin found only in some species of Plantain-eaters and even there is seen only in certain areas of the flight-feathers? Why patterns? Every theory copes with such puzzles in vain.

There is, however, recent information on the colouring of the wings of moths and butterflies that suggests the importance of colour, although not of the *particular* colour patterns they display. Burton (73) tells us that the wing scales are important for flight. Brush them off and the insect is partially crippled. He quotes studies of Paul Portier which demonstrate not only a circulation of blood through the wings in a family which includes the burnet moths, but also a circulation of air, both essential to flight. Plug either circulation and the insect cannot fly. Moreover, a wing scale is more than a flattened bristle. It is ornamented with ridges and is hollow, even compartmented. The wing colour is important in absorbing or reflecting heat and therefore in setting up such convection currents as will aid or impede the circulation of the blood and air in the wings. It was found, for example, that the red markings on the wings of a swallowtail butterfly are responsible for 98 per cent of the heat absorbed. This does not explain the patterns, of course, purely the surface areas involved. The beauty of the patterns still remains an evolutionary mystery.

Phosphorescence, Luminescence

Phosphorescence can be found in many animals, from protozoa to fishes, and in many bacteria and fungi, also in glow-worms and fire-flies. The hermit-crab carries about an anemone which gives off a strong light and which lives off the crab's rejected food. Then certain deep-sea prawns possess photophores (light cells) placed so as to illuminate the interior of the gill-cavities, a completely useless role, surely. The female glow-worm may use her light to warn birds she is unpalatable, but her mate has wings and no light! In the tropics even the winged forms carry a light, for there are more predators, bats and birds. There the palatable Gloteridae mimic glow-worm lights.

The abyssal fish, Opisthoproctus, has a rectal light organ directed downward. Its wall is thin and transparent, although elsewhere the skin is thickened. It even has a reflector, which suggests it may guide other like fish toward it, since they happen to have upwardly directed tubular eyes. Light organs communicating with the gut and emitting light through transparent structures are found in shallow water Pergomorphi.

Luminous microbes have no obvious use. For example Nicol says it has been calculated that if the dome of St. Peter's were covered with luminous bacteria this would emit only as much light as one candle.

Colour Changes

Many fishes in coral reefs can suddenly change colour. In cuttle-fish, fish, amphibia and some reptiles the skin can change colour due to its chromatophores and iridiocyte cells. Butterflies have their colour patterns laid out as exquisite mosaics of scales. Indeed, in Papilios the upper and lower surfaces may have totally different patterns with only a thin, thin membrane between.

Pycraft comments on the mystery that makes the beauty of the gorgeous Argus pheasant, where rods side by side in the feathers are coloured to make characteristic eyes and bars, always perfectly and uniquely the pattern of that species—and able to change to other definitive patterns in other seasons! Some species having just one annual moult have two distinct plumages, for example the Linnet, Brambling and Snowbunting! Curiously enough, the pigments of birds are never detectable in the making. Egg colours are even more elusive, since they are laid down in the oviduct, but no one has ever found these pigments in the walls of the oviduct!

The hairs of mammals may show various colours, so arranged as to form the specific patterns of Zebras or Tigers or Leopards, and there may be seasonal, sexual and age liveries as well. How can evolution explain this?

If bird colouring is determined by natural selection why are birds so differently coloured in an identical environment? Or why do they often change colour rapidly,—but sometimes as slowly as does the Great Black-backed gull which alters gradually over a period of three years?

What alters colour from intense pigmentations to none—as in the gannet which changes from white, to black with white spots, to white again—or in the lemming? Why should the two sexes in butterflies or birds often differ so widely in colour? No evolutionary principle can explain that, for "sexual selection", as Darwin proposed it, has long been dead. Wallace pointed out that female butterflies were not in the least influenced by male colours, for example.

Then there is the cone shell which has a conspicuous pattern which cannot be seen until the animal is dead and the shell has been scraped! Why should this beauty evolve?

86

A Few Remarkable Examples

The abyssal fish, Rhodicthys, is of a uniform bright red. Yet it lives at one and a half miles from the surface, in eternal night. Similarly the deep-sea Neoscopelus Macrolepidotus is brilliantly coloured with bright red, azure blue, silver spots and black circles! The deep-sea crustacea are vividly coloured in red or orange. More remarkable still are the eggs of some of the deep-sea genera, which may be a brilliant pale blue. The sea-cucumbers and sea-anemones at great depths are often brilliantly coloured, as are the branching crinoids.

The evolutionist is apt to cling to his "evolution of spots from stripes" theory, even when thinking of the Green Lizard, Lacerta ocellata, where the male loses the stripes but the more conservative female keeps the young's stripes! Imagine an evolution that evolves only one sex within the species!

"Protective colouration" is marked in the fimbriated gecko, Uroplates fimbriatus, which has skin flanges to aid its deception, and rests with its hind legs placed in unnatural positions, perhaps one directed forward and one lined up backward with the tail. Here one sees habit supplementing colour pattern. How did these evolve together, one being useless without the other,—as in bitterns, for example?

Unseen Beauty

Many structures are beautifully pigmented although rarely or never seen, for example the rose-pink down feathers of many bustards, the intense black of the body cavity of certain lizards, the greenish bones of such fish as the gar pike, African mud-fish and South American mud-fish, or the bright yellow of egg yolks, the green of bile, the bright red of blood. Why did these evolve? Some colour must be an accident of light, as that which colours the crystals of such gems as the ruby or emerald. Then there are sunrise and sunset, made by the refraction of the sun's rays on the dust and water vapour (clouds) of the atmosphere. This, like the blue of the sky ,is all an accident, but a pleasant accident for human eyes (and God's?)

The colours of many beautiful moths are swallowed up in the darkness of the night, notably such moths as the sphinxes and underwings. Sight can be no factor in their mating impulses.

Roberts (74) tells of the beetle, Emus hirtus, which closely resembles a bumble-bee—until turned over, when it is a brilliant cobalt blue. But it is quite nocturnal and lives hidden under dry cowdung!

Useless or hidden beauty must always challenge the evolutionist. Why the splendours of abyssal fish or crinoids or corals? Why the beauty in the desert or on mountain peaks or under logs? Why the beauty only to be found on shells after they are scraped, or inside animals, or in the mouths of nestlings, or in the gill-chambers of prawns, or in moths and fungi after dark? Why the cactus flower in the desert or all the vast variety of colour and form in **minute** insect eggs and the tiniest, newest caterpillars? And here we have talked only of colour, saying nothing of all that could be said about form, the architecture of the mollusc and the flower, of the mountain and the snake, the plan of the eagle and the walking-stick, or of the human liver. We have avoided the colossal beauty there must have been in the pre-human world, where no appreciative human eye could witness it for aeons upon aeons. All this means that beauty is either a happy coincidence, like the blue sky or red sunset, or the work of the greatest Designer and Aesthete of all. One must choose between a supremely stupid conclusion or the most obvious and overwhelming answer.

The colour of caterpillars is notoriously variegated, for example the larvae of the Cinnabar moth or the Buff-tip. Some larvae have brilliantly coloured, hairy coats, the hairs and body being differently coloured and altering with each moult! Indeed, the newly hatched caterpillar only 2mm. long may have its brilliantly coloured hairs arranged in complex patterns! The very eggs of butterflies, for example the Blues, may be sculptured, and that sculpturing can be resculptured! No evolutionary process could have found this either worthy of achievement or possible. How divine that it happens!

"Sexual selection", one of Darwin's brace of theories, was based largely on male colour and mating behaviour patterns. He thought male colours often evolved because thus the males were chosen by the females. Wallace promptly pointed out that this demanded more female aesthetic sense than the evidence supported, and also a uniform standard shared by all the females of a species, resulting in only one type of acceptable colour pattern.

Pycraft regards the sculpturing of wing scales in moths and butterflies, the nuances in colour of egg-shells, and the nervation and colouring of wings, as cases of "idiosyncrasies" of growth, mere free association which no inhibiting factors suppressed. Would not Design seem a better explanation?

Dinoflagellates usually have sculptured walls, minute as they are! Similarly, the two halves of diatoms fit together like a box and its cover. Their shapes are diverse, and their minute and intricate markings are the delight of microscopists. What finesse!

"Warning colouration" is often protective. Hingston (75) tells us of the Siamese toad, Callula pulchra, a brown species with a hidden yellow stripe which it shows only when alarmed and has sucked in air to become distended. The fire-bellied toad of Northern Europe, Bombinator igneus, is concealingly coloured—till alarmed. Then it turns on its back, revealing a bluish-black aspect splashed with weird red. Or it may stay on its belly and turn up its limbs, necks and the edges of its brilliant belly. It holds this posture while danger lasts.

The American toad, Bufa Americanus, also rolls over when in danger to expose a conspicuous, dark-spotted belly. Imagine this colour and audacious behaviour developing piece-meal by evolutionary processes producing the colouration which makes its actions reasonable!

Flies living in bee-hives are protectively coloured to resemble the bees. This argument could be expanded for countless other mimics, of course. Wallace told of a cricket which exactly resembled its foe, the sandwasp. Sir John Hooker found three ticks on an Indian lizard, each being coloured to suit the colour of just that part of the host's body on which it preyed—yellow, brown and parti-coloured,—probably for protection against the lizard itself.

Colour Vision

I have said very little of the beauty of form and colour in flowers. But much could be said. Why this beauty? Can it matter to the lily or the portulaca or the cactus that it should be robed more splendidly than "Solomon in all his glory"? Insects perceive colour very definitely, says Cott (76), although not in exactly the human range, and may vary widely in sensitivity, even inside an order. Colour and design are vital to some flowers, if not all. Whether shade or nuance or pattern is detected is very dubious indeed.

Allen (77) quotes old experiments on colour sense carried out by Sir John Lubbock on bees. The latter investigator found that bees could follow honey placed on paper of various colours as he interchanged the colours, usually orange and blue. Wasps were similarly alert to green and orange. Apparently ants could distinguish between the red and violet ends of the spectrum. Moreover, some plants such as the common violet have two types of flowers. The entomophilous type is beautiful, but the wind-fertilized one is inconspicuous in the extreme. Then there is the Lantana flower which has yellow, orange and purple flowers on three successive days—only the first two being touched by butterflies. In another species of the same genus, the lilac flowers show at the entrance of the tube a yellow mark surrounded by a white circle, calling visiting insects to hit a bull's eye. This lasts only one day—all that is needed, apparently. I contend that there is no use for most of such beauty unless man is that justification, or, better still, the eye of God that likes to see His creatures "good", as would any supreme artist and aesthete.

If there is some slight justification for the beauty of flowers which thus may attract insects or birds for purposes of cross-pollination, what is to be said for the beauty of foliage, even in parasitic plants? These may reveal striking colours. The maple leaf is a conspicuous example in Canada, but one could cite many another where beauty of marked character can serve no useful purpose whatever. It exists purely for beauty's own sake, apparently.

Then, too, as Allen points out, flower colouration may be nothing but an intensification of stem colour, as in Peperomia or Echeveria or Epiphylluma. Among parasites and saprophytes he cites Lastroea, Monotropa and others, whose rudimentary leaves may be as beautiful as their flowers. The design of leaves is varied and architecturally wonderful. Why? In essence such variation cannot reflect an evolutionary process based on need. What can it matter to survival if a leaf is palmate or serrate or cruciform, although the position and characters of its stomata can be quite a different matter.

Indeed, even before insect selection could ever have come into play there must have been flower colouration, for perhaps butterflies did not appear till the Tertiary, and honey-bees seem to be even more recent.

Summary

We should remember that colour and design are welded to the appropriate habit in all living things. Indeed, form and colour and habit are often necessary complementaries for survival. How could they evolve exactly pari passu? I believe that this is simply impossible, an absurd doctrine of coincidence, especially in view of the refinements and rationality of each.

Finally, why should evolution (if it be the responsible process), produce the greatest visual beauty in the flower, even the parasitic orchid, or in the coral or the goldfish or the canary or the coral snake or the shell of the Nautilus—and not in the "higher" forms, for example man or ape or cow? Can evolution have remembered the pheasant and forgotten man? Or does it move in two divergent directions at once, toward perfect colour and perfect sense, the two being incompatible? Here is a real dilemma I leave with you. The answer is still the same,—incomparable design by the Great Designer as He wills, and not for the utility that Evolution demands so consistently and inexorably, but with futility. Evolutionary theory offers no mental hand-holds on such vast uselessness brought to such glorious perfection.

CHAPTER X

Instinct and Its Puzzles

I always like a man to say
Whatever he thinks in the frankest way.
It's good to hear what he believes,
To catch the drip of his mental eaves.

—Vere Jameson

PROPOSITION—The perfection of instinct, its intricacy, its ubiquitous nature, its vital role in the preservation of thousands of forms, cannot be explained by the evolutionist. Instincts are useless unless perfect—hence could not be selectively produced piece-meal Occasionally the instinctive process can be analysed into component parts—which still does not give us any lead as to the origin of the whole.

Introduction

The study of instinct has long constituted a puzzle for the evolutionist. How explain the perfection of instinctive response appearing in such "lowly" forms as the butterfly or ant or wasp? How explain that this could develop by stages, as evolutionary theory postulates? How explain an unimaginable usefulness of imperfect instincts—instincts on the way in? How explain the correlation of instinct and colour pattern and life cycle or even of several cycles, where forms are inter-adapted? Where does instinct end and mind begin? What is instinct, anyhow?

Instinct in Predators

Fabre points out that the insects that kill their prey by instinctive skill understand the anatomy of that prey and of it only. In short, those that paralyze know how to paralyze certain species only. Thomisus, the spider that cuts bees' throats, knows the technique of the fatal blow as the Epeira spider does not.

The glow-worm, Lampyris, anaesthetizes the snails it attacks. The glow-worm can thus feed on the latter while life lingers in it. Otherwise it would decay. The snail is anaesthetized instantly and cannot escape, although fixed to a **precarious** perch by only the tiniest smear of glue. Actually the glow-worm transforms the snail into a liquid gruel where it sits, and drinks it slowly away **while the snail remains unmoved and transfixed!**

An Ammophila-grub eats its way into a caterpillar's side steadily, once it begins, never withdrawing its head. If moved to one side by force it hesitates and hunts for its old point of attachment; if the caterpillar is attacked at a new point it is apt to decay.

The Cercaris wasp stings beetles perfectly. No apprentice work here! The wasp Tachytes darts on a preying Mantis and **instantly** paralyses its arms—or the wasp would be lost! Yet to Crompton* (63) this is merely "habit so deep-rooted that it has become hereditary". He admits that his theories may be negated by aphids and cheese-mites, and, of course, I am sure they are denied by most parasites, which seem to have even more wonderful instincts that ants and wasps.

In Food

Fabre comments on the egg-laying hymenopteran, Eumenes, where the male is half the size of the female, and it therefore laid in a smaller cell. Surely its mother must have known its sex beforehand, for she leaves 5 caterpillars as food for male larvae and 10 for the others. What a wonderful example of instinctive care! The solitary bee, Osmia, does better, for she lays males or females in groups, depending on the size of the space available for her at the moment. She must be able to decide the sex of her egg at will! Apparently the impress of sex is given to the egg **at the moment of laying!** The same privilege is possessed by the wasps, at least in those species where the sexes differ in size.

Fabre was impressed by the botanical powers of Insects. The butterfly lays on a leaf whose plant has not yet put forth its identifying flower, after flitting about for just a moment. The Pieris recognizes the Crucifer before the expert botanist can. "Where science is apt to make mistakes, instinct is infallible", he said in wonder, for he himself had been an enthusiastic botanist for over 50 years. Moreover, the Pieris has a calendar that tallies with the gardener's, and lays her eggs just in time for cabbage leaves to develop in order to feed her young.

This type of analysis has been carried much farther. Leppik (78) says a flower is recognized as a whole by pollinating insects. He postulates a remarkable series of special symbols and numerals which anthophilous insects can remember and distinguish. It is really an "alphabet" analogous to the "language" and "dances" of bees. Thus a literate insect can distinguish hundreds of plant species from each other, and recognize food sources from far away.

Acworth (79) quotes Newman on the specificity of food plant and therefore of the egg-laying site chosen by butterflies. Where there are exceptions the botanical knowledge displayed by the insect excites admiration, for the nearest allied species is chosen. He goes on to enlarge on the stupidity of some instinctive acts. For example, the pigeon returning to her nest will miss it if it is displaced by two inches. Fish return to the same lake or pool to breed. A returning bee

*Quoted by permission of Wm. Collins Sons & Co. Ltd., London, England.

will return unconcernedly to another hive substituted for its own. Move the old hive but a short distance away, instead of replacing it, and the bee is nonplussed. Acworth quotes Frohawk on the Blue Butterfly, which will return to a particular solitary tree year after year. Instinct is more than "potted memory". He quotes Newman on the hibernation of the Purple Emperor. The little caterpillar rests between feedings on the mid-rib of the leaf it is eating. When ready to pupate it descends from the leaf, attaches itself to the twig, and goes through the winter safely after the leaf falls. How wise it was not to stay hugging that mid-rib! What a good knowledge of botany and memory (?) of weather is implied here!

Its Persistance

Fabre also comments on the absolute symmetry of the cricket's bows on its two wings. But the right always lies over and plays on the left. All cricket musicians he found to be right-winged. When he raised a cricket with the left wing case artificially displaced to cover the right the cricket tried to play in that position, failed, then corrected its wing positions to the usual, and played!

In the Young

Crompton (80) points out that the ability to make webs is inborn in spiders, for the babies make perfect miniatures the size of postage stamps—even young males do it well, something they scorn to do as adults.

Social wasp cells are manufactured upside down. Does the new grub fall out and die? No. The egg is glued to the top of the cell and the young larva anchors its tail to the egg when it splits open. Instinct should have taught wasps to build cells otherwise, but did not do so.—Hence this unusual pattern repeated endlessly!

In Reproduction

Many male spiders are eaten by their mates after fertilization. But some are too prudent to permit this. For example, Xysticus viaticus, while caressing his mate, ties her down to the ground by silken threads till he can escape. Drassodes lepidosus and others kidnap an immature female, guard her, raise her till she can be assaulted, then escape while she is too weak to resist.

Crompton comments on the specific reproductive distinctness of such African rats as the Verraux and Brant's rat. "Does the male, full of urge, count the mammae of the female, finding 6 instead of the necessary 10 walk away? Does another, staring at a female's eyes, notice the rings and give her the said news that union between them is impossible . . . We never find rats that are a mixture of species."

In Colonies

Haskins (81) tells us that the species of fungus cultivated by ants of the genus Atta no longer exists in a state of Nature. It belongs to the mushrooms, Basidiomycetes, but does not produce mushrooms. The ants are able to cultivate it so as to develop knobs on its hyphae, a sort of ant vegetable. These provide a liquid on which the ants live solely, although their larvae are fed bits of the vegetable itself. The smallest workers do nothing but tend these gardens and exclude every other fungus. What exacting and meticulous gardeners! The pure culture is maintained for generation after generation by the young queen habitually taking some of her last meal with her, located in a special pocket near the mouth parts. When she reaches her new burrow she first of all plants the fungus, then breaks her first eggs in it to fertilize it. Not till the fungus is flourishing does she raise her first brood—and this brood may not touch the garden.

The Formicine ants include gall-dwellers, with a special caste whose function it is to plug the entrance to the oak-gall home. The silk-building ants of India, of the genus Decophylla, use their cocoon-spinning larvae as shuttles to build silken formicaries, then themselves pupate without cocoons. Rows of workers line up on leaf edges, holding them together, till a larva can be carried down between to sew the edges together. When one larva is worn out, another replaces it.

Haskins* adds: "No true pre-ant, or missing link between the ants and the wasps, is known to us . . . either living or enshrined in rock." He adds that worker ants build as well when they are just emerged as when old, and yet within the general scheme of their habits are wide variations depending on terrain and location. Thus Solenopis molesta may live among the grasses, or as a thief ant, or as a house ant. Then he goes on to say that among ants only the brains of the females have evolved—the males having merely huge optic and antennary ganglia as in the solitary wasps. Ants have not only our type of cephalic brain above the oesophagus, but goitrous masses of brain around it. Imagine only one sex of ants evolving a brain!

Haskins goes on: "A whole system of signals, very readily recognizable for any given species of ants, has been developed . . whereby a hungry ant solicits a meal from one returning full-fed."

Parasitic queen ants of Bothriomyrmex are provided with little trichomes carrying a material attractive to host workers of nests they parasitize. Indeed, Haskins says that more than 300 species of insects are harboured in ant colonies in one guise or another!

Commenting on the unlearned activities of ants Haskins says: "Where else can we find evidence of a society so perfectly constituted, the basis of whose social adjustment is removed from the mental sphere?"

---

*Quoted by permission of George Allen and Unwin Ltd., London, England

He talks about slave-making forays, such as those of Polyergus. The entire expedition is coordinated and quick and purposeful. The slaves thereafter must carry on all the activities of the colony. They build the nest according to their own style, and raise the Polyergus young. The mandibles of Polyergus can squeeze or kill a slave, but cannot eat. The tongue is so shortened the host must be fed by the slaves,—and can die in the midst of plenty if not so fed.

Another slave-maker, Strongylognathus, has splendidly menacing mandibles, but rudimentary muscles powerless to use them. The bluff of force works as well as the act could. The workers are enslaved as effectively by the threat as by force. What a triumph of interlocking instincts! The slaves now fight in their master's forays, too, in the case of Strongylognathus huberi. The slaves of Formica sanguinea become ferocious when enslaved, although normally timid. Perhaps they **learn** to fight!

Haskins is struck by the timing of the slave-raids, and of the marriage flights where all the adult colonies of a single species over many square miles of land may release their males and young queens for flight within an hour of one another on the same day! Both slaves and workers seem to take part, for they have been seen restraining over-eager mistresses or winged forms who want to leave too early. Donisthorpe (82) reported that on August 8, 1915, swarms of the black garden ant and of another species were seen simultaneously over the greater part of England.

Puzzles

If workers are recurrent mutations how can they be carried in the germ plasma of a mother having none of their features and, when produced, conform to one standard? Why do we see well marked polymorphism among workers, where all must be equally well fed? Why the intersexes which occur in some colonies? Why the long and slender ants which live in the hollows of thin stems, the flat ants in cracks, the ants with truncated heads to stop the holes of tree-galls, and so on? How can the young fertilized queen keep live sperm in her spermatheca (sperm receptacle) for years of her long life?

An ant, moving at a constant angle to the sun's rays, can find its way back to its home; but if it is imprisoned in the dark while the sun moves through an arc, when released it will set off in the wrong direction. Moreover, if the source of light is, unlike the sun, nearby, moving at a constant angle will involve moving in a spiral; that is why the moth flies to its death in a candle flame. Bees also orient themselves by the sun, but can make a correction for the time of day, as can birds. In one experiment many shear-waters released in America were unable to direct themselves on an overcast day. But on a sunny day they oriented themselves correctly in 40 seconds, and flew across the Atlantic, each to his own particular burrow off the west coast of England. Curiously, the bee brain which can correct for changes in the sun's position with time, is only 1/10 inch in diameter.

Jordan and Kellogg (83) tell of the homing instinct of the fur seal, which takes it in winter more than 3000 miles from the Pribilof islands. In the spring it returns to the same tiny islands hidden in the Arctic fog, landing often on the same spot, and year after year returns almost to the day. Were this instinct not perfect the race would vanish. They mention the California woodpeckers (Melanerpes formicivorus) of whom a large number select a certain live-oak tree, bore its bark full of acorn-sized holes, then insert acorns. Only one tree in several square miles is so filled,—then all leave. At the right time all return, open the acorns and eat them. When the acorns ripen next season they return to the same tree and repeat the process—perhaps for 50 years or more. They cite the reproductive instincts of the king salmon or quinnat, so well known but so complex, and of eels.

Dice (84) cites the studies of Graham on the tendency of sawfly larvae in Minnesota to take up position on the slender tips of tamarack branches as a very effective protection against birds.

Von Frisch' (85) studies on honey bees are now a classic and will not be described here in any detail. He showed that a worker lucky enough to find a good source of nectar could return to its hive, give the news to other bees by the scent and taste of the nectar, direct the others by a "dance" to a source ample enough to justify such a visit, and could indicate the distance to be traversed by the character of the "dance" —which could mean a trip of a mile or more.—Moreover, the exact distance, even allowing for hills, is conveyed by the number of turns in the dance, and the bees are told exactly where. The language of these little creatures seems to be perfect. For they can dance at the appropriate angle to the sun's rays, and vary this with the movements of the sun with the passing hours, even on cloudy days. It is clear that the bees follow polarized light, hence the bee's eye (perhaps the ant's eye) must be sensitive to polarized light. What a lucky instinctive adaptation, but how infinitely complicated! Steche has recently proved that the duration of a bee's dance indicates the distance to the flower source—0.4 sec. for 200 yards, 1.3 sec. for 700 yards. A rich find is indicated by a faster wiggling of the rear end. He has now managed to convey his own messages and directions to bees similarly. Bees, moreover, have an abdominal scent organ by which they signal to other bees that the flower they have found is unusually attractive.

Shipley (86)* tells how the cells of the honey bee are so laid down that only two workers may pass each other between the combs. He goes on to explain ways in which the honey bee has "evolved" further than the solitary bumble bee. All that he proves is that the latter is in many ways

---

*Quoted by permission of MacMillan Co., New York, U.S.A.

superior, does not die after stinging, for example, is more versatile in selecting food plants, has workers that can serve when two days old rather than in two weeks, and then can maintain a longer working day, as well as having a self-supporting male. Its queen is not a mere egg-laying machine. He finishes by showing how a series of more complex bee-hives can be arranged to show that: "A clearer example of evolution could hardly be imagined"—All this has done is to produce a fine example of an arranged series, where every standard is arbitrary or human, and every stage still contemporary!

Honey bees fan a hive to air-condition it and encourage dehydration of the day's collected nectar, often working all night. On hot days they spread water over the combs, to permit cooling by evaporation. The number of bees needed to fan air in and fan it out is exactly what is needed. In winter they mass on top of the cells.

The instinct of the worker bees which leads them to prevent the queen from stinging the young queens to death until the correct time is remarkable. Thus they ensure perpetuation of the colony, however. How could the instinct arise, Graebner (87) asks, which warns two queen bees engaged in combat against inflicting the mortal sting which would kill both and leave the colony to perish without a queen?

Variations and Details

Honey bees respond to colour (von Frisch), and yet will ignore it in favour of light intensity (von Hess). Different reactions have thus been induced by different releasing stimuli. Tests on memory show very variable results, depending on the criteria used. Behaviour can be vital to the taxonomist. For example the pigeons (Columbidae) cannot be characterized by any common group or morphological characters, but all have one behaviour item in common—all suck when drinking. Among other birds only sand grouse also show this habit. Two sibling species of digger wasps have recently been recognized as two distinct species by a student of behaviour. Speciation is impossible, says Tinbergen (88), without **isolating behavioural mechanisms.** Morphological critteria alone are inadequate. He goes on to indicate how sense perception plays a large role, some animals having a very acute perception of light, and responding positively or negatively to it. For example, minnows can distinguish half-tones in the pitch of sound.

Yet it can be just isolated features of the sensory field that provoke instinctive reactions. The red belly of the male three-spined stickleback provokes fighting amongst other males. The red breast of the English robin acts likewise on other robins. The red spot on the bill of the herring gull attracts the pecking of its begging chick. Short-necked bird-like shadows alarm gallinaceous birds. Tinbergen gives examples of all sorts of physical "sign" stimuli which release typical instinctive responses.

Posture and behaviour are also vital in releasing instinctive responses. Thus the female stickleback responds to the courting male when he displays his red belly and "zig-zags" to her. Definite sign stimuli control the "ceremonies" of the mating grayling butterfly, of the gaping reaction of young thrushes. Different colours may produce feeding reactions or laying reactions in the cabbage butterfly. Different stimuli are needed by the female stickleback for various phases of mating.

It can be shown, too, that normal stimuli are not always optimal The ringed plover prefers a well-marked egg to its own, and oyster-catchers prefer big eggs or five egg clutches to the normal three eggs. Many major instincts are chain reactions and can be analysed into component instincts, each setting off the next in line. Examples are a bee lighting on a flower, a digger-wasp hunting bees, or the courting movements of a pair of sticklebacks. If two reactions are antagonistic, a conflict of instinctive responses can be seen. Some cichlid fish can be conditioned to accept other species' eggs and raise them, after which they will never raise their own.

There are many puzzles, of course. How does a young cuckoo recognize and select its mate when it has never before seen its own kind? How does a male stickleback labouring under the same difficulty select pregnant females of its own kind? How do insects repeat per-formances they have never seen but which are characteristic of their race and species? These must all be examples of innate behaviour, in-explicable by any knowledge we now possess. Instinctive drives wax and wane with the seasons, with satiety, hormonal stimuli and such. Thus "injury-feigning" in the white-throat usually cannot be released a fourth time in a row. There is vacuum-behaviour, too, where instinc-tive reactions occur in the absence of stimuli, for example young honey buzzards trying to dig out a wasp's nest before they have left their own, or a male stickleback's zig-zag dance in an empty tank. Male and female hormones injected into castrates often reproduce part or most of their sex behaviours. Muscle groups are often coordinated reflexly, for example the trunk muscles of eels or the pectoral-dorsal fin rhythm in fish. "Sign" stimuli have been studied carefully and many variations in motion and special relationships uncovered. A stimulus of this type may be both releasive and directive. Apparently, Tinbergen says, the higher centres involved in instinctive reactions can be purposive, but the lower centres make the consummatory act rigid. Yet he would call all these levels "instinctive". Each instinctive mechanism is con-stantly primed. The various levels are coordinated and can inhibit one another.

Part of some instincts is learned by "imprinting" (89). We will not discuss this puzzle here, however.

Certain behaviour is certainly innate. For example, tadpoles do incipient swimming while still in the egg! If the tadpole is raised under continuous anaesthesia, then released with other normals of his age, he swims as well as they do. The locomotion of lizards has the same features. For instance, grafting new tendons together, or reversing right and left fore-limbs produces no change in the muscle responses. The muscles do what they would have done before—even after a year's experience with the new attachments. Young pigeons or dragonflies prevented from flying fly perfectly when allowed to do so. Innate behaviour may appear very early in imperfect form, as in the "quivering" part of nesting in cormorants only two weeks old. Only later do they get hold of twigs, then proceed to quiver and so lock them. The development of sand-digging in the stickle-back shows recognizable stages. The ability to learn motor responses by imitation is very restricted. Tinbergen knows of only one example, the song of nightingales, goldfinches and some other songbirds! Here is a real point against the evolution of instinct after instruction.

Woodbury (90) discusses bird and other migrations, and remarks on the absence of learning in the Monarch butterfly which makes tremendous migrations, one complete trip each generation. Some insects have each leg of the migration journey performed by different generations. This is true of grasshoppers, for example. Then he talks about birds leaving the Antarctic which must cross temperate and tropical regions. Birds returning from the tropics must start under conditions like those prevailing when they arrived. A great variety of environmental conditions must be sorted out by them before they decide to migrate and while this is in process. Fish migrations are even more puzzling, extending over a period of years. Then there is the great problem of the exact returnpoint, achieved by eels and salmon or the golden plovers.

Behaviour in a victim species can be almost "perfectly adapted", and yet predators still prey on it successfully. Verwey* (91) tells of the instinctive relations of the shrimp, Crangon crangon, and the cuttle-fish, Sepia: "As a rule the animal (shrimp) lies hidden below the sand during the day and is busy during darkness. But much of its time is used in migration; to the shallower warmer water in spring and a good deal of summer, back to saltier water in autumn and part of the winter; it also moves up and down from the channels to the shallows, thereby following the tides. These movements are not restricted to the hours of darkness; they also take place during the day. Moreover, the animals creep out of the sand at the slightest inducement. All this causes a great restlessness so that their hiding is far from permanent.

"In this connection it is right that the shrimp does not only possess its innate burrowing behaviour, but also the possibility for active colour change. It is not only dark on a dark background and light on a light one, but it assumes an appropriate tint for a yellowish

---

*Quoted by permission of the Clarendon Press, Oxford, England

or more brownish background by movements of appropriate types of pigment. This means that, when not on the move, the animal is not so easily seen.

"Enemies of the shrimp are, among others, the bullhead, the plaice, the dab, and the cuttlefish.

". . . the one, acquainted with the shrimp probably best of all, is the cuttlefish. It makes its way just over the sand bottom, its head somewhat lower than its rear. Its funnel is directed on to the sand below and in front of it. It blows small water jets on to the sand. They hit a shrimp, which feels itself more or less exposed and begins to shove new sand over its back. I believe this is what the cuttlefish sees. Instantly it has seized its prey.

"The shrimp's hiding is perfect; its camouflage is perfect. But the animals preying on it are also perfect, each in its own way."

The "fixed patterns" of species seem to be taxonomically conservative. But social releases can vary widely between related species. The courtship preening of ducks differs with their colour patterns, as could be expected, else it would be useless. Tinbergen* stresses that this is evolutionary, since "specificity is a demand imposed by their function as isolating mechanisms." It is true, of course, that such specificity would be "demanded" of evolutionary processes—or a Creator! Fiddler crabs wave their courtship claws in ways differing for each species—as would be expected. Closely related species may lose a behaviour component entirely, or may replace a call note, as in fintails and teals, with a behaviour elements like the aufstossen of ducks.

Bostock (92) points out that instinct can alter slightly with a colour mutation, as in yellow males of Drosophila melanogoster, which have deficient wing vibration, hence a less effective courtship, hence reduced success in fertilizing females.

In the closely related species of African Cichlid fish, Tilopia hendeloti and Tilopia natalensis, the males display mating patterns to females of either species, but females usually respond only to their own males. Yet the courting movements in the males are identical. One can think of no isolating mechanism here but colour.

Summary

It would seem that instinct is seen in every type of creature. It must be best defined in such lowly but complex creatures as the parasites, for example, where it has rarely been studied, outside of the ants, wasps and termites. It would seem that instincts are most complex, coordinated and essential in the simplest creatures. They are often chain reactions, but at lower levels are innate. However analysed and

---

*Quoted by permission of the Clarendon Press, Oxford, England

dissected, most of them are as inexplicable as they are enormously varied. No clearer demonstration can be found in Nature of the impress of a Designer on the acts of His creatures, and none show His versatility and even His humour better. Darwin realized long ago that instincts were as important as corporeal structure for the welfare of a species. He clearly saw that they could not be perpetuated habit. He stressed the variation in instinct between domestic strains, then proceeded to knock out his own argument by citing the cuckoo's nesting habits. He was puzzled by nursing instincts, particularly as he said he knew nothing of the origin of the mammary glands. He should have been puzzled, for here is a hopelessly difficult problem for the evolutionist. He was most bothered by the neuter forms of insects. How could they be developed by the natural selection of their so-unlike parents? Then he found wide variation, real castes, amongst the workers of some ant species, differences as great as could exist between genera. He concluded that the parents able to produce such a variety of neuters could have been selected for just that ability, however well hidden! What was the causal mechanism which underlay such a variation so obviously needed, or how selection could operate on characters invisible in the parents in order to produce life-saving and widely different characters in their progeny, Darwin did not try to theorize. There was no easy answer by his methods, of course.

CHAPTER XI

Protective Colouration, Form and Habit

Secrets that lurk
Behind trees.
Silence, red eyes,
—Enemies.

—Vere Jameson*

PROPOSITION—The problem of colour in living things is one of extreme complexity. It defies evolutionary explanation because of that very complexity, the differences between sexes and even successive moults of the same creature, mimicry, and its perfection. Here again, half perfection is not perfection.

Introduction

From the earliest times men have noticed the phenomena of adaptive colouration or protection by colouration, for they have hunted or bred creatures so protected. In their turn they have suffered as the prey of creatures adaptively coloured for hunting. And all together have suffered from perhaps the most supremely camouflaged of all creatures, the bacteria and viruses recognized only in the last century, creatures escaping notice by the simple (?) device of extreme smallness.

Protective Colouration

Protective colouration is so widespread amongst living things that one scarcely knows where to start in discussing it. It ranges from the whale's or shark's grey back, to the giraffe's spots, to the grey or white rabbit in its form, to the tree frog, to the cuckoo's egg, to the praying mantis or clearwing moth, to the plankton in the sea. Camouflage implies the ability to merge with the environment. There is also the protection ensured by imitating or mimicking a safer species. Both of these types we should discuss here, but especially the latter. Books on the subject are plentiful, and all one can do here is touch on it—and give references for further reading.

Cott points out that human camouflage devices derive from animals. Our balloon barrages are gigantic spider webs, our smoke screens recall the cuttle-fish's defence, our sonar was first used by the bat and dolphin. The modern study of this theme dates from the publications of an American naturalist, Abbott H. Thayer, as recent as 1896 and 1909.

---

*Quoted by permission of the Ryerson Press, Toronto, Canada.

Concealment in the environment largely depends on avoiding shadow beneath, and in having countershading colours, darker on top where the sun shines on the creature, and paler beneath. This is not so marked in animals living in dim light, but is more marked in animals living on sunny open plains, for example antelopes and larks. Countershading can be reversed, as in the larva of the eyed-hawk-moth (Smerinthus ocellatus) which rests belly up. In the same way spots tend to shrink ventrally, and bars, as on zebras, tend to narrow ventrally.

The best example known of the evolution of a new variety or strain occurring under our eyes is the recent melanism of British moths living in industrial areas. The Handbook on Evolution (1958) of the British Museum points out that of 780 species of British Macrolepidoptera fully 70 are undergoing the most striking evolutionary change which has ever been actually witnessed. The first melanic form of the Peppered moth was seen in Manchester in 1848. By 1900 this was 99 times commoner than the original light form which persists elsewhere. Birds eat this moth selectively, depending on the colour of the background. Undoubtedly the dark or melanic variety is protected from birds in that dirty locality. But all is not so simple, as Ford and also Kettlewell (93) make clear, for melanic mutant dominants of the same sort are found in the Caledonian forests of Scotland, the Canadian sub-Arctic, and in the rain forsets of Southern New Zealand. In Prussia there are both black *larvae* and black moths of this same species of peppered moth. A few moth species have female melanics only. Are these females the only forms evolving protective colouration? For melanic varieties have also increased in hardiness, due to gene changes involving more than colour, changes advancing melanism in rural areas as well. Up-to-the-minute evolutionists rarely mention this last and slightly disconcerting finding.

It is Widespread

Colour resemblance to the environment is widespread, though not general. Thus in the tropics one finds a preponderance of green birds, toads, snakes and insects in the trees, and brownish forms dwelling on or in the forest floor. Shore birds are mottled. Even animals of one type, such as spiders, often differ in colour, depending on their environments. Indeed, this colour range may occur inside one species, as in crested larks of the genus Amenomacies in Northern Africa, or amongst deer mice and pocket mice in the American Southwest. Seasonal changes occur in the ptarmigan, some northern grouse, and the Arctic fox. Rapid colour changes can occur in chameleons, for instance, or in other lizards such as iguanas and geckos, although terrestrial lizards usually rely on speed for safety. Experiments on flounders show that they can alter colour in relation to their backgrounds—even changing the finenesss or coarseness of their pattern. Reef fishes alter colour shades as they drop or rise in the water. Some even wear different colour bars for resting and swimming. Some squids wear stripes for swimming and bands for resting. Crustaceans and cephalopods may change colour rapidly. The pupa of some species of butterflies, for example Vanessa and Pieris, alters colour appropriately for background. Naturalists have found that 80 to 85 per cent of crab spiders select flowers of their own colouration.

Some little butterflies, the blues or Lycaenidae, have "tails" on their hind-wings resembling antennae, and even move them like feelers. A spot nearby resembles the eye. If a hungry birds snaps at this butterfly it bites only the tail, permitting the insect to fly away relatively unharmed.

Many spiders and mantises in flowers and on leaves hide from their prey by protective colouring. In Manilla a white spider with yellow legs hides in white flowers having yellow stamens, and in Malaya the mantis, Hymenopus, hides in a special rhododendron of matching colour. Azilia, a Guianan spider, sits on a nest of lichen to hide.

Disruptive colouration is important for ring-necked plovers, as collar bands on sandy plovers, or as dark lateral longitudinal stripes on pale antelopes. The eye loses the concept of form in such examples.

Constructive shading creates powerful visual illusions. The banded pattern of many frogs, where the bands of the body seem continuous when the creature is at rest in particular and characteristic stance, is a fine example. In many fishes body bands extend out on to the fins. Many insects have patterns involving their legs and antennae. Cott first emphasized the camouflage of the eye achieved by bands of colour on the head crossing over the pupil, which otherwise is so revealing, or by means of black masks adjacent to it.

Concealment of shadow is effective in ptarmigan crouching in the snow, or in butterflies like the green hairstreak which approximate their wings in the sun to leave no breadth of shadow. Many reptiles and amphibians, such as the horned toad, have lateral flanges which hug the ground. Certain caterpillars conceal themselves by patterns resembling leaf veins.

The sphingid caterpillar of the Guiana forest, whose congeners the natives eat, can transform its thorax to show two great black, threatening "eyes". It also distends its anterior segments and twists about like a small tree-viper.

Disappearing colouration is often used. A brightly coloured butterfly or bird suddenly sits down colourlessly and in trying to locate it we overshoot it, as in the common tortoise-shell butterfly. The leaf butterfly, Kallima, is boldly coloured—until it rests on a leaf.

Ants are mimicked by beetles, two-winged flies, grasshoppers and spiders, even in habit. For example, spiders elongate their bodies, use

104

their first pair of legs to resemble feelers, colour the body to resemble an ant's waist. Clearwing moths resemble hornets and wasps—even have decided to fly by day! Lizards are deceived by this, for example. The hawkmouth, Xanthopan, imitates tree bark only because it always settles there head upward. On the other hand the geometrid tissue moth imitates bark by settling on it horizontally. Insects mimicking bees and wasps pretend to sting when threatened.

Several harmless snakes puff and hiss like dangerous snakes. The small European bird, the wryneck, nests in holes in trees. When disturbed it flattens against the side of the hole, and oscillates back and forth, hissing like a snake.

Protective Form

Body form can be altered, as in the extreme thinness of such leaf insects as Chitomiscus and Cycloptera—even the body parts can conform to leaf structures. Leaf resemblance is also found in some fish, chameleons and other forms. Bark resemblance is common, as in moths, beetles, spiders, tree frogs, lizards and a few birds. Whole families of moths such as the genus Catocala have utilized this principle. Lichen is also used thus, for some birds use lichen to hide their nests, for example the ruby throated hummingbird, wood-peewee and the blue-gray gnatcatcher. The walking-stick insect should be mentioned here. Even its joints resemble plant nodes. The posture of this insect and of many caterpillars is protective. Wallace told of some found in the Malay Islands and America which carry moss-like processes on their bodies in order to increase their resemblance to twigs. In the sea many fish and crustaceans have velamentous and filamentous appendages, especially those in the Sargasso sea, where there is much seaweed.

Sir Julian Huxley (94) has recently discussed an interesting case of mimicry. He describes the Dorippe japonica, a common edible crap in Japanese waters whose thorax bears the likeness of a mediaeval Japanese warrior, and which the Japanese refuse to eat because it reminds them of the warriors who threw themselves overboard rather than surrender in a legendary battle of the 12th century. Huxley therefore ascribes this crab's appearance to artificial selection by the hungry Japanese of the last 800 years. Unfortunately, we do not possess an old crab of the 12th century not marked in this way in order to substantiate his claim, nor do we know how many of these crabs now fall prey to less superstitious and less respectful predators, nor do we know at what late period in that 800 years the gradually developing resemblance became so striking as to induce popular avoidance. If these crabs always looked like this there is no point worth discussing, of course, and I suspect that they did. Certainly there could have been no resemblance before a long process of "selection" (and selection for what?) had produced at least a noticeable resemblance to the dead

Heike warriors. What an illogical argument!—and yet this is necessary to explain such mimicry on an evolutionary basis and present it as "evidence".

Even Huxley seems to realize this and refers to the little English shore crab, Sorystes, whose thorax is also so like a face as to induce taxonomists to call it cassivelaunus, after an ancient British chieftain— but this crab is small, fortunately, and so is not used as food. What produced the selection here, by men who did not use it, but would be the only species of predator to be deterred by a human resemblance, Huxley does not indicate. He should—otherwise his argument works in reverse!

There are leaf insects resembling big green leaves, or dead leaves, or leaves with dead spots. There are leaf frogs and leaf toads, and even a leaf fish on the Amazon which gets close to its prey by floating down current like a dead leaf.

Insects of the family Membracidae are defenceless little bugs sucking sap from leaves and twigs. On the forepart of their thorax is a large hood. This has been elongated to make some resemble a seed, or has sharp hooks to resemble thorns, or is large and orange-coloured to hide the rest of the bug and resemble a nauseating chrysalis. One species has it enlarged and shaped to resemble a worker ant of the vicinity,—and ants do not make palatable tid-bits.

Combined Mimicry

The common nightjar crouches among dead leaves when nesting— but the South American nightjar, Nyctibius, lays in a broken stump— then broods rigidly erect, to look like a splinter of that stump. One type of shrike has its nestlings rise up and freeze together like a broken-off branch when endangered. The only other example of combined mimicry Huxley mentions is plant bugs of the genus Flata which cluster together on stems like flowers. The green bugs resemble buds and the pink bugs the recently opened flowers.

Many Remarkable Examples

Mimicry among insects can deceive the most skilful naturalists even while the latter are alerted to the possibility. This indicates its perfection. It may be so good that it can deceive other insects being mimicked. For example, Crompton tells us that many spiders disguise themselves as ants, have the shape and even the habits of ants. Some spiders have even imitated the unusual protuberances that occur in certain ant species. An ant has two antennae and six legs—therefore mimicking (eight-legged) spiders hold their front pair of legs over their foreheads and wiggle them like antennae. They also imitate the jerky gait and feeding movements of the ant. In Brazil, Bristowe found a black spider carrying over its head and shoulders the hollow skeleton of an ant. Later Hingston saw the same thing in British Guiana. These mimicking spiders may protect themselves thus against enemy spiders, which in turn run off and erect a defensive silk barrage if touched by the false antennae of the actors. A wolf spider and a jumping spider of Uganda imitate the stinging Mutillid wasps, even in having four white spots on the abdomen. Indeed, such spiders often run with the wasps as intimates!

The cuckoo egg is a remarkable example of mimicry. It may be very dissimilar from the eggs in the cuckolded nests in which it is laid, but often is quite indistinguishable by any but an expert, and then only by careful weighing! And it must be laid in the nest of one of the scores of species it parasitizes at such a time as to hatch just before its stepbrothers, in order that it may heave them out of their nest and not itself be crushed by them.

The little Himalayan cuckoo lays red eggs in one nest and white in another to match the respective fosterer's eggs. Indeed, the same species of cuckoo can lay blue eggs in the nest of a blue-egg fosterer and brown eggs in that of a brown-egg fosterer. The Burmese plaintive cuckoo lays two distinct types of eggs—a white egg with red spots in the nest of the Franklin's warbler when the latter lays white eggs, and a blue egg in nests of the same warbler if they contain the blue eggs the warbler is also able to lay.

The Drongo-cuckoo is so like the pugnacious Drongo-shrike that it gains easy access to the latter's nest to lay its eggs. The Indian cuckoo, the Koel, victimizes a starling, the Mynah. The young and adults of the Mynah are black—so the **black** male Koel draws the owners of the nest away to let his **brown** partner lay her eggs—which hatch out into **black** fledgelings!

In Java there is a spider which lies on its back on leaves and thus exactly resembles a bird's droppings. The crab spider, Misumena vatia, changes its colour to fit the flower it haunts, from white to yellow to pink to pale green. The colour changes are due to pigment on its back. A Brazil spider, Spicadua heterogaster, has an unspiderlike shape and white prominences tinged with pink to resemble petals.

The Bee-hawkmoth flies by day because it seeks to resemble the bee. Indeed Pycraft says that no less than 16 species of British day-flying lepidoptera are "clear-wings". The Hornet-moth and Lunar Hornet-moth are very like hornets, even in their mode of flight. There is a butterfly (Leptocircus virescens) which resembles a dragon-fly, even in its flight habits.

Even conspicuous and distasteful butterflies may mimic each other, as Bates observed among the Ithomiinae and Heliconinae in South America. "Mullerian" mimicry is based on such phenomena, indeed. All Papilios that serve as models have larvae which feed on poisonous plants. Even certain large day-flying moths mimic these butterflies. Those wasp mimics which are moths, all of the family Syntomidae, are day-flying. It is well-known, of course, that moths tend to fly by night only. In New Guinea the rare Papilio laglaizei mimics the common day-flying moth, Alcidis agathyrsus. The resemblance from above is good, but underneath is truly marvelous. For the moth has an orange belly on the underside, conspicuous when at rest. The wings of the butterfly fold differently at rest, but in such a way as to hide its dull abdomen. However, it shows the same orange spot, this time on the wings, when these are folded!

The model and mimic may be limited to a small area of land, and both may change markedly in another adjacent area. In other cases, a different distribution of food plants separates model and mimic. Indeed in Ceylon the Danaid model is a low-country inhabitant but the Fritillary mimic lives thousands of feet up. Poulton has conceded mimicry between Hypolimnas misippus in Africa and Indo Malaya and Athyma punctata and Limenitis albomaculata found in China! Perhaps migratory birds are the enemy all are protected against! Other examples of geographical separation are the South American Vanessid genus Adelpha and the African Planema paggei—or the South American Phyciodes leucodesma and the African Neptis nemetes. How can the evolutionist explain this, where an ocean separates mimic and model?

Caterpillars mimicking twigs often have a deeply notched brown pattern, or lumps on the head end producing an even better resemblance to a budding twig. This is extremely well done by the Early Thorn moth where the head and first two body-rings are bent backwards at right angles to the rest of the body. Some caterpillars resemble snail shells. The larva of the large Emerald moth feeds on catkin. Its colouration is also helpful here.

The caterpillar of the Lobster moth of Britain has modified its doubled up legs to hang down like the brown scales surrounding the buds of the beech tree. They are of the proper colour, length, number and even shape for this purpose! When this larva is attacked it assumes a terrifying posture. Attacked more savagely it lowers flaps on its sides to display conspicuous black wounds there, like the wounds that would have been made by an ichneumon fly, marks which indicate that it can no longer be of interest to an insect enemy, for another parasite has already taken the premises! What can the evolutionist say in the face of such an intricate, precise, and exquisitely reasoned deception?

Major Puzzles

Pycraft frankly admits: "It passes the wit of man to discover the agency by which living bodies can obliterate all semblance of their original form, and come to assume a likeness to inanimate objects."

"Mimicry rings" constitute one of the most remarkable phenomena in all insect mimicry. In this case only the females mimic, and the males are utterly different. Could adaptive evolution have been limited here to one sex? Can **slight** differences mislead birds or lizards—for otherwise the initial small changes in type and colour could scarcely have had selective value.

Small initial protective variations are valueless, of course, as even Darwin and Wallace recognized—even when model and mimic approach each other pari passu.

Summary

The vast extent, variety and resourcefulness of mimicry throughout the world of creatures, notably insects, spiders, fish, and molluscs almost defy comprehension or description. It can be so perfect as to deceive even the best expert on the watch for this very thing. The mimicry of colour is frequently combined with an appropriate mimicry of gait or noise or other habit. Incredible versatility can be found, as in the modification of egg colour and size by the parasitic cuckoo, or in the symbiotic modes of other plants or animals. The mimicry may involve major structural changes. It can be as versatile and extensive in the immature as in the mature forms—and yet be utterly different in type and resources. The perfection of detail achieved is so great as to defy description. No obvious reason for mimicry holds water. Predatory birds, mammals, lizards or other insects are not the answer. There is a striking absence of **partially** successful attempts at mimicry. Sometimes only one sex mimics a model. Mimics often deceive their enemies with complete success and can live among them safely. Mimics may mimic plants or flowers as well as other creatures. Evolutionary processes cannot explain the perfection, versatility and variety, the absence of imperfect efforts, the absence of adequate causes, the mimicry of females only in many species, the perfection and variety and different styles assumed by mimicking larvae and adult forms—nor the concomitant mimicry of form, colour and habitus. Mimicry is one of the really great and unanswerable arguments against the evolutionary doctrine.

CHAPTER XII

Plant Evolution (?) as it Looks at Present

Grass recipes
For syntheses
We cannot match!
Who made the keys?

—Vere Jameson

PROPOSITION—Botanists have the greatest problems of all evolutionists, unless one mentions experts in fungi, bacteria, viruses, and parasites, who also have real difficulties. Perhaps the worst problems of the evolutionary botanist are those that deal with parasitic plants and insects, and with carnivorous plants.

Introduction

Textbooks on Evolution usually say much more about animals than plants. There is good reason for this, of course. The evidence for plant evolution is very incomplete and inadequate. Even its exponents depend for their argument on the succession and obliteration of plant forms pointing to the gradual development of flowering plants, although any genetic relations escape them. **Theories** of relationship they can advance, but these are admittedly very tenuous. Indeed, Gager (95)* says: "If we had a museum collection of specimens of all the kinds of plants that have ever lived, botanists believe that such specimens could be so arranged as to represent their genetic relations and to give us a true picture of the evolutionary development of the present plant world. But probably no such collection can ever be made." Therefore the "evolution" of plants remains largely an act of faith. Now let us consider the problem in greater detail.

Classification and its Difficulties

Any classification is difficult to make, and this is truer still if it is to be a natural classification. The basis of artificial classification may be such arbitrary characters as the number of stamens or height of stem, features which may have no geneological value. Sinnot and Wilson** (36) say: "The task of separating the plant kingdom into several main groups is therefore a difficult or impossible one, for the plant population of the earth today includes the descendants of stocks which have been distinct for so long that their original relationships are obscure. The major divisions which we recognize today are therefore in

---

*Quoted by permission of the MacMillan Co., New York, U.S.A.
**Quoted by permission of the McGraw-Hill Co. of Canada, Toronto, Canada.

many cases artificial ones, valuable for their convenience in classification rather than as expressions of natural relationship." They go on to point out that fossil evidence is the surest basis for a reconstruction of plant evolution, but that this is very inadequate and, in any case, the simpler, softer-bodied plants left few or no fossils. Indeed, even the separation of algae and fungi is unnatural, for among the algae are included many groups of simple, chlorophyll-bearing plants that have little relationship to each other, and it is difficult to decide whether some of them should be placed in the plant or the animal kingdom. This is also true for the Slime Fungi.

The simplest plants, the Blue-green Algae, are sometimes classed with bacteria as Schizophyta. They have been found as fossils in some of the most ancient rocks. In some there is no chlorophyll, but its substitute is another pigment called phycocyanin. Do the Green Algae, with a nucleus and sexual reproduction, stem from the Blue Algae, so alike but so unlike? The stoneworts (Charophyceae), too, seem unrelated to all other forms.

Among fungi there are several major types; their interrelationships are obscure. Probably evolutionists must regard them as polyphyletic, derived from many original sources, together constituting only an artificial group.

Viruses have races or "strains". They may or may not be living things. Apparently they can mutate. But they can grow only in the presence of living protoplasm and cannot be cultivated indefinitely on nutrients. They have not been shown to breathe. Some, both vegetable and animal viruses, have been crystalized and in such a state can exist almost indefinitely. If introduced into animals or plants these again develop into typical virus bodies. They are probably single molecules, and so probably cannot carry on the various activities of organisms. They may be merely degenerate micro-organisms.

Slime molds can move like animals (amoeboid), but reproduce by spores as do plants. The individual organisms can fuse into a pseudoplasmodium, but in this they preserve their identity, and the mass moves about as one amoeba glides over another. Later the amoebae may differentiate for various roles, and the "plant" may even send up a stalk.

The Bryophytes (mosses, liverworts and hornworts) lack a root and a highly organized vascular system, but have elaborate sex organs and an alternation of generations. They show sex chromosomes, too. They have not been found earlier than the Carboniferous, and palaeontologists cannot detect their "origin". The mosses have few fossil forms and these are strikingly like modern mosses. Their origin is quite unknown and mysterious.

The Psilopsida has only two living genera—the rest are all very old fossils. They are widely different from the algae and bryophytes to which evolutionists would like to relate them. They belong to the so-called vascular plants.

The Lycopsida or club-mosses, and the Sphenopsida or horse-tails, are classed as Pteridophytes, along with the ferns. They have a complex sporophyte generation alternating with a much simplified gametophyte generation.

The seed plants or Spermatophytes have two main subdivisions, the Gymnosperms and Angiosperms, the latter being the flowering plants. The angiosperms are subdivided in turn into the monocotyledons and dicotyledons.

Curiously, the first parasitic Gymnosperm has just been found. It is a rare species of Podocarpus, a conifer, from New Caledonia (96).

California Examples of Microevolution

Clausen (97) has taught us much about the speciation going on in modern plants. He refers to viola tricolor and the forms it has developed on Californian coastal dunes, along a stretch of only 200 miles; to the subspecies of the rose Potentilla glandulosa also seen in California. He shows the wide variation in form among the many geographical races and five major groups of the California tidy tips, Layia platyglossa, each perhaps a mere four to ten miles from its neighbours. Significant and marked morphological variations have developed. Because many local populations are well separated spatially there they constitute isolated breeding units rather effectively. Where a species occupies many kinds of environment it is because it has developed physiologically distinct races, each of these able to compete best in one locality. California represents an excellent place to study such race formation, as in the climatic races of the yarrows or milfoil in the genus Achillea of the Sunflower family. Undoubtedly environment plays a role in selection, for different species develop parallel biological races in parallel environments. Thus Achillea borealis and Achillea lanulosa have evolved parallel ecotypes or climatic races on the coast of California, Oregon and the Aleutians. But the California tarweeds have evolved species and genera rather than ecologic races on the California coast. Some species of the tarweeds have evolved seasonal ecotypes in the same locality. Such races can freely interchange their genes and have a fluid variability. Probably such races evolve readily, says Clausen.

An ecological race can be very persistent, as in Clausen's original report of the inland and maritime races of Viola tricolor, as discovered on the tip of Denmark and near Lyngby, 150 miles inland. The maritime race persisted against drastic environmental changes through many generations over a period of 20 years in Europe and America, even when its genes were sent through the contrasting inland race. The differences in form between some races of Layia chrysanthemoides can be so marked that they were once classified in different genera. A subspecies of Layia glandulosa is so different from the usual type specimens as to compare to the differences between even larger classificatory groups.

Do subspecies change to species? Yes. The two coastal races of the Californian coast tarweed, Hemizonia augustifolia, are an example. The Santa Lucia Mountains divide them at the sea. When the plants were crossed, only 57 percent of the F_1 generation were as vigorous as the parents, some being very weak. Ecological races or subspecies are more flexible than distinct species and better material for micro-evolution. If intervening sectors are wiped out, the distant remnants can become distinct species. Ecological races can be similar morphologically but not genetically, and often the latter discontinuity comes first. Very remarkable morphological changes can develop without breeding barriers appearing, as in Layia glandulosa, or in the genus Penstemon of the figwort, where the hybrids are fully fertile, although the two parent species remain distinct, perhaps because one needs humming birds and one needs bumble bees for cross fertilization. The species of wild Columbine of the genus Aquilegia, enormously different in appearance, also interbreed freely. They use humming birds or hawk-moths for their needs. Bumble bees visit both. Maize is another such plant.

We do not know much about the factors which keep a species together. But a species may contain hundreds of races, as in the Achilleas or Milfoils. A race from Mount Kiska may cross readily with a race from the San Joaquin Valley, the parents obviously differing by many genes. But a San Joaquin race and one from Northern Iceland may produce a hardy but sterile hybrid. Why? No one knows. The causes of crossing over and chromosome repatterning we do not know. Single chromosomes can be lost, indeed. Thus two adjacent strains of Viola arvensis, when crossed, lost a suppressing gene and a new 16 paired chromosomal form arose of large size, breeding true. This is not really "progressive evolution" but represents a loss. Another 16 pair chromosomal segregant has been made that is altogether different because made differently. When Viola tricolor is crossed with Viola arvensis three new constant types arise, with different colours, sizes, and other characters, even one with 22 pairs of chromosomes, unlike the 13 and 17 pairs of the parents.

On the other hand, there are often effective barriers to plant hybridization. For example, there are hybrids where the nucleus and cytoplasm do not fit, as in certain Epilobium hybrids. Chlorophyll disturbances occur in certain interspecific hybrids of Geranium and Hypericuna. Crosses can have a pollen tube too short, as in crossing Polemonium and Zea-Tripsacum. The embryo and endosperm may not fit, as in hybrids between species of Linum and of Datura. Separating these surgically leaves the endosperm free to develop! The pollen tube may develop too slowly in a foreign style, as in Violas—or may not germinate on a foreign stigma. It is hard to encompass all the patterns by which species and races can become isolated. Remember, in all this we have been talking only of microevolution—not megaevolution.

Clausen concludes that we still do not know what makes living things develop as they do nor how they first appeared. Our researches have merely brought us face to face with the wonderful and still quite incomprehensible structure of life. Up against such a situation, he says, the scientist feels humbled, for at this juncture he comes upon the Great Unknown.

The Troublesome Taxonomy of Fungi

Fungi present their own special difficulties. Many a species has had different generic names given to its sexual and asexual stages before it was recognized that they were a unit. But thousands of fungi, called Imperfecti, are known only in the asexual stage. There is little foundation for the belief that any sexual stage exists in these. What shall we say of fungal strains, which may amount to more than 100 in Botrytis cinerea? Are these varieties, or just inside or outside a species? Then, too, fungus colonies mutate, and such a saltation may become characteristic—or even reversible. **A different strain may grow out of minor branches of the same hypha,** when isolated! The saltations, as in Phytophthora Omniona, may be tremendously different morphologically. Moreover, fungus hybrids between different "species" can be produced.

Fungal parasitism is so strict that it can be used to distinguish its host-plants, as in rust. There are physiologic as well as morphologic species of fungi. Perhaps Puccinia has at least 1000 such. Are all these one species? No one knows. In fungi even "genera" have been crossed, by the way. The genera of Agaricaceae were actually based on spore colour! Surely enough has been said here to illustrate the confusion an evolutionist must feel as he faces the problem of fungi. What is a species or genus, how variable is each, what are its relationships and origins, and so on?

The Taxonomic Problems of Angiosperms

The classification of the Dicotyledons is very imperfect, and need reshaping with reference to natural groupings and the evaluation of characters. Yet Sprague (98) points out that to do this properly for the Dicotyledons alone would exhaust the lives of a team of taxonomists. In other words, such a vital item as the taxonomy of this important and common plant division is beyond us. Where does this leave the evolutionary status of this group, genealogies obviously depending on knowing such details? Sprague admits that any claim that a complete classification of angiospermous or even dictyledonous families can be based on their probable phylogeny need not be given serious consideration. Some genera are obviously artificial, as in the families Cyperaceae, Leguminosae, Rubiaceae and Compositae. No one knows, for example, what are the unit characters of such a plant, or of a leaf! So little is known on this score that wild confusion can develop, as in the cases of Anopyxes and Diclidanthera. Two great herbaria got specimens of the former simultaneously and classified them in different **families**, for example Meliaceae and Rhizophoraceae. Diclidanthera has been placed in at least 4 different plant **families** by various experts.

Our Ignorance of Nature

Allan (99) also stresses our inadequate knowledge of Nature. The Hebes of the Chatham Islands have species named only on the most casual inspection. No one knows how many species of Alseuosmia occur in the northern part of the North Island of New Zealand. They are multitudinous, perhaps.

Wide crosses are known, even between radishes and cabbages, and between bamboo and sugar cane. What are the limits of hybridization? No one knows enough to classify the wild hybrids of the country, some undoubtedly being treated as species. Hybrids can "mimic" specific forms **very** closely.

Among the mosses, admits Simpson (1), peristome characters diagnostic of orders, families and genera can occur "in species living in the same way and place"!

Cultivated Plants

Single gene differences often produce varieties, these occasionally almost reaching specific rank, such as in some cultivated raspberries. Crane (109) points out that the two pea species are really not species genetically. A single gene can even control such a distinct character as opposite and alternate leaves within the genus Ulmus. Chimaeras are known, which produce different types of plants, depending on which part of their tissues propagate, for example the Bouvardias Bridesmaid and Hogarth, or the potatoes Golden Wonder and Langworthy. In Nature examples are the American blackberry and the common wood-sage, Teucrium scorodonia.

Indeed, no sharp line can be drawn between cultivated hybrid species and spontaneous new species from the wild. Many hybrids are totally or partially sterile, but some have overcome this by doubling their chromosomes, (for example Primula kewensis), even at a single step.

Naturalists have found more than 800 botanical varieties of wheat and dozens of new species of potatoes. Crane admits that many thousands of new species are yet to be discovered. Knowledge of Linnaean species is only a first step in biological knowledge and very superficial for actual plant and animal breeding. Nor does it meet the requirements of a thorough evolutionary study of species.

In short, Darwin et al spoke too soon. The newer knowledge has revealed a world the first evolutionists did not dream of, and one which certainly complicates and overflows all the evolutionary theories of the textbooks. The problems of fungi or algae or bacteria alone would drive a conscientious evolutionist to distraction.

Plant Parasites

Let us conclude with come remarks on plant parasites and carnivorous plants, discussing their incredible adaptations to their unusual role.

The Cynipids, or gall-flies, lay eggs on leaves or twigs, the number depending on the resources of the plant. The ovipositor is a remarkable organ, with associated levers and supports. When the eggs hatch, the larvae feed on the plant juices. The plant then forms a gall there in response to the irritating salivary secretions and the physical presence of the maggot. The gall may include several or many larvae. The larvae and gall mature coincidentally, differing with the particular gall concerned. Then the gall dies and hardens as a protective chamber The adult fly gnaws its way out. But this new fly may seek a new plant, there incite **entirely different galls,** and the new fly may have a markedly different appearance when its larvae hatch. This second generation of flies lays its eggs on the first host plant, where galls and flies now revert to the first type. Here is an alteration of generations, formerly described as two species of Cynipid flies. Of course, many gall-flies do not alternate generations thus. But where it appears, one generation appears to be female only, so that the other generation, which has both sexes, develops only from unfertilized eggs. The great puzzles are the alternate galls, the instinct which leads the adult flies to the proper plant and position on twig or leaf for oviposition, and the gall formation itself, which shows nearly infinite variety. The jumping seed-gall of the oak leaf is a small one which develops on the leaf, falls off, then the active larva inside causes it to roll or even jump a quarter inch into the air. Stratton has pointed out that intelligence or memory can be of no use to the Cynipidae; no gall-fly ever sees its progeny, and none ever pricks buds a second season, or lives to know the sequel of that act. The number of eggs laid is exactly proportionate to the space suitable for them, to the size of the gall that will later develop, and to the food available for their nourishment. No matter what form the gall takes, the potentialities of tissue growth later demonstrated by it must be present at the very spot selected by the fly. The first act of the injured plant is to throw out a blastem, and it is noteworthy that only those larvae survive to hand down their skills which come out of an egg so wisely placed as to incite the growth of that nutritive blastem. Probably the morphological character of the gall depends on the insect and not the plant. An amazing number and variety of other insects parasitize these galls, even other Cynipids.

The Smyrna fig needs a Chalcidid fly, the "caprifying" fig-wasp, Blastophaga grossorum, to complete its development. The wingless males never leave the fig in which they are bred, but the females fly freely about. A fig is a fleshy, hollow-walled receptacle with minute flowers scattered over its inner surface. The only entrance into it is a tiny opening at one end nearly closed by scales. The eggs are laid by the females at the base of the little flowers in certain figs. The hatching larvae lie in little galls. The wingless males come out ,do not leave the interior of the fig, but crawl about over the galls, puncturing those containing females and fertilizing the latter where they lie inside! The fertilized female gnaws her way out, leaves the fig and flies about to crawl into other young figs. But only the wild, inedible "caprifigs" attract her, not the Smyrna fig flowers. In them no eggs are laid—but as she walks about these figs, she cross-fertilizes the female flowers with pollen from the male flowers of the caprifig by "caprification". Lacking this, no Smyrna fig flowers could be fertilized. Thus fig-growers suspend branches laden with caprifigs containing the insect among the branches of the Smyrna fig. The female Blastophaga entering a Smyrna fig and dying there leaves no progeny, for she lays no eggs in that type of fig. Thus a plantation of caprifigs must be kept near every Smyrna orchard. California fig-growers grew very poor figs till the Algerian Blastophaga was imported and raised on this continent.

Darwin's great contribution to this general theme was in 1862 in his book on the Fertilization of Orchids. He found that among one group the various parts of the flower were so accurately developed for cross-fertilization that without the aid of insects not a single plant in the whole group of 29 genera could produce seed. The pollen was usually acquired by the insect on its way out of the flower. Commonly, too, **the pollen masses slowly changed positions while attached to the insects, in order to assume the position proper for contact with the stigma of another flower,** perhaps while the insect took time to fly to another plant!

The Milkweeds of the genus Asclepias are unique in the device they use, for example Asclepias cornuti. This flower has a slit in the sides of its paired anthers, a slit wider at the bottom than at the top, which catches a bee's foot as it strives for a foot hold on the slippery flower. As the bee struggles to escape it pulls two pollen masses united to the corpusculum through the narrow slits at the tops of the pollen sacs and fertilization occurs. This happens on flower after flower. Some smaller bees and other insects cannot pull free, indeed.

One of the most amazing examples of insect-plant dependence is the Yucca-moth (Pronuba) and the yucca. Riley discovered this relationship in 1872. The pollen is sticky and agglutinates in masses which cannot get to the stigma without help. The nectar of the yucca is secreted at the base of the pistil, where it is unhelpful. The flowers are borne high, with a strong odour. The Pronuba moth mounts a stamen, makes a pollen ball and packs it against the under side of its head by means of a **specially developed maxillary tentacle,** not developed in other moths. In gathering pollen the moth hooks its tongue over the end of the stamen. After loading on its pollen, it flies to **another** flower, lands on the pistil and thrusts its ovipositor through the wall of the ovary to lay one egg. Then it climbs the pistil and rubs pollen carefully down the inner side of the stigmatic tube. Next it descends the pistil to lay another egg between another pair of stamens. Up it goes to rub more pollen on another stigmatic surface. The process goes on till each of the six lines of ovules has one egg and pollination has been achieved as often. The larvae hatch among the developing seeds and eat them. But they **never eat all the seeds** before they escape from the seed-pod. If they did this there would be no new yuccas. How considerate of these maggots to diet so cautiously! Then they sqeeze out a thread which drops them to the ground to hibernate for the winter; they come out as mature moths next summer at the time the Yucca flowers. The mature moth seems not to eat. Kellogg* (101) says: "It seems certain that it is prompted to place the pollen in the stigmatic tube after each act of oviposition solely by the instinct to provide for its young, for it is readily understood that if the ovules are not fertilized the seeds would not develop and the larvae would be without food. The Yucca prohibits self-pollination by its tubular stigmas and its relatively short and reflexed stamens. Moreover, the Pronuba moth always cross-pollinates by securing pollen from one flower, then flying to another to lay its eggs!"

Carnivorous Plants

Darwin's studies on Insectivorous Plants (102) were among his best. He records that the plant Drosera could respond to a foreign particle weighing less than the millionth of a grain. "Hardly any more remarkable fact than this has been observed in the vegetable kingdom," he observes. The leaves of Drosera rotundifolia, a bleak Arctic form, could withstand brief immersions in water at 145 degrees. He deals with the remarkable bending of the tentacles toward different stimuli. In discussing the Venus fly-trap, Dionaea, he mentions the marginal spikes on the lobes being arranged in such a way that they interlock when the lobes close, and the sensitive protruding filaments on the leaves have articulations which let them lie flat at such times. He goes on: "It is a strange fact that Dionaea, which is one of the most beautifully adapted plants in the vegetable kingdom, should apparently be on the high road to extinction." Finally he

---

*Quoted by permission of Appleton-Century-Crofts, Inc., New York, U.S.A.

comments on the remarkable convergences in the moving parts of many plants, not only carnivorous types. All these adaptations, so diverse and wonderful, must have puzzled the great evolutionist.

Lloyd (103) says there are 450 or more species of carnivorous plants, representing 15 genera, belonging, aside from the fungi, to six families. They are divisible into two main groups, widely different. Thus, apart from the fungi, the evolutionist must believe that the carnivorous habit has arisen at least twice. This does not make his views easier to hold. There may be passive pitfall traps, passive lobster pots, snares, fly-paper traps, active traps, steel-traps and mousetrap types. Odours act as lures sometimes, or nectar may be put forth for this purpose, or bright colours, movements, enzymes and acids, special hairs, glands, stomata, tentacles, and such. Many fungi are wholly carnivorous.

It is of evolutionary interest, too, that among the Lentibulariaceae are examples of the simplest traps (Pinguicula), the most complex pitfalls (Genlisea) and the incomparable trap of Utricularia.

Lloyd* goes on: "About the origin and evolution of the carnivorous plants, however much these questions may intrigue the mind, little can be said, nor have I attempted to discuss them. The evidence from fossils is meagre . . . a utricularia . . . is recorded from the old-diluvial of Oberohe . . . No others, so far as I know, have been recorded. . . . The fact that they have originated at two or more distinct points in the phylogenetic tree is of major importance. How the highly specialized organs of capture could have evolved seems to defy our present knowledge." There are Australian Utricularias, for example. Were these ancient types able to develop the most unique of all traps in parallel after the ancient isolation of that land mass? Lloyd says aptly: "Since we cannot answer these questions, it is perhaps as well to say no more." If only evolutionists had come to that wise conclusion in Darwin's day!

Tait noticed a peculiar point about Heliamphora. The pitchers cannot bend over, but yet maintain a constant water level in them despite rains. It has been found that each leaf has a pore so placed as to drain off excess water. Imagine evolution doing that!

The fungus Cordyceps invades the bodies of various species of caterpillar, eats them away, then sends up a stalk from each sclerotium now used as a root. The wonderful fungus, Arthrobotrys oligospora, traps live animals. Its hyphae leave a tangle of loops lying about, but these traps are formed only if nemin is produced in their immediate vicinity by nematodes. Living eel-worms when caught in such a loop cannot escape, die, and are then invaded by branches of the loop. Dactylella bembicoides forms a loop which instantly clamps down on

*Quoted by permission of the Ronald Press Co., New York, U.S.A.

119

any eel-worm poking into it, due to the simultaneous swelling of the three cells of its ring! There are at least three other predacious species of fungi. Some fungi, like Dactylaria candida, have loops plus adhesive knobs. From these knobs an haustorium soon penetrates the animal's body, sucks it clean, then leaves the empty shell. Zeophagus insidians bears short branches which, if any armoured Rotatorian seizes, the creature cannot let go of, for the end of the hypha promptly swells. Thereafter a branch invades the body of the prey.

Dionaea, or Venus' fly trap, is a wonderful device, as was mentioned above. Two lobes have spiked margins, and six sensitive hairs on the top of the leaves. Bright pigment covers the surface of the leaves. The two leaves can swiftly clasp a fly or other prey. As hours pass the trap tightens even more closely. The glands now secrete a digestive fluid, and the insect is absorbed. In about ten days the trap opens again. If one wanted to construct a plant for trapping insects, it would be difficult to imagine a form and organization better adapted to secure that end than the devices of Dionaea muscipula. The mechanism in this and similar traps, for example Aldrovanda, are hard to explain, mostly because of the speed of closure, less than half a second in the latter. Lloyd reviews the problem at length. Imagine such numerous, complex and wonder-arousing mechanisms developing piece-meal, or by one stride as in a mutation.

Summary

No satisfactory origin for or relations of the great families and orders of plants can be found in the vast fossil material so far studied. The first plants often resembled modern species closely, and were even more complex. Certainly they seem to make their first entry on the stage full-bloom. Modern experimental studies on both wild and cultivated plants show how new genetic and morphological species can arise. These two features of such plants are not necessarily correlated. But usually geographic isolation plays a part here, and the distinctions that develop go only as high as genus production, if to that. Hybridization and gene mutation can make new genetic species. There has been much confusion in taxonomy introduced by ardent but ignorant evolutionists.

Fungi present wonderful examples of the difficulties of phylogenetic taxonomy, as do the angiosperms. The adaptations of plants to life, and to insects especially, can be too extraordinary for evolution to begin to explain. Carnivorous plants provide very notable examples of plant specialization, far too intricate to explain on the basis of piece-meal or mutational development.

CHAPTER XIII

Extraordinary Adaptations

By whose decree
The supple knee
A small boy bends
So carelessly,

That perfect thing
The sea-gull's wing,
To catch a midge
On bank or swing,

The paint upon
The crack of dawn
Or moth at night
Or hidden fawn?

—Vere Jameson

PROPOSITION—The world of living things contains many thousands of such complicated adaptations as defy evolutionary explanation. They are the work of a super-intelligent and careful Creator.

Introduction

Living forms are all adapted to their environment or they could not survive. The list of their adaptations would fill an encyclopaedia— or be much larger. We give little heed to chlorophyll or the hollow bones of birds or the fins of seals or haemoglobin or the antennae of insects because such adaptations meet our eyes, ears and nose everywhere. The theory of evolution is based on such multiple adaptations, but assumes that they developed by tiny spurts or gradually, since either earlier creatures were not well adjusted or the environmental conditions of life have altered through the ages. How can life always remain adapted while the milieu changes, unless it be self-adapting?— or did the Creator always make creatures well endowed for the conditions of their existence, which are usually very stable during their brief lives?—or does He let them make small adaptive changes while setting a boundary to the possibilities of major change?

Every text on Evolution or on Biology is replete with illustrations of adaptation. I do not wish to repeat too many of these, but to adduce a few of the little known and more extraordinary adaptations—adaptations so complex and refined that evolutionary theory must be very hard pressed to explain them. The notion of a designing, all-wise

121

Creator fits them much better. Almost every Naturalist who reads this chapter will wonder why I have left out so many good examples he knows of. My answer is Dr. Johnston's: "Ignorance! Pure ignorance!" Caullery says: "It goes without saying that questions of a general character can only be treated through facts that are concrete and exact. In the field of biology the general exists only through the particular."

A most remarkable example of current evolutionary argument is Simpson's: "the best and I think quite conclusive proof that very small values of (selective pressure) are often effective in Nature is precisely the evidence so often cited against the effectiveness of selection. This evidence shows that adaptation may begin and proceed on the basis of very small variations and may reach a very intricate and high degree of perfection, so that its initiation, its continued trend, and the point reached must have involved very small selective values **if selection was involved** (italics mine)." Since adaptation has occurred, the argument "that adaptation does frequently . . . involve changes of low selective value can thus no longer be cited as evidence against selection but becomes the strongest sort of evidence that selection is, indeed, effective in producing adaptation." What a wonderful argument in a circle!

For Food

Ant soldiers soon specialize. Some gather seeds and some crush them. Some become great sacks of food and so become incapable of movement, hanging from the roofs of specially prepared chambers, receiving nourishment continually and doling it out by regurgitation when needed. About one in every 100 workers shows this physogastry. Termitophiles, as well as Claviger and myrmecophilous aleocharines, develop this physogastry. The termitophilous carabid beetles also have this happy and altruistic arrangement.

A British spider, Scytodes, is the only one able to spit gum over its prey. But in Australia, Dicrostichus magnificus sits quietly, smelling like a flower (?), till a moth flies by. Then she whirls a weighted line around her head and strikes the moth with the sticky wad of gum on its end. She then fishes the moth to and fro like a troutfisher. In South Africa, Cladomelea does about the same, whirling her lasso over her head for as much as 15 minutes on end. Then she pulls it in, puts on new bait, and tries again. Two Australian spiders are retiarii, and fling small webs about the size of postage stamps.

Pycraft tells us of the Angler-Fish (Lophias piscatorius) hugging the seabottom, where it lies partly hidden in mud of its own colour. A series of ragged flaps of skin about the head and fore-part of the body, as well as the split rods of its dorsal fins are remarkable. The first rod is stationed just above the upper jaw and a small flag marks its tip. The flaps and flag are agitated as the fish lies in wait for prey. If a small fish touches the flap, it is triggered into the mouth at once.

The larva of the water-beetle, Hydrous piceus, preys on snails. These are caught by pressing them between the folds of its back, whence they are pressed forward by the most improbable coiling movements to the mandibles that finally crush the shell.

All complete instincts are perfectly adapted—but some are more elaborate and complicated than others. For example, the wasp Bombyx dislocates one wing of any fly it paralyses, places the fly on its back on the floor of her cell, and lays her eggs on its sternum. In this way the fly cannot turn over on the very delicate young wasp larvae which hatch later. As has been mentioned before, the mother wasp can distinguish between the sex of her eggs, and thus can regulate both the size of the egg's cell and the amount of its provender to deposit there.

The hairs of bees are wonderfully varied, but are designed to hold pollen. The pollen may be carried in a special pollen basket or on special abdominal hairs. Some bees have their breeding-season exactly coincident with the blooming period of a single plant, for example Halictoides nova-Angliae and the purple pickerel weed, Pontederia cordata. The mother bee of the genus Allodape leaves bee-bread for her young. The larvae hold one packet apiece by special long appendages and each eats its packet just in time for pupation. The size of the packet corresponds to the size of the species, and each packet nourishes one larva.

In some species of the desert kangaroo rat the animal's cheek pouches, in which it carries home its sun-dried food, are lined with fur as further insulation.

Parasitism

The modification of body parts for the parasitic life are enormous and sweeping. The organs of locomotion may disappear or atrophy or become organs of attachment, hooks and suckers. The sense organs and central nervous systems may be reduced. The hind gut, or the whole bowel may disappear, as in Cestodes and Acanthocephala. Anticoagulants may appear in the blood-sucking forms. The ovaries can hypertrophy and become enormous. The gastropod, Gasterosiphon, for example, has lost its shell completely, but a visceral hump remains and there are vestiges of a foot. No cephalic tentacles, nor a true mantle, nor gills, kidney or heart are seen. The central nervous system is condensed. There is neither intestine nor anus. The ovary and testes are distinct but senile. Analogously, the Cryptoniscidae among the Epicardiae are merely sacs of embryos when adult, dying when the brood emerges. They have disconcerting shapes, bearing no resemblance to a crustacean. They show no traces of segmentation or appendages, have only a vestige of an alimentary canal and no mouth. The nervous system is reduced to a few ganglia. Moreover, the various types are extremely divergent in their degenerative alterations.

The Sitaris grub clutches the hair of a passing Anthophora bee by a wonderful pair of spikes. Carried thus, it enters the bee's cell and is laid on the latter's egg at the **precise and only moment** it could jump on. For the Sitaris grub itself would die if dropped in the surrounding honey. Thus the bee's egg is both raft and provender for the little parasite. Only one Sitaris ever rides one egg—the egg is too small to hold more! The grub eats and grows, splitting open its skin to expose a "second grub"!

Lull tells of the ant, Lasius brunneus, which gathers the young larvae of the corn-root louse in the fall and keeps them safe till spring, when they are transported to the roots of certain weeds until the corn germinates, then to the roots of the growing corn, and there are herded till autumn mating time. At this time they are allowed to pair and their offspring are preserved as before.

The Coelenterate, Polypodium, has a stolon which is parasitic within the egg of the sturgeon. Here it turns inside out till spawning occurs; then the stolon splits and turns outside in. Some of the egg yolk adheres to its buds and is now used by the parasite for its nourishment for a time. The freed polyp can walk about on its tentacles on the river bottom.

Then there are the extraordinary adaptions of plants. Darwin called attention to the mistletoe, "which draws its nourishment from certain trees, which has seeds that must be transported by certain birds, and which has flowers with separate sexes, absolutely requiring the agency of certain insects to bring pollen from one flower to the other." The fruit is eaten by most frugivorous birds, notably the mistle-thrush. The bird wipes its beak on the bark; there the viscid pulp soon hardens to protect the seed. This sends its roots into the bark of the host tree. The parasite can thus live as long as the host tree.

For Reproduction

Nicol tells of Sphaerobolus, the fungus mortar about 1/5 of an inch in diameter and about as high. As the fungus matures the covering over the mortar is pulled back and a pocket of spores can be seen in a cup-shaped bed containing fluid and itself a web of tissue. Suddenly the cup everts and fires its missile, the eversion taking about one-thousandth of a second. Only the web moves. The fungus mortar can fire its shell at least 18 feet.

Wallace comments on the fact that in open, cup-shaped, regular flowers self-fertilization is often prevented by a physiological variation, "the anthers constantly emitting their pollen either a little earlier or a little later than the stigmas of the same flower, or of other flowers on the same plant, were in the best state to receive it." How could such a delicate and accurate provision of flower physiology ever arise in stages?

Even more inexplicable is the provision by the plant, Duvana dependens, of a special gall to cherish the moth, Cecidosis eremita. Karl Frank showed that it shaped a cover of exactly the right size **at the right time,** not earlier and not later, so that when the moth crept out of the gall the chrysalis skin only was torn off. Why does the plant help the moth by such a marvellously complex adaptation?

Acworth tells of the remarkable year 1893 when Pearl-bordered Fritillary butterflies hatched into mature butterflies in about a month in place of the normal 330 days. Imagine any other gestation period altering so much, promptly at need!

When grayling butterflies are mating the female alights and the male stands in front of her. At the climax he bows, a movement by which the female's antennae, containing chemoreceptors, are caught between the male's forewings, where his scent organs are. Mating cannot occur otherwise.

The male of the spider, Hypomena bituberculata, has two hard knobs on his head. As he approaches the female, who is so often dangerous, he lowers his head. The female, lunging at him to kill him, seizes these knobs. Her jaws enter specially prepared grooves at the base of the knobs. Thus she is locked to him and cannot hurt him although she holds him down till the sex act is performed. Other males in other species can hold the female's fangs either together or apart, and thus keep her harmless.

Wood Jones (104)* tells of the chit-chuit, the tropic island white tern, which lays its eggs on a bare branch of a tall ironwood tree in the tossing wind of a tropical island; for three months egg or baby balances there. He concludes: "It is a thing almost beyond belief."

The sand grouse can hatch its eggs when the air is very dry and the desert soil too hot to touch, the vegetation parched and all available seeds nearly desiccated. To sustain the nestlings the male, before drinking, rubs his breast violently up and down on the ground to ruffle his feathers, then wades in the water to saturate his underparts. The nestlings suck these wet underfeathers on his return.

The emperor penguin has no nest but carries and incubates its eggs upon its feet. Its young learn to walk on the parent's feet, hiding behind a parental apron. Both sexes and all the birds in a colony may help in the incubation.

A helminth, Polystoma integerrimum, lives in the bladder of some frogs. In spring its eggs are laid simultaneously with the frog's, and hatch at the same time to infect the young tadpoles. It matures in 3 years, like its host. But if the tadpole infected originally is less than a week

---

*Quoted by permission of Edward Arnold (Publishers) Ltd., London, England

old the parasite develops in a month, lays eggs and dies during tadpole metamorphosis. Thus this bladder fluke provides a generation at the correct time to infect both old tadpoles and younger ones! What an adaptation in timing!

The new-born kangaroo is only an inch long and unable to suck. It seizes a teat, whose end swells at once so that the young can scarcely be pulled off. A sphincter muscle in the mouth of the young also helps it to hold its grip. Its mother has a special adaptation of the cremaster muscle as well, which enables her to squirt milk down its throat, past its larynx, otherwise the infant would drown in milk. Nipples in marsupials and placentals would be useless unless the young possessed soft muscular lips—which no "lower" form has. How did lips and teats evolve pari passu? (105)

Moulting

The caterpillar moults in a remarkable way. Acworth* (79) quotes Kirby and Spence on this: "The head, antennae, jaws, and legs of the caterpillars are persistent ,and their hairy covering only is shed at the period of moult. Swammerdam recorded that not only the hairy covering of these parts and the skin of the body come away at each moult, but also the throat and part of the stomach, and even the inward surface of the great gut, change their skin at the same time. But this is not the whole of these wonders, for at the same time each of some hundreds of pulmonary pipes within the body also casts its delicate and tender skin. These several skins are afterwards collected into eighteen thicker, and as it were compounded, ropes—nine on each side of the body—which, when the skin is cast, slip gently and by degrees from within the body through eighteen apertures or orifices of the pulmonary tubes, nine on each side. Two other branches of the pulmonary tubes, that are smaller and have no points of respiration, cast a skin like-wise. If anyone separates the cast little ropes or congeries of the pulmonary pipes with a fine needle he will very distinctly see the branches and ramifications of these several pipes, and also their annular composition." Imagine this process happening by mutation or piece-meal by any process!

The grub of the locust has its boring tool on its neck. This area swells and subsides alternately, striking the obstacle before it like a piston. When the grub reaches the surface this blister splits and the skin is cast off. The final moult is wonderful. For along its corselet is a weak line, and there waves of blood can be seen throbbing within, till the skin distends and splits as if the halves had previously been barely soldered together. The split runs back between the wing roots, then goes forward up the head to the bases of the antennae, where it splits. The back then escapes, then the head, leaving the mask behind. The sheaths of the antennae, without a wrinkle or any derangement,

---

*Quoted by permission of Eyre and Spottiswoode, London, England.

and in their usual positions, hang over this dead face of the discarded skin! Then the fore-legs and intermediary legs withdraw from their sheaths without wrinkling those gauntlets. But the great shanks are barbed in a double row, and 4 large spurs mark the very tips of the feet. This spur fits inside an identical gauntlet, each spur inside a spur, and the whole sheath as tight and thick as varnish. Yet the spur is softened and withdrawn without wrinkling it; a few minutes later the legs and spurs are hardened.

In the Water

Crompton tells us how the Water Spider (Argyroneta aquatica) does a tricky flop and plunge on the surface of the water, by which it collects a globule of air in the hairs at its middle. It carries the air underwater, then collects its bubbles at the top of its underwater house, —having long ago discovered the "diving bell"!

Another remarkable bubble adaptation is that of the floating barnacle, Lepos fascicularis, which manufactures a bubble when its body has become too heavy to float on a piece of seaweed.

The pelican dives hard into the water to catch fish. Therefore it needs and has a built-in shock absorber, a series of air sacs, not only in the bones, but sacs branching out from its lungs which run along its neck, on up to its skull and into some of its muscles. It even has a set of these air sacs under the skin.

A Few Unexplained Items

One of the most puzzling items for an evolutionist is the sex difference in the beaks of the Huia bird of New Zealand, now presumed to be extinct. The cock-bird had a short, stout beak for breaking up rotted wood in order to reach the hu-hu grub. The female had a long, curved beak for deeper probing. The only observer to report on them (Buller), reported that they cooperated in feeding. It may be that such cooperation was essential. Here is evolution (?) producing a marked sex differential which concerns so vital a process as feeding, a differential which might distinguish genera among Darwin's finches, for example, But—if the male could get food with a short beak, why did the female need a long one? If the pair had to cooperate to eat, what did young unmated birds do for food? (73).

The Miracle of the Eye

Let me begin by quoting Darwin on this subject, as is so frequently my custom. (That lets me begin at the first and often at the next to the last, for he was an admirable naturalist). Darwin admitted: "To suppose that the eye, with all its inimitable contrivances for adjusting the focus to different distances, for admitting different amounts of light, and for the correction of spherical and chromatic abberation, could have been formed by natural selection, seems, I freely confess, absurd in the highest possible degree" . . . "the difficulty of believing that a perfect and complex eye could be formed by natural selection, though insuperable by our imagination, can hardly be considered real" . . . "Amongst existing Vertebrates, we find but a small amount of graduation in the structure of the eye (though in the fish, amphioxus, the eye is in an extremely simple condition without a lens), and free from fossil species we can learn nothing on this head. In this great class we should probably have to descend far beneath the lowest known fossiliferous stratum to discover the earlier stages by which the eye has been perfected." He gives a long paragraph on the eyes of crustaceans, and concludes: "With these facts . . . which show how much graduated diversity there is in the eyes of our existing crustaceans, and bearing this in mind how small the number of living animals is in proportion to those which have become extinct, I can see no very great difficulty . . . in believing that natural selection has converted the simple apparatus of an optic nerve merely coated with pigment and invested by transparent membrane, into an optical instrument as perfect as is possessed by any number of the great articulate class," (which includes vertebrates and incidentally, man, of course) . . .

"He who will go thus far, if he finds on finishing this treatise that large bodies of facts, otherwise inexplicable, can be explained by the theory of descent, ought not to hesitate to go further, and to admit that a structure even as perfect as the eye of an eagle might be formed by natural selection, although in this case he does not know of any of the transitional grades. His reason ought to conquer his imagination; though I have felt the difficulty far too keenly to be surprised by any degree of hesitation in extending the principle of natural selection to such startling lengths." This belief demands great faith, but Darwin insists on it, for "If it could be demonstrated that any complex organ existed, which could not possibly have been formed by numerous, successive, slight modifications, my theory would absolutely break down." He says elsewhere: "The belief that an organ as perfect as the eye could have formed by natural selection is more than enough to stagger anyone." Never think that only Christians require faith!

Now, as Merson Davies points out, nothing in palaeontology indicates that creatures of the past had poorer vision than have corresponding types now. O'Toole* (106) quotes Professor Dwight, who remarked: "—the eyes of certain mollusca and crustacea are on stalks, and this is found also in various very different families of fishes. How did this happen? Was it by way of descent from the mollusca or the crustacea? If not, how could chance have brought about such a similar result in diverse forms?" Convergence is now the word for this phenomenon, although it merely describes rather than explains the difficulty. O'Toole himself goes on to say: "The cephalopod mollusc

---

*Quoted by permission of the MacMillan Co., New York, U.S.A.

Nautilus, for example, solves the problem of light perception in the identical manner in which it is solved by the vertebrates. This mollusc has the perfect vertebrate type of eye, including the lens and all other parts down to the minutest detail . . . the genetic interpretation (of this) is positively rejected by the evolutionist, who interprets the occurrence of similar eyes in molluscs and vertebrates as an instance of accidental convergence. Paley said, speaking of the fish's eye many long years ago: The laws of light "require, in order to produce the same effect, that the rays of light, in passing from water into the eye, should be refracted by a more convex surface than when it passes out of the air into the eye. Accordingly we find that the eye of a fish, in that part of it called the crystalline lens, is much rounder than the eye of terrestrial animals. What plainer manifestation of design can there be than this difference?" The spherical lens of the fish compensates for its flat cornea, and is adapted for near vision at rest, unlike the eye of other vertebrates.

On the other hand, J. B. S. Haldane (107) observed that "if the eye consisted of a thousand independently variable parts, all of which had to fit more or less adequately, then their fitting would deserve the title of a miracle. But actually things are not like that."—for "the eye is formed before its bony socket, and largely determines the form of the latter, and so on." The question then is: "How many variables in the specifications of the eye, which must alter together to produce an improvement in its function, are independent heritable characters? If you can prove to me that there are a hundred, I must of course abandon Darwinism . . . Personally, I suspect that ten is an overestimate." That "suspect" marks the evolutionist, of course. Lunn and Haldane (107)* quote Alfred Noyes, the astronomer, who has other things to say on this last matter: "Suppose, for instance, one of the surfaces of the crystalline lens of the eye to be accidentally altered, then I say that unless the form of the other surface is simultaneously altered in one only way out of millions of possible ways, the eye would not be optically improved. An alteration in the two surfaces of the crystalline lens, whether accidental or otherwise, would involve a definite alteration in the form of the cornea, or in the distance of its surface from the centre of the crystalline lens, in order that the eye might be optically better. All these alterations must be simultaneous and definite in amount, and these definite amounts must coexist in obedience to an extremely complicated law" . . . my apprehension then that so complicated instrument as the eye should undergo a succession of millions of improvements, by means of a succession of millions of accidental alterations, is not less improbable than if all the letters of the Origin of Species were placed in a box and on being shaken and poured out . . . should at last come out together in the order in which they occur in that fascinating work."

---

*Quoted by permission of Sheed and Ward, Inc., New York, U.S.A.

Fisher claims to have proved mathematically that for a sufficiently small alteration the chance of improving an organ such as the eye is exactly one half, and not a minute fraction. "Unfortunately his argument is mathematical," says Haldane, and "like many mathematical results, it is rather paradoxical."

Perhaps the outstanding defect of the eye as a visual instrument is its chromatic aberration. The different components of white light are bent differently by a lens, so that on the retina there is apt to be a coloured edge on visual images, indicating the splitting up of the light fractions at the lens. However, no mobile, adjustable lens could be thought of that would correct for this peculiarity of white light; namely, that it is not a unit but a fusion of red, yellow, and other factors. One might as well say Nature has ordered light defectively as that she had formed the eye on inadequate principles of physics.

Evolutionists discussing the evolution of the eye say curious things. Walls (108) says that there are vestiges of visual ependyma in the mid-brain or diencephalon which receive some illumination even through the whole side of the head. Hence the regulation of breeding seasons in birds by the changing light of day. But the writer (109) and other workers have shown an analogous sex hormone variation in man and rodents, depending probably not on light but on seasonal diets. We do not need to find a vestigial use for rudiments (?) of visual apparatus in the mid-brain, therefore.

Walls,* an evolutionist, also says: "The origin of the lens is the most mysterious thing about the whole evolution of the eye. It is not possible to say just why, when, or how it arose, or how it managed to get inside the meningeal envelopes of the retinal brain-tube." In some inexplicable way it developed focussing power! In its early development it is pinched off from the skin layers and drops into the retinal cup long before the meninges are formed. Walls comments: "We are thus able to imagine that in the embryo of some crucial early vertebrate, purely as an accident of mutation, the lens came to occupy this much more favourable position by getting the jump on the meninges. It has remembered to get an early start in development ever since." Further on: "Luckily, the vertebrate eye has just happened to evolve as a hollow ball with a tough outer coat . . . It was thus enabled to secure the requisite rigidity, holding lens and retina in the proper optical relationship" as if it were a small basket ball. To hold the lens forward, two kinds, of fluid developed in the eye-ball, the jelly at the back holding the lens forward, as in the lamprey. The eye had to be more moveable, so "commandeered" adjacent paired muscle-masses. These are fine instances of how the evolutionist commandeers words to explain the inexplicable! A hole forms in the iris because the latter becomes

---

*Quoted by permission of Ciba Pharmaceutical Products, Inc. Summit, N.J., U.S.A.

pigmented! This is an explanation, isn't it? Fishes accomodate by moving the lens to and fro, but use different mechanisms for this "and one cannot say which arrangement is the most primitive." Rhodopsin or visual purple has been "invented" and "re-invented by many animal groups," Walls says.

Then fish came on land, says the evolutionist, and became amphibious. But "A fish eye out of water is the most useless part of the fish." It could not see and must have dried up promptly and become infected. Lids and lubricating glands had to be produced at once or these animals could not maintain their beach-head, and at least one lid must move. Simultaneously these first venturesome fish had to invent a way of secreting fluid inside the eye ball. As the refractive system was all completely changed in the air, the lens had to be made flatter and pushed back to keep an image on the retina. The lens also had to learn at once to stop ultra-violet light in order to prevent it sunburning and blinding the retina. What a clever and quickly adjustable fish that first land-invader was! The teleost fishes developed an eye which aimed at an object, as well as colour vision. Colour vision in reptiles and birds had to be evolved **de novo**, because they chose to develop from a different class of fishes, unfortunately!

Moreover, all photoreception, in any phylum of animals, is dependent for its light-sensitive pigments upon the carotenoids, such as vitamin A. The light intensities under which animals can see may vary by a billion times.

The "lowest" mammals "lost" most or all of their retinal cones, as they needed only nocturnal vision. They "lost" the oil-droplets in what cones they had, and hence their color sense. They "lost" the power to accommodate and the disadvantageous striated muscles in the ciliary muscle and papillary sphincter. This placed a great handicap on the evolution of the eye in higher animals, such as man. Apparently, evolution here took a wrong and irreversible direction! The first placental mammals, the insectivores, did even worse things to their eyes, leaving a terrific bottleneck in development for all higher forms! Many of them "lost" all the double cones in their retinae, and all their oil-droplets in the cones. Thus, later hoofed and flesh-eating mammals at best are indifferent to night and day, and few have been able to become truly diurnal. The lowest primates, for example, are nocturnal only, with pure-rod retinas. The lemurs have no colour vision.

But monkeys made the eye over, says Walls! "since the results are all to be seen, in full bloom, in even the lowest of the true monkeys (Capuchins, Macaques), one cannot determine the order in which these were accomplished historically." In brief, the re-evolution of the primate eye is incapable of even theoretical reconstruction! But we evolved cones again—poor by comparison with those of reptiles and lower mammals. A shallow fovea was re-evolved, but one nearly as good as that of teleost fishes or reptiles. The retina at the fovea and about it became impregnated with a yellow pigment and this, plus a yellowish lens, (which cuts out the short wave-lengths of the spectrum where colour error is greatest) forms the colour filter which we had to have to replace the lost cone oil-droplets evolution should have saved for us from the lower animals such as frogs! Indeed, evolutionists hold that colour vision evolved separately at least three times among the vertebrates, and that which we possess "duplicated" perfectly its forerunners in teleost fishes and sauropsidans, as nearly as we can tell. Remember that such assumptions, and the evolutionist makes them repeatedly, are due to the fact that he had arranged animals in a family tree, according to such features as the backbone, type of eating, protective external pouches for the young, and so on, long before he thought of colour vision—which just did not fit into his pre-arranged family tree. **Had he made vision his criterion, animal "relations" could be much different than they now are said to be.** "In man, too, a completely new mechanism of accommodation, since imitated half-heartedly by some of the flesh-eaters and perhaps the diurnal squirrels . . . had to be devised." Here is a wonderful example of evolutionary loose talk.—Are we to assume these carnivores and squirrels evolved from man? The lens became elastic and therefore could become more spherical for near-sight, although this mechanism is not nearly so nicely "evolved" as the constrictor muscle of reptiles applied directly to the lens. Our ciliary muscle is non-striated, and so works more slowly than that of birds and reptiles. Our eyes "accommodate" the hard way and lose this power as age hardens the lens. If only we had evolved as good a lens or eye as that of the snake! O! Evolution, thou false jade! Man has been cheated.

All the visual pigments known in animal eyes, says Wald (110) are made with a specifically bent isomer of retinene. This isomer is the only one which can fit the point of attachment on the protein, opsin. Light acts by straightening out the retinene (from a cis to a trans isomer), hence detaches it from the opsin. What a beautiful biochemical mechanism to evolve as perfectly as it has, and so generally in all eyes, despite their different evolutionary origins!

There are some remarkable eyes in the animal world, too, which must stagger the evolutionist—if he can be staggered. For example, the fish called the mud-skipper goes out on mud-flats occasionally. Then to protect his eyes, which have no lids, of course, he pulls his eyes down into their sockets and rolls them about to look inward into his head. In the flatfishes the youngest fishes have an eye on opposite sides of the head. But soon the young fish starts to lie on its side, and the "downside" eye migrates to the new "topside". In one flounder (Pseudo-pleuronectes Americanus) this process is reported to consume only three days, although it involves twisting the skull as well! The Central American freshwater fish, Anableps, has a pupil crossed by a dark, horizontal line composed of narrow projections of the iris. When the fish swims this line lies just at the water-level, so that half

132

the eye is in the air to see above the water and half below to see under water. One lens must therefore provide two focal lengths—hence the fish needs an egg-shaped bifocal lens. Some desert salamanders have transparent eyelids, or even windows in the lids. It must try evolutionists' imaginations to evolve such specialized structures. Usually such things are conveniently ignored. At least they rarely creep into the college textbooks which set out to prove the plausibility and credibility of the theory.

For Defence

The Hunting Wasp carries a director in its tail which has a tiny point with a hole in it through which two lancets shoot out to sting its prey. These needles are three-sided, their outer V-shaped edge retained in a slot on the inner wall of the director. The inmost sides of the two needles in the centre are concave, forming a poison tube. The extremities of the needles are also barbed with six flat barbs and at the base of each barb a channel is cut through into the central pipe. This lets the poison squirt out of the end of the pipe and through the sides at the base of the barbs. What a magnificent weapon to evolve piece-meal!

The cockroach, Diploptera punctata, has a defensive spray it can eject from only one side of the body or from both; it can aim this spray, can use it up to four discharges at a sequence, and by this means can repel attacking ants and carabids and temporarily palsy them.

The Malayan hooded locustid (Capnoptera) does not resist when picked up, casually lowers its head, opens a cleft between its head and thorax, thus forcing out a scarlet bladder or hood, as if its entrails were extruding in a frightening way. The Singhalese grasshopper, Acridium violescens, if chased by Mynah birds, rolls over on one side, and deliberately draws up a hind leg to expose a series of grey and black eye-spots. The bird usually withdraws, even after several approaches. The rolling over is done deliberately and slowly. How could such an unusual habit evolve to reveal the warning colour pattern so perfectly? How did the insect know it was there, and could be menacing? The mantids also reveal menacing bright colours and make a noise when attacked. Their predators show fright,—as do humans, indeed.

An Australian worm, Didymogaster silvaticus, when handled roughly, squeezes itself and shoots a fluid out of some 20 perforations in its body to a height of perhaps four feet.

The sloth of tropical forests is often coloured green because a symbiotic green alga lives in its grooved hairs and gives this protective colouring to its host. Put the sloth in a zoo and its colour fades as the alga dies. How prescient of the sloth to provide these unique grooved hairs! How wise of it to let only a green fungus live in the grooves! How accommodating of the fungus!

Tinbergen* (88) quotes Kepner from Lashley on the adaptations of Microstoma. "Microstoma, related to the more familiar Planaria and liver flukes, is equiped with nematocysts or stinging cells like those of the hydroids, which it discharges in defence and in capture of prey. In discharging, the stinging cell evaginates a threadlike, barbed tube through which poison is ejected. The striking fact about the creature is that it does not grow its own weapons, but captures them from another microscopic animal, the fresh-water polyp, Hydra. The Hydras are eaten and digested until their undischarged stinging cells lie free in the stomach of Microstoma. The nettles are then picked up by amoeboid processes of the cells lining the stomach and passed through the wall into the mesoderm. Here they are again picked up by wandering tissue cells and carried to the skin. The stinging cells are elliptical sacs with elastic walls, which are turned in at one end as a long coiled tube. In discharging, the wall of the sac contracts and forces out the barbed poison tube from one end of the sac. The nettle cells can therefore fire in only one direction. When the mesodermal cell carries the nettle to the surface, it turns it around so as to aim the poison tube outward. It then grows a trigger, and sets the apparatus to fire on appropriate stimulation.

"When Microstoma has no stinging cells it captures and eats Hydra voraciously. When it gets a small supply of cells these are distributed uniformly over the surface of the body. As more cells are obtained they are interpolated at uniform intervals between those already present. When a certain concentration of cells is reached, the worm loses its appetite for Hydras, and, in fact, will starve to death rather than eat any more of the polyps, which are apparently not a food but only a source of weapons.

"Here in the length of a half a millimetre, are encompassed all of the major problems of dynamic physiology." Indeed, the whole process is simply incredible, on an evolutionary basis.

In the Nematode life-cycle there is an abrupt change in the third-stage larva, in many forms, from an aerobic to an almost anaerobic environment, and from a metabolism depending on the catabolism of fat to one mainly depending on glycolysis, and from a free life to a parasitic one. The biochemist will be puzzled by this.

Adaptations for Arctic Climates

Among the most remarkable adaptations of animals are those which inure them to extremes of cooling and even to freezing. A recent study by A. V. Smith (111) gives details of some of these.

---

*Quoted by permission of the Clarendon Press, Oxford, England.

Larvae of the wheat-stem sawfly can be supercooled to between 20° and 32° below zero Centigrade before freezing occurs. Certain insects survive even the formation of ice within their tissues, for example larvae of the European corn-borer and hibernating prepupae of the Japanese moth, Monema flavescens. However, if these prepupae develop intracellular crystals in the heart the organ disrupts after thawing. Larvae of an Alaskan midge survive in frozen mud or ice at temperatures as low as -40°C for months at a time. The blood of some frost-hardy insects contains glycerol, which may be very significant. The horse mussel and other mussels may survive after 71 to 76 per cent of the body water has been frozen, then thawed. At this stage the concentration of salts in the residual cell fluid is quadrupled.

The famous Alaskan Blackfish does not revive nor does the heart respond to stimuli after the whole body is frozen at -26°C. Freezing the rear end of it kills that part, although the front end may still survive. Arctic shallow-water fish may double the osmotic strength of their blood in the autumn in order to become almost isosmotic to freezing water.

The vessels in the webbed feet of gulls or the fins of whales in polar seas have a brisk circulation. The venae comitantes are arranged around the arteries to rewarm the venous blood and precool the arterial blood before it reaches the extremities. Alternative venous channels can be opened up for emergencies. What an interesting adaptation to evolve!

The peripheral nerves of Arctic birds and mammals conduct impulses at lower temperatures than do those of tropical animals. The fats in the peripheral tissues of Arctic animals have lower melting points than the fat in the interior of the body.

In hibernation the activity of the cerebral cortex ceases completely. Breathing and heart beating continue slowly. If the environmental temperature drops below zero the hibernating animal compensates by increasing its metabolic rate.

Sloths, the anteater, the armadillo, even the lemur, are not homeothermic, but vary their body temperature with their environment. Does this relate them closely to the cold-blooded reptiles?

Smell and Other Senses

Griffin and Grinnell (112) claim that the group of Megachiroptera among bats are visual, but the rest use sonar. They catch insects by reflecting sound off the insect's body. The oil-bird, Steatornis caripensis, of South America, and perhaps swifts of the genus Collocalia use a method quite similar. Many bats can make long distance homing and migration flights at night under conditions in which echo-location can be of little, if any, help. The fish-eating bats detect echoes from fish beneath the surface of smooth water, a surface which must be almost completely reflecting even to the intense high-frequency sonar of the bats. Strangely, too, bats can avoid collision with smooth water surfaces when drinking.

Anatomical

The scales of butterfly wings lie on the wings like shingles, although sometimes they lie on edge like Venetian blind slats. As they lie there they form **exactly** the structural condition necessary for the production of the correct refraction of colour desired for that species. Moreover, the outer surface of this scale is ruled like a diffraction grating, the best our physics laboratories can produce. What an intricate device to arise by chance?

Crompton describes the web-weaving device of the spider Aranea. It has 6 teats, each having about 100 tiny taps. Each of these taps is connected by an individual tube to a separate gland in the spider's body. The spider can use any number of tubes desired, can move her teats about for the manufacture of separate threads, or can join them together to produce a broad band of silk. Seven kinds of silk are manufactured by spiders, no species having all seven, but all have three and Aranea has five. The 600 little pipes do not all make silk, for the spider also makes and extrudes glue. When she makes her web with its 13,000 lines, she anoints each thread with this glue in globules arrange exactly **equi-distant.** The spider's feet exude oil like sweat, and this enables her to avoid being entangled in her own net. The spinnerets must replace abdominal legs, Thomson claims. The spider gorges when she can, but can starve for 18 months on end and survive.

Graebner comments on the strange problem of the spider's silk. The glands producing silk would be useless without spinnerets. Legs must have been modified to perform as spinnerets, as has been claimed by evolutionists, but how could locomotive legs have been pierced with more than 1000 apertures through which the web is later drawn? How could these organs have served their purpose while the requisite instincts were still imperfectly evolved?

De Beaufort (113) mentions the Homalopteridae found in mountain torrents in Northern Borneo. The whole flat underside is surrounded by the much expanded pectoral and pelvic fins, forming a large sucker by which the fish can cling to stones or rocks.

The fish, Phyrrhyhina filamentosa, lays its eggs outside the water, then by expert work with her tail, constantly splashes them to keep them moist for the next three to five days. When the young hatch, back they slide into the water.

Non-Adaptation

A word could be said on the non-adaptive features of life, often very complex items, for example, the forms of antelope horns or the random distribution of the three main kidney types in mammals, whether on land or sea. Simpson (1) observes: "If, as claimed, the large sabres (teeth) made it difficult (for ancient cats) to eat, the animals took 40,000,000 years to starve to death."

But hypertely, the overdevelopment of adaptational features, has long been regarded as a major objection to evolutionary theory. Haldane, Waddington and Huxley seem to find it unusually difficult, says Simpson. An outstanding example is the Mesozoic mollusc, Gryphaea, developed until one valve pressed on the other and would not let it open.

Simpson strives hard to neutralize this difficulty (pp. 283 et seq.), but is not very successful. Roberts has adduced another remarkable "adaptation" hard to explain on evolutionary reasoning, the mechanism by which a python swallows an unusually large animal. It actually dislocates its occipital condyle from the atlas vertebra, with an associated stretching of the spinal cord. Snakes occasionally die when swallowing a prey that has proved too large for them to manage.

Summary

Extraordinary adaptations in Nature are common. They are often far too complex to be explicable on an evolutionary basis. Physogastry, the degenerative alterations of parasites, the moulting of caterpillars, the adaptational habits of the water spider, the sting of the hunting wasp, the spiracles of insects, the castes of termites, ants and bees, the web-weaving mechanism of spiders, the lassoes of spiders, their sex habits and organs, the sex habits of the grasshopper, the mechanisms by which the grasshopper escapes from its gallery, the cricket's wing, the moult of the locust, the skill of the grub of the Anthrax fly, the larynx of the howler monkey, the sense organs of insects, snails and birds, the mating of grayling butterflies, the fiddler-crab's waving arm,—and so on, and on, including all instincts, all mimicry, all parasitism, these seem quite beyond understanding on the basis of evolution. These phenomena could not develop in stages, as they are useful only when perfect and complete. They are so numerous and varied that they provide too many exceptions to evolutionary rules. Their number and complexity are simply enormous, for they pervade Nature, both its plants and animals.

CHAPTER XIV

Convergence

Words slip carelessly past our teeth
Blessing or damning men beneath
The roaring stars and jealous sun
Where articulation has not begun
And never a word for ether leagues
The crowded ear of God fatigues.

—Vere Jameson

PROPOSITION—The phenomena of convergence of form and function are so widespread in Nature that they lead to hopeless confusion in tracing relations between living forms. Moreover, the parallel development of identical structures and biochemical systems in widely diverse types of creature tasks the evolutionist to the uttermost. Is this Convergence—or one Creative directed impetus?

Introduction

Evolutionists were early aware that very similar organs, colours and habits had appeared in widely dissimilar types of animals. It was hard enough to explain how evolution could have produced an organ once. It was much harder to explain how the organ could have developed twice or five times, each time starting from a completely dissimilar structural beginning. There are many striking instances of this sort of thing, for example, the production and laying of eggs, or the mimicry of butterflies, so many, indeed, that biologists developed the idea of "convergence" from numerous, even widely different phyletic origins. Nowadays this extraordinary philosophical principle is a commonplace biological conclusion, polyphyletic origins are frequently postulated in both plants and animals, and no one pauses to look at the very high bar the evolutionist has here leaped with a splintered semantic pole.

Indeed, we can never be sure any longer that any structure is derived by immediate descent from another, since we never can tell how much of the similarity is due to convergence.

Let us look at "Convergence" a little closer, at least closer than did Darwin, who dismissed it in one brief paragraph in The Origin, saying that: "This is an intricate subject which need not be here discussed," and that if genera could diverge by evolutionary principles they could probably converge as easily by similar means.

Even phyla, the primary divisions of the animal kingdom, can converge, for example humming birds and hawk-moths, (Trochilidae (chordates) and Sphingidae (arthropods).)

Environment

Jordan and Kellogg say that similar environments tend to produce similar adaptations in unrelated groups of animals. As examples they quote the density of fur in Arctic animals, the white winter dress of Arctic creatures, the gray colour of desert beasts, the swift, darting motions and bottom-hugging of unlike fish in swift streams, the black colour, soft bodies and luminous organs of deep-sea fishes, eel-like and snake-like forms in creatures quite unlike eels and snakes, the blinding of many unrelated species of cave fish and cave salamanders. Certainly we could agree with Gadow* (11) that "these cases of analogy, homoplasy, convergences have become of supreme interest in (our) science. Their solution implies the greatest of problems"—

Convergence in Invertebrates

The death feint is a wonderful example of protective mimicry, used by many unrelated creatures. The Mexican leaf butterfly not only mimics a leaf when at rest, but in the way it drifts to earth and even in alighting. Yet the colouration of these butterflies varies greatly between individuals. Surely such intensely useful colour variations either should become fixed by natural selection or be swamped out by inter-breeding. The evolutionist cannot explain why neither happens, and why such major variants persist. As a general rule the butterfly's eggs, too, resemble plant seeds. The convergance in such widely different phases of one life-history as the egg and the adult wing to totally different features of plants is certainly an intricate problem for an evolutionist to solve.

There are two Antarctic ten-legged Pantopods or sea-spiders which converge only in this detail, but otherwise belong to two widely different genera, all other forms having eight legs. A third ten-legged form has lately been found, this one quite unrelated to the other two.

As an adaptation to permit ectoparasitic insects to glide through mammalian fur, the apterous earwig, Hemimerus, has a projection from the back edge of the head, over-lapping the pronotum slightly. This is exceptional among insects, is best known in fleas and in some Hemiptera parasitic on bats. In the beaver parasite, Platypsyllus castoris, an analogous comb of spines bridges the gap between head and thorax.

Small freshwater annelid worms, the Tubificidae, live half-buried in the mud of water-courses, breathing through their weaving tails.

---

*Quoted by permission of the University Press, Cambridge, England.

Living among or near them are the larvae of midge flies (Chirononomus) doing the identical thing—and, most remarkable of all, the blood of the insect larvae is coloured red with haemoglobin, like that of the worms.

Willey (115) comments on the remarkable convergence of ant and termite habits, which we need not stress here since other chapters have dealt with it.

The tracheae of insects and spiders are similarly histologically and physiologically—but have separate origins, say the modern evolutionists. Indeed, to make it more remarkable, even among spiders they have evolved twice—from ectodermal tendons and lung-books. The latter may be analogous to the pulmonate mollusca, where the lung-chamber has replaced a gill-chamber. The internal tracheae seen amongst arthropoids as well are regarded as polyphyletic (of multiple origins).

A Note on Plants

Gadow tells us how plants use similar devices for the same climate. In deserts there are no broad-leaved plants, most being spiky, as in yuccas, or large, thick and juicy under an air-tight and water-tight epidermis, like the African aloes or American agaves. Or the plants may be leafless and have thousands of spikes instead, with a green rind on the stem. The chlorophyll is then spread over the stem instead of the leaves, for example in the American cacti and African euophorbias. In arid areas the vegetation is patchy on every continent, for reasons unknown. It is hard, on looking at any desert on any continent, to miss the resemblance, though the plants may be quite unrelated.

Convergence in Vertebrates

Willey discusses convergence in a book on the subject. He mentions that electric fishes all impart shocks by a peculiar device. Yet here we are speaking of the ray and eel of South American rivers, and the catfish of African rivers, quite unrelated creatures. Moreover, many species closely related to these have no trace of this endowment.

The porpoise has a most efficient sonar and can recognize and locate a tiny pellet of shot dropped into a murky tank, or swim through a maze, as Kellogg (116) has recently shown. The bat has an equally effective system. Griffin and Grinnell showed that the latter can act on information contained in one or a few echoes having no more than 1/2000 of the noise energy simultaneously present in the same frequency band. One would have expected these ultra-faint signals to have been lost in the surrounding babel of noise.

The very unlike fish genera, Dactylopterus of the Triglidae, and Exocoetus of the Teleosteae, are fliers. Both live in the Mediterranean and Indian Oceans. Although so different, both fish fly over the sea due to an analogous elongation and expansion of the pectoral fins.

Some Clupeidae of the bony fishes have a continuous perforated membrane over the eye like the Olgopsid cuttlefishes. Both the Mugilidae family (grey mullets) and Clupeidae (herring) family have adipose eyelids, transparent or perforated. Yet the evolutionist concedes that these must have arisen independently.

Romer (117) shows that the development of long spindles to support a dorsal tail occurred in at least three and perhaps five separate lines, and Redfield suggested to him that these were heat-regulating mechanisms—no other good use for them has ever been proposed, alas!

Lepidosteris, the North American garpike, is unique amongst living fish in having opisthocoelous vertebrae (concavities behind). But the same type of vertebrae are seen in Bombinator, the European fire-bellied toad, Pipa, the Surinam toad, Alytes, the mid-wife toad, and Discoglossus, the painted frog found near the Mediterranean. What a series of unexpected coincidences!

Geiling (118) was able to study pure extracts of the anterior and posterior lobes of the pituitary gland because he caught beluga whales in the St. Lawrence, and with the aid of their glands and those of chickens and armadillos, (in all of which obviously closely related forms the parts are distinct) was able to secure adequate preparations.

Many fishes have the pyloric gizzard seen in birds. Indeed, the earthworm and some molluscs have gizzards. Both of the former two are direct but independent modifications of the gastric pylorus. Even sand may be found in fish gizzards. Willey* found "an almost precisely similar gizzard" in Mugil olivaceus as in a Clupeoid fish, Chatoessus nasus, found living in the same waters as the former. "I confess that at first acquaintance with this case I began to distrust my own eyes," he says, for these fish are from widely different families.

Buccal incubation is seen in the males of the fish Arius boakei in Ceylon, the hinder gut being nearly closed. This is found in the allied genus Osteogeniosus, also, and in a South American species of Arius. Compare this with the comparable phenomenon in the Chilean toad-like batrachian, Rhinoderma darwini, where the male broods the young in the mouth. Then there is cutaneous incubation in both fish and batrachians, in both male and female. Indeed the needful variations of fin and disc are amazing in this regard, and the eggs may be carried on the back or belly. In an amphibious waterbug, Belostomatida, the eggs are also carried similarly in a disc on the male's back.

There is a large accumulation of yolk in the eggs of Arius and Gymnarchus, sharks and rays. Cephalopod molluscs also have a yolk-sac, the most ancient existing genus, Nautilus, having the best developed yolk-sac!

---

*Quoted by permission of John Murray, London, England.

The respiratory apparatus has many convergences in Nature.—The Jumping Blenny, Salarias, the Jumping Goby, Periophthalmus, Saccobranchus and Ophiocephalus. They are all air-breathing, and Clarias and Saccobranchus are both Siluroids, but the coral-like dendritic appendages in the suprapharyngeal chambers in Clarias are much more like the lamelliform labyrinthine organs in Anabas than the diverticula of Saccobranchus. Such fish must breath air or drown.

Warm-bloodedness must be a convergence between birds and mammals, for palaeontology and physiology will not hear of a common origin.

The arteries which supply the lungs of Dipnoi, and the air-bladder of some other fishes such as Polypterus, and the lungs of frogs and all higher air-breathing vertebrates arise as branches of the fourth branchial artery. But so do the vessels supplying the air-pouches of Saccobranchus —which also has a true air-bladder. Here, then, is "a very delicate example of vascular convergence," says Willey. At the same time, the air-bladder of the Clupeoid fish, Megalops cyprinoides, is not vascularized from the branchial arches.

Raymond (119) indicates that the hypocercal tail is known in animals only among anaspid fish, cholyosaurs, and marine crocodiles, totally unrelated forms.

Gadow remarks on the parallel development of the arboreal Hylidae, but, since in Africa and Madagascar there are no Hylas, the Ranidae supply the "tree-frogs". Indeed, one cannot distinguish between them externally—till they are dissected. If they lived side by side, as they do not, they would be examples of mimicry. It is merely "convergence as things now stand", for apparently tropical forests must have tree-frogs. The same is true of tree-snakes, whether the contributing stock be boas, harmless colubrines, cobras or even pit-vipers. Prehensile tails or special climbing feet are seen in chameleons, monkeys, lemurs, pangolins and sloths among edendates, palm-martins among carnivores, arboreal porcupines among rodents, and oppossums among marsupials.

He cites other examples, for example the Malay frogs of the genus Rhecophorus which "glide" by means of webs between their fingers and toes. Then there are the Agamid lizards of India and Malaya with folding parachutes whose stays are furnished by elongated posterior ribs. In Borneo is a tree-snake which can glide by spreading its ribs and flattening out. Then there are bats, and the Malayan Galeopithecus, an insectivore, flying phalangers (marsupials), Anomalurus of West Africa (rodents), and flying squirrels.

The male frog in Africa and the Seychelles often glues a few (but large) eggs on the female's back. In some Brazilian tree-frogs a slight fold of skin along the sides of the back prevents the eggs slipping off. In Hyla goeldi this enlarges to a hood during the hatching season. In a few tropical American frogs (Nototrema) such a hood forms a permanent pouch on the back.

Gadow goes on to tell of the like habits of desert animals on any continent, for example the Cystignathid toads of Australia which hibernate under the clay with a bladder full of water till the rains come, but can spawn at once with rain, have fast-growing tadpoles which soon become frogs, then rapidly fatten themselves to prepare for their hibernation which may last several years. The genera Ciroleptes and Heleioporus thus are always ready to spawn!

The horned toads, Phrynosoma of North America and Mexico, which are Iguanids, closely resemble the Moloch of West Australia and Phrynocephalus of Turkestan, both Agamids. Desert lizards tend to converge on similar body types. Wonderful means of protecting the nostrils and eyes can be found among them. For example the Lacertid, Ophiops, has a transparent lower lid permanently fused to the upper lid—as in the skinks, Ablepharus of the Old World and Xantusia in California and Mexico. Lizards may have lateral fringes on their feet to help them run over sand, for example the North American iguanid Uma, the Persian Agamid, Phrynocephalus—as also do desert geckos, Ptenopus and Stenodactylus of Africa and Teratoscincus of Turkestan.

Long jumping legs appear in the kangaroo, the jumping hares (Pedetes) (a rodent), and in the insectivore Macroscelides, the elephant shrew, in the little Jerboa, Dipus, in S. E. Russia and Asia, in the jumping mice of North America (Zapus). All have also a long balancing tail, often tufted.

A case of double convergence is in the coiled prehensile tail and great rolling eyes, moving independently, of Hippocampus, the seahorse, and Chameleons!!

Tropical snakes often confuse even the experts as it is so difficult to distinguish poisonous from inocuous forms where both are coloured so similarly.

The milk of mammalian breasts resembles pigeon's milk, but the latter is made of protein with oil and contains no lactose nor casein, and is really formed by the breakdown of a cell layer. Similarly the rays secrete milk for the young while the latter are in utero.

Woodbury stresses the convergence of the forest birds, creepers and wood-peckers, both of which climb tree trunks and use the tail as a brace in doing so, and have peculiar sharp tail feathers to help them. Both towhees and song sparrows jump up in the air and while in the air turn over leaves to find insects. Here is a convergent habit.

Wings appeared four times in Evolution, in insects, bats, pterodactyls and birds. Just once would be hard to explain—but four times!

Jordan and Kellogg tell of Merriam's study of nine species of California chipmunks (Eutamias), which he found to be unrelated genealogically. For some came from closely related forms in remote geographic areas, some from extinct forms, and only three or four from local species. Here is "convergence" with a vengeance—if it is!

The Platypus, which lays eggs and has a duck-like bill, is an example of double convergence. Indeed, Willey says: "Instances of parallel convergence are so numerous and so common that we begin to realize that convergence is a regular and not an exceptional phenomenon." He instances the relations of the Marsupials and Placental Mammals, the Insectivores and Rodents. The central nervous systems of annelids and arthropods, on the one hand, and the vertebrates on the other, are convergent.

The Old World hystricomorphs (porcupines) and those of South America seem to be unrelated. They even have different lice. What perfect convergence, however!

The placental arrangement by which the blastocyst is surrounded by the decidua capsularis is seen in man, the anthropoid apes, different genera of rodents, the spiny hedgehog, Erinaceus, in the spineless Malayan hedgehog, Gymnura, and even to some extent in bats. Similarly the discoid placenta of man shows convergence with that of the mole, Galeopithecus, the rabbit, Tarsius, and the hedgehog.

Simpson points to the carnivorous Marsupial, the Tasmanian Wolf and to certain South American carnivorous Marsupials as examples of convergence with true wolves and other members of the dog family. He says the latter are actually more like man in ordinal relationship than like the Marsupial carnivores! Such duplication of adaptive types or ecological roles is not rare.

Now the rabbits are regarded as convergent with rodents, rather than belonging to the latter group. In the Palaeocene and Eocene these types were distinct, and what resemblances have developed since are superficial.

Histological Convergence

Examples of histological convergence are even more remarkable and puzzling. In the excretory tubules of Amphioxus are clusters of long, pin-shaped cells identical with the solenocytes in the nephridia of Polychaete worms. Goodrich observes (see Willey): "If two such excretory organs as the solenocyte-bearing nephridia of Phyllodoce, and the solenocyte-bearing kidneys of Amphioxus could be shown to have been independently evolved we should have to give up structural resemblance as a guide to homology." He says that the only case which seems to him at all comparable is that of the nematocysts in Coelenterates, Planarians, and Molluscs. To this we may add the myoepithelial cells in Coelenterates, Nematodes, and Tunicates, As Goodrich admits, the flame-cells of flatworms, Rotifers, and Polyzoa (Entoprocta) are probably of the same nature as solenocytes.

Here, certainly, is an absurdity in evolutionary theory. The "convergence" is a little too perfect and too difficult to credit. I, for one, reject the idea.

Willey says: "The most remarkable histological resemblance is manifested between the lateral sense-organs of the Capitellidae and the lateral sense-organs of Vertebrates (different phyla!). In both cases the essential organs consist of small, solid, roundish, epidermal buds, from which fine stiff sense-hairs project freely into the surrounding medium; and the resemblance is further enhanced by their segmental arrangement. The correspondence could hardly be greater, the convergence could hardly be closer, the homology could not be more remote than infinity."

. . . "An instance of nuclear convergence has been noted recently by Minchin. In the collar-cells of some calcareous sponges (Clathrinidae) he found that the nucleus occupies a position at the base of the cell, and the flagellum arises independently from a granule or blepharoplast situated at the surface of the cell in the centre of the area enclosed by the collar. In the Leucosoleniidae the nucleus occupies an apical position and the flagellum appears as a direct continuation of the pointed end of the nucleus.

"Minchin quotes a parallelism to these alternative positions of the nucleus in the case of two species of Mastigina described by Goldschmidt. Such a character, adds Minchin, in the case of sponges, can have but little importance in the struggle for existence, and yet in his opinion it indicates the deepest phylogenetic divergence in the pedigree of the calcareous sponges."

Muller (120)* asks: "Why was it, for example, that tracheae arose at least twice independently among land arthropods but nowhere else? Wherever there are parallelisms of evolution (and where are there not?) there is evidence of deterministic processes of some kind . . . We must bear in mind how very rudimentary our knowledge usually is of the ecology of existing organisms, not to speak of long extinct ones." If only the early Darwinians had been so modest!

Summary

Throughout the whole world of plants and animals there are many examples of "convergence" of structure or habit or physiology in widely different types of creatures. What does this mean? Is it the effect of similar demands of the environment on different creatures, practically compelling the emergence of similar structural and physio-logico-biochemical responses? This undoubtedly explains such features as the white colour of all Arctic animals, or the cylindrical forms of fishes and lizards, or the blindness of cave animals. But it cannot

---

*Quoted by permission of the Princeton University Press, Princeton, N.J.

explain situations where the resemblances are exact, and complex, and more spectacular and puzzling, such as in the excretory tubule cells of Amphioxus and Polychaete worms, the equilibratory organs of the different phyla, the types of eggs and the methods of incubating them (notably in buccal brooders), the gizzards of fish and birds, the discoid placenta, the ten-legged Pantopods, opisthocoelous vertebrae in the garpike, toads and frogs, and all mimicry in general.

I believe it is too difficult to imagine the piecemeal evolution of any complex structure or habit, and still more difficult to imagine like structures arising from widely different anatomical origins and habits by evolutionary processes. Convergence merely multiplies the difficulty, particularly the cases of "double convergence". Where the final resemblances are histologically identical, the evolutionist must be staggered. No evolutionary process achieved that, I feel sure.

What I do understand from the scrutiny of such phenomena is that the Creator found all flesh and plants plastic to His design, and, although He multiplied infinite variety and produced infinite variation on every theme, yet He had the tendency on occasion to elaborate the same or closely similar structures by different means in different creatures, as another example of His pride of craftsmanship and His virtuosity.

Convergence is a very subtle exposition of His powers.

CHAPTER XV

The Geographical Distribution of Animals and Plants

"The things of heaven and earth are so wide a realm that even all created beings together can only begin to grasp it."

—Von Goethe

I reach only
with this weak hand,
Nor touch Heaven
Nor understand."

—Vere Jameson.

PROPOSITION—The ancient geographical isolation of animals and plants has produced new species, genera and families. This is obvious. But it never has produced more divergent types, however long the isolation. Moreover, evolutionists cannot edequately explain the peculiar distribution of animals and plants that is now known. So many new forms of life have been discovered of late that it is obvious that the theory was propounded before the evidence was nearly all in. This has proved very uncomfortable to the supporters of evolutionary dogma.

Introduction

It appears that the idea of evolution presented itself to Darwin's and Wallace's minds after a study of the peculiarities of animal distribution made by Darwin on the Galapagos Islands off South America and by Wallace in the Malayan region. Indeed, the evidence in these areas is inescapable, up to a certain point. For many isolated islands like these have developed peculiar species, genera and even families, which have varying degrees of resemblance to corresponding groups on adjacent land masses. Examples of this are almost too numerous to mention, but some may here be given, largely limited for brevity to instances in the animal kingdom and excluding marine forms,—although the latter present such good illustrations as the differences in fauna between the eastern and western shores of Central America.

Darwin's Ideas

Darwin admitted: "Undoubtedly there are very many cases of extreme difficulty in understanding how the same species could possibly have migrated from some one point to the several distant and isolated points where now found. Nevertheless, the simplicity of the view that each species was first produced within a single region captivates the mind." He goes on: "In America, Dr. Hooker has shown that

147

between forty and fifty of the flowering plants of Tierra del Fuego, forming no inconsiderable part of its scanty flora, are common to Europe, enormously remote as these two points are; and there are many closely allied species. On the lofty mountains of equatorial America a host of peculiar species belonging to European genera occur. On the highest mountains of Brazil, some few European genera were found by Gardner, which do not exist in the wider intervening hot countries. So on the Silla of Caraccas the illustrious Humboldt long ago found species belonging to genera characteristic of the Cordillera. On the mountains of Abyssinia, several forms characteristic of Europe and some few representative of the flora of the Cape of Good Hope occur. At the Cape of Good Hope itself a very few European species, believed not to have been introduced by man, and on the mountains, several representative European forms are found, which have not been discovered in the intertropical parts of Africa. On the Himalaya, and on the isolated mountain-ranges of the peninsula of India, and the heights of Ceylon, and on the volcanic cones of Java, many plants occur, either identically the same or representing each other, and at the same time representing plants of Europe not found in the intervening hot lowlands. A list of the genera collected on the loftier peaks of Java raises a picture of a collection made on a hill in Europe! Still more striking is the fact that southern Australian forms are clearly represented by plants growing on the summits of the mountains of Borneo. Some of these Australian forms, as I hear from Dr. Hooker, extend along the heights of the peninsula of Malacca, and are thinly scattered, on the one hand over India and on the other as far north as Japan.

"On the southern mountains of Australia, Dr. F. Muller has discovered several European species; other species, not introduced by man, occur on the lowlands; and a long list can be given of European genera, found in Australia, but not in the intermediate torrid regions . . .

"And it is a striking fact . . . that all the flowering plants, about forty-six in number, common to Tierra del Fuego and to Europe, still exist in North America . . .

. . . "I do not pretend to indicate the exact lines and means of migration, or the reason why certain species and not others have migrated; why certain species have been modified and have given rise to new groups of forms, and others have remained unaltered . . .

"I have said that many difficulties remain to be solved: some of the most remarkable are stated with admirable clearness by Dr. Hooker in his botanical works on the Antarctic regions . . . As far as regards the occurrence of identical species at points so enormously remote as Kerguelen Land, New Zealand, and Fuegia, I believe that towards the close of the Glacial period, icebergs, as suggested by Lyall, have been largely concerned in their dispersal. But the existence of several quite distinct species, belonging to genera exclusively confined to the south, at these and other distant points of the southern hemisphere, is, on my theory of descent with modification, a far more remarkable case of difficulty. For some of these species are so distinct, that we cannot suppose that there has been time since the commencement of the Glacial period for their migration and for their subsequent modification to the necessary degree . . .

". . . In the Galapagos Islands there are 26 land-birds; of these, 21 (or perhaps 23) are peculiar, whereas of the 11 marine birds only 2 are peculiar; and it is obvious that marine birds could arrive at these islands more easily than land-birds. Bermuda, on the other hand, which lies at about the same distance from North America as the Galapagos Islands do from South America, and which has a very peculiar soil, does not possess one endemic land-bird; and we know from Mr. J. M. Jones' admirable account of Bermuda, that very many North American birds, during their great annual migrations, visit either periodically or occasionally this island. Madeira does not possess one peculiar bird, and many European and African birds are almost every year blown there, as I am informed by Mr. E. V. Harcourt . . . Madeira again is inhabited by a wonderful number of peculiar land-shells, whereas not one species of sea-shell is confined to its shores: now, though we do not know how sea-shells are dispersed, yet we can see that their eggs as larvae, perhaps attached to sea-weed or floating timber, or to the feet of wading-birds, might be transported far more easily than land-shells, across three or four hundred miles of open sea." (Did Darwin believe that only water-birds got dirty feet and by this means became able to transport small shells?) "The different orders of insects in Madeira apparently present analogous facts." The absence of terrestrial mammals in any island situated more than 300 miles from a continent or great continental island, often islands well suited to such forms of life, is a conclusive argument against local creation, says Darwin. There has been time enough, too, since some of these islands are old.

Darwin also stressed the degree of affinity of the mammalian inhabitants of islands and its relation to the depth of the seas separating them from a neighbouring continent. He candidly faces two great difficulties: "I do not deny that there are many and grave difficulties in understanding how several of the inhabitants of the more remote islands, whether still retaining the same specific form or modified since their arrival, could have reached their present homes. But the probability of many islands having existed as halting-places, of which not a wreck now remains, must not be overlooked . . . Almost all oceanic islands, even the most isolated and smallest, are inhabited by land-shells, generally by endemic species, but sometimes by species found elsewhere. Dr. Gould has given several interesting cases in regard to the land-shells of the islands of the Pacific. Now it is notorious that land-shells are very easily killed by salt; their eggs, at least such as I have tried, sink in sea-water, and are killed by it. Yet there must be, on my view, some unknown, but highly efficient means for their transportal . . .

"The most striking and important fact for us in regard to the inhabitants of islands, is their affinity to those of the nearest mainland, without being actually the same species. Numerous instances could be given of this law. I will give only one, that of the Galapagos Archipelago, situated under the equator, between 500 and 600 miles from the shores of South America. Here almost every product of the land and water bears the unmistakable stamp of the American continent. There are 26 land birds, and 21, or perhaps 23, of there are ranked as distinct species, and are supposed to have been created here; yet the close affinity of most of these birds to American species in every character, in their habits, gestures, and tones of voice, are manifest. So it is with the other animals, and with nearly all the plants, shown by Dr. Hooker in his admirable memoir on the flora of this archipelago. The naturalist, looking at the inhabitants of these volcanic islands in the Pacific, distant several hundred miles from the continent, yet feels that he is standing on American land. Why should this be so? Why should the species which are supposed to have been created in the Galapagos Archipelago, and nowhere else, bear so plain a stamp of affinity to those created in America? There is nothing in the conditions of life, in the geographical nature of the islands, in their height or climate, or in the proportions in which the several classes are associated together, which resembles closely the conditions of the South American coast: in fact, there is a considerable dissimilarity in all these respects. On the other hand, there is a considerable degree of resemblance in the volcanic nature of the soil, in climate, height, and size of the islands, between the Galapagos and Cape de Verde Archipelagoes; but what an entire and absolute difference in their inhabitants! The inhabitants of the Cape de Verde Islands are related to those of Africa, like those of the Galapagos to America . . .

. . . "Thus the plants of Kerguelen Land, though standing nearer to Africa than to America, are related, and that very closely, as we know from Dr. Hooker's account, to those of America; but on the view that this island has been mainly stocked by seeds brought with earth and stones on icebergs, drifted by the prevailing currents, this anomaly disappears. New Zealand in its endemic plants is much more closely related to Australia, the nearest mainland, than to any other region; and this is what might have been expected; but it is also plainly related to South America, which, although the next nearest continent, is so enormously remote, that the fact becomes an anomaly. But this difficulty almost disappears on the view that New Zealand, South America, and other southern lands were long ago partially stocked from a nearly intermediate though distant point, namely from the Antarctic islands, when they were clothed with vegetation, before the commencement of the Glacial period. The affinity, which, though feeble, I am assured by Dr. Hooker is real, between the flora of the southwestern corner of Australia and of the Cape of Good Hope, is a far more remarkable case, and is at present inexplicable; but this affinity is confined to the plants, and will, no doubt, be some day explained." He stresses the opportunity of chance immigrants to run riot in new surroundings, although he forgets how great aeons of time should have repeatedly duplicated almost all such fortuitous visits and so obliterated the differences, for instance between neighbouring plants, or between islands in the Galapagos Archipelago. A lesser problem in this island group is that the new species formed in the separate islands have not quickly spread to the other adjacent islands. But the Galapagos islands, "though in sight of each other, are separated by deep areas of the sea; in most cases wider than the British Channel, and there is no reason to suppose that they have at any former period been continuously united. The currents of the sea are rapid and sweep across the archipelago, and gales of wind are extraordinarily rare; so that the islands are far more effectually separated from each other than they appear to be on the map. Nevertheless, a good many species, both those found in other parts of the world and those confined to the archipelago, are common to the several islands . . . In the Galapagos Archipelago, many even of the birds, though so well adapted for flying from island to island, are distinct on each; thus there are three closely-allied species of mocking-thrush, each confined to its own island. Now let us suppose the mocking-thrush of Chatham Island to be blown to Charles Island, which has its own mocking-thrush; why should it not succeed in establishing itself there? We may safely infer that Charles Island is well stocked with its own species, for annually more eggs are laid there than can be possibly reared; and we may infer that the mocking-thrush peculiar to Charles Island is at least as well fitted for its home as is the species peculiar to Chatham Island." How can such a tiny differential as exists here prove to be of **total** value in excluding the invader? One of the real paradoxes of Darwin's theory in this connection is the considerable difference between the fauna and flora of western and eastern Australia, even if we concede an ancient separation by an arm of the sea.

Scott (121) has given one of the best and briefest recent presentations of the evidence in this field.

The Problems

de Beaufort* presents the zoogeographical evidence in great detail, beginning by quoting Darwin's objection, made as early as 1856, to those who make continents "as easily as a cook does pancakes", but adding that nowadays "with palaeontologists as the wheel ,there is less chance of landing in the ditch." Certainly the studies of zoogeographers have left the situation much more complicated than

---

*Quoted by permission of Sidgewick and Jackson, Ltd., London, England.

in Darwin's and Wallace's day. These enthusiasts have shaken the earth's surface up and down throughout the geological ages like children bobbing waterlogged apples. Let us examine three aspects of the problems involved.

(a) Do ancient geographical separations clearly produce new races, species, genera, even families?

(b) Does such variation ever go on to create orders, subclasses, classes or phyla? (Here is the perfect laboratory for a decision on this vital point.)

(c) Were species—genera—families created twice or three times, or always but once?

A fourth question, the fixity of certain species in Nature, even in widely sundered environments, we will not discuss now. How many "species" are examples of "convergence"? Vast areas of ignorance cloud these issues. This is as evident in de Beaufort or Gadow or Woodbury or Simpson, as in Wallace a century ago. Many creatures are left high and dry on the shelves of ignorance, for example the Megapoda of the Nicobars, or the fresh-water crayfish Astacoides, or the origin of Platyrrhine monkeys in Madagascar and South America. Scarcely a continent has not been joined to every other by at least two hypothetical bridges. Every island has been joined to its neighbours by rising and falling land links. Many times glaciers have crept down from incredible distances, then retreated as many times for unknown reasons. Great gaps in the fossil record exist, even where they are most essential for our understanding of past ages and their life. The explanatory data Darwin and Wallace looked for so confidently have not accumulated to any great extent since their day, despite a full century of intensive exploration.

The Hawaiian Problem

Sinnott and Wilson remark that the Hawaiian Islands "present an especially interesting set of problems. They are far more distant from the continent (than the Galapagos), for more than 2,000 miles separate them from the coast of California. Their flora is a rich one, having nearly three times as many species as the Galapagos, and is highly endemic, with about 80 per cent of its species native to these islands alone . . . The Hawaiian flora seems to have been derived from many sources. Some species are related to common Polynesian and Malayan types. Others have their nearest allies in Australia, and still others in New Zealand and among the 'Antarctic' floras. A considerable part of the flora is closely related to American types, mostly tropical; but some of these, like the blueberry, buttercup, strawberry, and Silene, are genera characteristic of temperate America . . ." There are real puzzles here, the puzzles of alikeness persisting in the most prolonged isolation, and, on the other hand, of local differences developing into genera. "Some botanists hesitate to assume the existence of such land bridges (as postulated above) even though the seas are relatively shallow there today . . . With the plants of American origin, a land bridge seems out of the question, for the ocean between Hawaii and our continent is very deep. Many of these species, however, especially the characteristic Compositae, are well adapted to wind dispersal. The whole problem of the origin of the plant, animal, and human populations of Polynesia is still far from solved and awaits the accumulation of many more facts than we now possess" . . . Unfortunately, the theory of evolution was propounded and generally accepted long before we had more than a small fraction of our present volume of information!

The Geographical Dispersion of Races,—Species,—Genera,—Families

There are vast numbers of examples of these, whether the "islands" which originally produced them by isolation were really oceanic islands, or terrestrial mountain-tops, or ecological niches, or inland lakes. De Beaufort mentions the bean goose, where specimens from the tundra of Northern Asia have become morphologically different from those occurring in the adjacent taiga, the northern woods. The flying squirrels (Glaucomys) show the sabrinus species living in the northern pine woods of Canada, and volans, a species inhabiting deciduous forests in the eastern United States to Guatemala. The British tree-creeper, Certhia familiaris, a bird of coniferous woods, belongs to a species found in the Alps, Pyrenees, and the mountains of Corsica. Elsewhere it has been replaced by Certhia brachydactyla, a bird of the deciduous forests.

The deepest lake in the world, Baikal, contains many peculiar forms, for example genera of sponges, genera of molluscs, the fish **families** Cottomephoridae and Comephoridae, and many genera of worms, crustaceans and other groups. It also has a seal, Phoca sibirica, related to another species found in the Caspian, Phoca caspica.

In Borneo the genera of freshwater fishes in the Mahakam and Kapuas rivers differ widely, because in opposite watersheds. In mountain torrents in north Borneo are two endemic species of Homalopteridae, fishes which can apply their bellies to stones or rocks and hang on. Closely allied forms appear in the streams of South China.

In Africa the potto, Perodicticus ibeanus, lives on the Mumias mountains in Uganda and in the Kakumega forests of British East Africa, remote and isolated from the other species of the genus in western Africa. Different subspecies of the monkey, Cercopithecus albogularis, are found on the eastern mountains and in western Africa— as is true of the squirrel Heliosciurus. In the great eastern African lakes the number of endemic (local) species of cichlid fish is amazing, reaching as high as 99 to 91 to 75 per cent of the whole number of species in the lakes, this being highest in the oldest and deepest lakes, for example Tanganyika and Nyasa. Lake Tanganyika is the second deepest lake in the world, next to Baikal, and has an impressive number of very peculiar forms of gastropod molluscs belonging to endemic genera.

Madagascar has Insectivora which all belong to the Centetidae, or tenrecs, except for a couple of shrews. This family is almost restricted to the island, the western African Potamogale being the only exception, (and very widely different). All the members of the family Lemuroidea live in Madagascar and neighbouring islands. However, fossils of the family have been found in Europe and North America. Madagascar has half a dozen endemic genera of Viverridae, all other families of Carnivora being absent. All rodents are missing but one peculiar family of rats, the Nesomyidae. Some Madagascar birds belong to peculiar genera which are hard to classify, for example Mescenas and Monias. A number of extinct ostrich-like birds of the genera Aepyornis and Mullerornis, peculiar to the island, may have persisted into historic times. A genus of Geckos, Uroplates, placed in a separate subfamily, is endemic. There are four endemic genera of the cosmopolitan Colubrinae snakes, one of these living alone in the Seychelles. There is an endemic genus of land tortoises, Pyxis. There are a few species of the genus Pachypanchax, a Cyprinodont fish, restricted to Madagascar, the Seychelles, and probably Zanzibar also. The freshwater crayfish, Astacoides, having such characteristic freshwater parasites as Temnocephala, is found here. The Scorpion, Heteroscorpion, is an endemic genus, and another endemic genus lives in the Seychelles and Mauritius.

In the Seychelles is one species of the endemic genus Cryptopsophis (of the Apoda). 67 per cent of the insects there are endemic or local!

One can scarcely call Australia an island. Its marsupials belong to an order that is not peculiar to this area, however, for many are found in the Americas. Only one order, the Monotremata, is now confined to this continent, Tasmania, New Guinea and Salawatti. De Beaufort says: "It is hard to say when and whence the Monotremes and Marsupials entered Australia."—"several suggestions have been advanced to link the recent Monotremata to Mesozoic or early Tertiary mammals from the northern continents."

In southern New Guinea is a genus endemic to its rivers, Carettochelys insculpta. A peculiar genus of tree frogs (Hyla) here, Nyctimantis, has a vertical pupil. Many genera of birds of Paradise are endemic here, and great variation in their types of bill occurs. New Guinea is also rich in genera of pigeons, notably the crowned pigeons. There are also curious endemic genera of kingfishers.

In New Zealand is the endemic family of the wren-like Acanthisittadae, passerine birds. Another group of genera endemic there is composed of Heterolocha, Creodon and Callaeas. The kea is an endemic parrot genus. The kakapo and the extinct moa were endemic, as is the kiwi, the latter two being flightless. A primeval type of reptile is the tuatera (Sphenodon punctatum), the only living member of the Rhynchocephalidae **family**. There is an endemic frog **genus**, Liopelma.

Fiji has an endemic poisonous elapid genus of snakes, Ogodon. The iguanid, Brachycephalus, is here found in isolation. Two local frogs of the genera Cornufer and Platymantis resemble species in the Solomons. Among birds four are endemic genera and three endemic subgenera. Samoa has two endemic bird genera, one of them being the pigeon, Didunculus.

Hawaii has an endemic genus of flycatchers and one of the honeyeaters. Its most remarkable creature is an endemic **family** of passerine birds, the Drepanidae, whose bills vary from sickle-shaped (Drepane) to hooked, or even to parrot-like (Pseudonestor). This must be an ancient family. There is an endemic **subfamily** of land shells, the Achatinellinae, with a great variety of local, often very local, species. The insects are also highly endemic.

Thus our rapid survey of the world's islands illustrates clearly that prolonged isolation of animals there can lead to the production of characteristic species, genera, even subfamilies and families. But the differentiation goes no further, given almost any amount of time, it seems. Thus distinct families are found only on Madagascar, Hawaii and New Zealand, and in Lake Baikal, an equally long isolated sea. Even such family formation is rare, amounting to only four examples, which shows how exceptional such an event has been.

How long has this change taken? Lake Baikal was formed in Tertiary times, and there is no evidence of sea connection since. Madagascar has probably been isolated ever since the Upper Eocene, if not earlier. Hawaii seems to have been isolated a long time, how long being uncertain. Finally, New Zealand seems to have been isolated since the end of the Mesozoic period. This information perhaps tells us something of time scales in animal development.

The Creation of Orders, Sub-Classes, Classes and Phyla

It is easy to trace the development of new plant species, even plant genera, possibly plant families, as see a recent chapter, but beyond that we cannot go. The major classes, orders and phyla came into being in an altogether different way, by Creation. For life is not a limpid but a very viscous fluid. It easily clots, as in the numerous species remaining unchanged since primeval times. It is an amoeba whose pseudopods move out in many directions at once but which cannot flow over certain trivial barriers. Barriers are there, which we are foolish to ignore.

Life is a long hurdle race which most runners cannot negotiate because they cannot leap high enough to move down the track. Nature is a snug sit-by-the-fire conservative as well as an explorer. She is content at the "family" level.

That is why, as was mentioned earlier, an article could be written in the journal, Evolution, in 1957 by Wood entitled, "What, if anything, is a rabbit?"—the author finding that he could not trace the origins of this beast beyond family level!

The problem can be put more graphically in another way. If I pick up in my arms all the cats in the world and you take up all the finches it is easy to see at a glance that they differ generally and profoundly. They are different "kinds", or different classes, as we say. No matter how many different types of cats or finches we can gather into one group or the other they still remain utterly different. Along comes another friend whose capacious arms enfold all the rodents there are. I still see that these are quite a different "kind" from my cats, and no aggregation of his or mine, however extensive, could convince us that perhaps some members of our groups should be traded as being imperfectly classified. Our "orders" remain distinct, as they have always been historically.

But along comes a fourth person, and he has similarly collected all the extinct kinds of cats in his arms. I can see that this batch resembles my armful closely—much more than did the armfuls of my previous friends. For they are obviously of one family. divergent in diversity, as life tends to be, but fundamentally alike—of one "kind".

Now Simpson stresses that every order began as a species, and that only in retrospect was one species of the order of Reptiles and another one nearly like it and adjacent to it a Marsupial. All our taxonomic groups are thus merely psychological conveniences and constructs of some late-living taxonomist. This must be the evolutionist's point of view, but it begs the question. It assumes the fact of evolution.

For at any time on the earth since life began one could encounter groups of diverse animals, like the armfuls mentioned above, in large numbers. There were no single animals or plants ar groups of one or two, as far as palaeontologists can tell us. It has always been possible, in theory, to carry out part or all of the quaint little experiment of three paragraphs back. Our orders and phyla are not retrospective mental constructs only, but represent a cross-section of life which could always have been observed. They are partly vertical and partly horizontal—but not entirely vertical, and any acute student of the world scene before the days of the study of palaeontology could have been pardoned for regarding them as purely and solely horizontal, whether he lived in the day of Alfred, the Great, or in the Mesozoic.

Were orders, classes and phyla created in one area of the primal earth or many—at different epochs or several? Certainly they have long been distinct. It is impossible to come to any conclusions about the widespread phyla, and no one would try. The same is true of the classes. Some ideas about orders exist, but they are very vague. For example, it is held that Xenarthra, the order that includes the sloths, armadillos and anteaters, originated in South America.

Were Species—Genera—Families Evolved more than Once?

Darwin insisted this question should be answered with a categorical "no". But the data of zoology alone present some puzzling problems to confuse an issue as simple as this reply would leave it, and with great abandon zoogeographers have tossed continents and landbridges around (frequently in mutual contradiction) to meet the contingencies of this unitary theory. Of late, there has been greater acceptance of polyphyletic (genetically diverse) origins, even for man. This, of course, demands so much of evolutionary process, especially in view of its well-known conservative nature, that most scientists balk at this point.

What are some of the puzzles?

The monkey, Macacus inuus, occurs in Gibraltar, Algiers, Morocco, then skips a large area, appearing again in southern Asia and as a closely related species, Macacus speciorus, in Japan, The oil-beetles of the subfamily Eleodinae are seen in California and the Mediterranean region, only a few species being in Asia. The same phenomenon is found in the ants. Of the Californian snails and slugs, several are related to European species, only a few species ranging into Siberia and China. The genus Potamobius, a freshwater crayfish, has representatives in Europe, eastern Asia and western North America. Other aquatic animals have similar distribution. The newt, Hydromantes, has one species in the high Sierras of California and two species in Sardinia, Italy, and northern France. One authority explained this by a landbridge, but others conclude that this is due to the dispersal of Siberian fauna.

Of two genera of the family Polyodontidae, the spoonbill, Polyodon folium, inhabits the rivers of the Mississippi system, the other one, Psephurus gladius, lives in the Yangtse and Hoangho in China. This really involves a puzzling dispersal, for these are divergent genera, not species. The Cryptobranchidae have two genera; one is Cryptobranchus in eastern North America and the other is the giant salamander, Megalobatrachus, of Japan and China. Among tortoises and lizards are similar cases. Thus the genus alligator has one species in Florida and one in the Yangtse. It is assumed that these are "relics' of a wide Tertiary distribution!

The Procyonidae, including the racoons and coatis, so typically American, has one member, the lesser panda, Ailurus fulgens, in the Himalayas—a "relict"! The Camelidae have fossils in North America, then spread to Asia and to South America, to survive as camels at the former site and llamas in the latter.

The catfishes, Amiuridae, are nearly restricted to North America and Mexico—but for one species in China. Umbra, a pike, lives as U. Crameri in Southeastern Europe, but as U. limi, the mud-fish, in Canada and northeastern United States. The North American Ascaphus is a very simple recent tailless Amphibian—but its nearest relative lives in New Zealand. More "relicts"?

The freshwater fishes, the Cichlidae, are found in Africa, Madagascar and South America. A few species occur in Palestine. Two genera of the simple teleost fishes, Osteoglossidae, live in South America, another in Africa, a fourth has one species in Siam, Malaya, Sumatra, Banka and Borneo, and another in New Guinea and Australia.

Lanthanotus is a remarkable genus of slow-worms found only in Borneo. The only other member of the family is the Gila monster of New Mexico and Arizona. The Lacertidae lizards occupy all the Palaearctic, Ethiopian and Oriental regions—but only one species, Tachydromus sexlineatus, lives in the east, in the Greater Sunda and nearby islands. The non-poisonous snakes, the Uropeltidae and Xenopeltidae, occur in the Oriental regions, Xenopeltis unicolor also being found in the Celebes.

The Pelomedusidae, a family of freshwater tortoises, has a genus, Podocnemus, which has several species in South America, one species in Madagascar and none in Africa. The freshwater Cichlid genus Etroplus is found in Ceylon, but three genera, Ponatilapia, Ptychochromis, and Paretroplus occur in Madagascar, and the last of these resembles Etroplus. Even though they occasionally enter brackish water, how could such a migration occur? The freshwater crayfishes, Parastacidae, have Parastacus in Neogaea, Astocopsis, Paracheraps, Cheraps, Engaeus, and Paranephis in Notogaea, and Astacoides in Madagascar. All have the same kind of freshwater parasites, such as Temnocephala. How could all their ancestors have entered fresh water from the sea independently in South America, Australia and Madagascar?

When de Beaufort faces this and the other problems to be stated, he says: "In the face of so many contradictory facts, the safest way is to plead ignorance."

Extinct ground sloths are found in South America, Cuba and Porto Rico. De Beaufort wryly comments: "It is hard to imagine these huge animals arriving in the West Indies on rafts."

Among toads, the Criniinae, are restricted to Australia, New Guinea and the Aru Islands, very closely related to the Psendinae of South America. A New Guinea genus of the tree frogs, Hylidae, has a vertical pupil—a hylid with a similar pupil is found also in the West Indies. But this must be convergence. How did Hyla get to Australia—from Asia or South America via Antarctica? The evolutionist goes back to its parasites for an answer. The hylas of Australia and South America have an infection with a different parasite, hence it probably spread from South America to North America to Asia to Australia. This does not tell us where the Australian hylas came from, however.

Both the South American and Australian marsupials are infected by tapeworms of the genus Linstowia.—(also found in Australian bandicoots and in Echidna).

All this means that **widely** scattered all over the world there are identical or similar genera or even species. Some of these can be explained by transportation on flotsam or birds' feet or icebergs, some by land-bridges now sunk, some by swimming, some by the appearance of new mountain chains or volcanic islands,—but some have no current explanation! The land-bridges postulated do not find general acceptance, and, as has been implied before, rise and fall at the convenience of any puzzled zoogeographer almost too divinely. Simpson refines these to "corridors", "filters" like the Sahara or Himalayas, and "sweepstake routes" (like the East Indies Islands). The dilemma remains, however.

The Puzzle of Isolated but Like Species

The puzzle is currently solved (?) in a variety of ways. An isolated species can be called a "relict", no one being quite sure how long it has been isolated, or why, or why all its congeners should have been wiped out over a whole continent or two (as is so often assumed), which separates it from any near ally. Some of these forms have no fossil predecessors known, for example the mollusc Lamilifera of the Iberian peninsula, several families of Ethiopian Insectivora, the Cape jumping hare, the platyrrhine monkeys of South America, the Hystricoidea of South America, the characin fish of Central America, South America and Africa, the Monotremata of Australia, or the Australian marsupials or emus. Nothing could be more puzzling than the problem Darwin raised in his effort to solve the problem of speciation. How explain the numerous and important exceptions to every known rule all over the world?

How explain the fauna of St. Helena or Hawaii, so long not connected with any other land mass, and whose ancestry cannot be easily suggested?

Why, for example, since it is now held that insectivores and marsupials have lived together since late Mesozoic times, did not placental mammals enter Australia with its marsupials?

How can freshwater fishes (even those which occasionally are seen in brackish waters) or frogs have crossed hundreds of miles of sea, for example the New Zealand frog, Liopelma? What about New Zealand's crayfishes (Parastacidae) and mussels (Mutelidae)? De

Beaufort says: "We cannot do without a land-bridge" for these. How, then, explain the lizard Brachylophus in Fiji, or its two frogs of the genera Cornufer and Platymantis? These seem to be hopeless puzzles to de Beaufort.

Then there is the land mollusc, Placostylus. De Beaufort quotes Mayr on this: "To me it seems incomparably simpler to assume a still unknown method of transportation, than a land-bridge that is unsupported by any other fact!" And goes on: "This is indeed simple, but then one has still to explain why the unknown method failed when Placostylus reached the Andesite line" (which divides the Pacific islands geologically between their eastern and western parts)—or, really "between the islands with and without Placostylus."

Gadow challenges many examples of "relicts", and says they are really convergences, the principle he personally stresses. He cites the so-called boreal remnants on far southern mountains, really very rare, according to him. This theory of relicts was first based on the similarity of the Arctic hare in the Alps and Scandinavia—but no other typical Arctic animal appears in the Alps. Nor do the creatures on mountains in temperate countries extend their range to the polar regions. A striking "convergence" is the shoebill of the Upper Nile and the boatbill in Tropical America.

The antiquity of isolated species and genera has been well illustrated by much of what has been said here, and need be no further emphasized. This is of great theoretical interest. It emphasizes the conservatism of Nature, its specific and certainly its generic rigidity. Runners can run a faster and faster mile till they do it in four minutes. Thereafter it is increasingly difficult to cut the time, and no three minute mile can be envisaged. Species ebb and flow, it seems, and even genera flow, but it becomes increasingly difficult to make bigger jumps, and the family, a group of obviously similar genera, appears to represent the final achievement of radiation in Nature. Outside that boundary only God can change His creatures—if He does.

Simpson says: "Analysis requires inference and even some speculation, because the most pertinent faunas, those of the late Cretaceous and early Paleocene, are very poorly known.—Late Cretaceous mammals are known only from restricted areas in Asia and North America, early Paleocene mammals only from a small part of North America. However, reasonable speculation labelled as such also has a legitimate place in science and can be interesting."

Gadow dismisses as of little significance the instances of casual dispersal of island creatures and goes on: "Land tortoises (genus Testudo) have reached the Galapagos by land, not astride a log, just as certainly as lemurs in Madagascar and elephant remains in the Andes are evidence of former land connexions." He goes on to put the case for numerous and extensive land connections throughout the oceans.

160

"There are but few countries which have not been submerged at one time or another, and most of the great chains of mountains, Andes, Rockies, Pyrenees, Alps, Himalayas, are only of Tertiary date . . . it is futile to chart a geological epoch." For example, he believes there was a South American-African bridge in the Mesozoic.

Dice* appropriately quotes Grinnell as saying: "If a new ecologic niche arises, or if a niche is vacated, Nature hastens to supply an occupant, from whatever material may be available. Nature abhors a vacuum in the animate world as well as in the inanimate world." A remarkable example of an adaptive radiation are the Hawaiian honey-creepers of the family Drepaniidae, mentioned earlier in this chapter. All have the characteristic goat-like odour. Each island of the group has its own species, even each area of each island. One has a delicate bill for searching for insects among foliage and flowers, one is more like a woodpecker, one can chisel bark, one can crush bark and twigs to find beetles; five species of the genus Psittirastia have finch-like heavy bills.

Jordan and Kellogg cite the geographical species of the golden warbler, Dendroica aestiva, and say: "When the geographical relations of the origin of a species cannot be shown it is usually because the species has not been critically studied, from absence of material, or from absence of interest on the part of naturalists." Gulick's study of the Hawaiian land snails is a classic of the type, in which he found 175 species split up into 700 or 800 varieties. Allied species may occupy adjacent valleys, sometimes feeding on the same or similar plants. A minute gradation exists between the degree of variation and the geographic intervals. The American oriole has many subspecies all across the Antilles and the United States and Canada. Each species, beside colour variations, has its own song and its own way of weaving its hanging nest—not one of these new traits being of obviously selective value, as Kellogg and Jordan point out.

The fact that the goldenrods are practically confined to North America, the Eucalyptus to Australia, and the tobaccos to the Americas, suggests strongly that they arose there.

The existence of 700 genera of plants, notably the southern beech (Nothofagus), in southern South America and New Zealand suggests an old land connection. But how explain that more than 1/3 of the plant genera in New Zealand also appear in Europe, 58 species being actually identical. In Fuegia and S. Chile are 40 floral species identical with those in Europe and the Arctic—but unknown over thousands of intervening miles. The differences between Australia and New Zealand are also striking. Of 7 large genera of plants highly characteristic of Australia only one species occurs in New Zealand. Seven

---

*Quoted by permission of the University of Michigan Press, Ann Arbor, U.S.A.

tropical Australian families are not found, indeed. On the other hand, 100 species are identical.

Wallace was early aware of the problems of zoogeography. He said: "We shall thus be led to an intelligent comprehension of the phenomena of distribution in all groups (of animals), which would not be the case if every specialist formed regions for his own particular study. In many cases we should find that no satisfactory division of the earth could be made to correspond with the distribution even of an entire class; but we should have the Coleopterist and the Lepidopterist each with his own Geography. And even this would probably not suffice, for it is very doubtful if the detailed distribution of the Longicornes, so closely dependent on woody vegetation, could be made to agree with that of the Staphylinidae or the Carabidae which abound in many of the most barren regions, or with that of the Scarabeidae, largely dependent on the presence of herbivorous mammalia. And when each of these enquirers had settled a division of the earth into 'regions' which exhibited with tolerable accuracy the phenomena of distribution of his own group, we should have gained nothing whatever but a very complex mode of exhibiting the bare facts of distribution. We should then have to begin to work out the causes of the divergence of one group from another in this respect; but as each worker would refer to his own set of regions as the type, the whole subject would become involved in inextricable confusion. These considerations seem to make it imperative that one set of "regions' should be established as typical for Zoology; and it is hoped the reasons here advanced will satisfy most naturalists that these regions can be best determined, in the first place, by a study of the distribution of the mammalia, supplemented in doubtful cases by that of the other vertebrates."—What an amazing confession, by one of the most honourable and sincere figures in the history of evolutionary theory!

Summary

The occurrence on long isolated islands of peculiar species and genera proves the local evolution of these types. Only in Hawaii, New Zealand and Madagascar has this process gone on to the formation of endemic families, although these land masses have been isolated for very long periods and are of a size able to provide a great variety of environment to local forms. This proves that evolution has not passed the "family" level, despite the vast aeons of time available for such a leap. Where and how "orders" arose is not clear, but most or all were created in Eurasia, it appears. They have always been separate, and arise as entities wherever first discovered. This is also true of plant life. The relative fixity of species and genera—although they do evolve—is well illustrated by the persistence unchanged from ancient times of many, many animal and plant types in widely separated parts of the world. Numerous examples are cited here, these providing many puzzles for the evolutionist.

CHAPTER XVI

THE SPECIES PROBLEM

"all the lions and tigers which lie perdus in a drop of spring water"

—Lord Tennyson

Had I the power to turn off rain
Or make white brain cells splay insane,
Design a root tip or mold a thew,
What would this frightened scholar do?

—Vere Jameson

PROPOSITION—If evolution is a study of the origin of new species the term species should be accurately definable. That has not been done. There is no greater confusion in modern biology than at this crucial point.

Introduction

Since evolutionary theory is concerned primarily with the picture of change in living forms, and since species have been regarded for centuries as the unit type of life, it follows that the gradual transition of species into other species or genera is a vital consideration in any discussion of our general theme. Nowadays this is a real problem, one much more in the forefront of thought than even in Darwin's day. Indeed, two great international symposia of biologists have lately concerned themselves with it and the discussions of both have appeared in print under the title of this chapter. Usually popular texts on evolution ignore the issue and assume that species are recognized entities which none dispute. Then they go on from there. But that is not good enough for scientific students of the issue in hand.

Crompton recalls that the British Association has ruled in this matter by saying that a species is a group of animals that has been defined as a species by a competent systematist. Even the expert systematist has his difficulties, however, for he is apt to disagree with others.

Specific differences are puzzling

Thomson asks, after mentioning the fact that the Origin of Species was published in 1859, who today can feel clear as to the origin of any single species. He goes on to quote Bateson* (122):

---

*Quoted by permission of the American Association for the Advancement of Science, Washington, U.S.A.

"Ideas which in the abstract are apprehended and accepted with facility fade away from the concrete case. It is easy to imagine how man was evolved from an amoeba, but we cannot form a plausible guess as to how Veronica agrestis and Veronica polita were evolved, either one from the other or both from a common form. We have not even an inkling of the stages by which a Silver Wyandotte fowl descended from Gallus bankiva (the guinea fowl of ancient India), and we can scarley even believe that it did."

Darwin himself admitted that the different breeds of pigeons, if found in the wild state, would be regarded as separate genera by ornithological morphologists.

Caullery remarks on the sexual dimorphism of the Gnathidae amongst the Isopoda. It is so great that for a long time (1817-1885) the males and females of a single species were placed in different genera, Anceus and Praniza. Even today our knowledge of the life histories of ocean fishes is utterly inadequate—99 per cent of such are unknown. The classical example is the recent study of sailfish by Gilbert Voss (123) or the tracing of the transition of the Mediterranean Leptocephalus into elvers. The metamorphoses of such fish as the Stylophthalmus, which proved to be the larval stage of Idiacanthus, or of the snake-mackerel, Gempylus, or the surgeonfish whose larva shrinks as it metamorphoses, then suddenly grows huge again, have puzzled taxonomists for decades. Wheeler tells us that in most ants the castes are so unlike they have often been described as separate species.

Micro- versus Mega-evolution

Carson (124)* points out that the geneticist **must** study microevolution as a rule. "His work is of necessity usually at or below the species level." This emphasizes the difficulty of reducing our problem to experimental dimensions. Any conclusions we derive as to microevolution need not by any means extrapolate into macro- or megaevolution.

Do Species Really Exist?

Darlington** (125) says of species: "In the virus the definition of a species is clearly a matter of molecular structure. In the asexual protozoa the classification is beyond any genetic experiment and has no necessary genetic significance. In the higher plants a morphologically uniform species may conceal intersterile diploid and polyploid forms. In the higher animals, similariy, cryptic (hidden) species may arise by the differentiation of mating instincts establishing a genetic isolation without any change of form . . ."

---

*Quoted by permission of the American Association for the Advancement of Science, Washington, U.S.A.
**Quoted by permission of The Clarendon Press, Oxford, England.

At the recent British Symposium on speciation Haldane remarked that specific distinction was more linguistic than biological. Hall George has said elsewhere that species were really of pyschological convenience, an idea, for a species is not discovered but made.

The Botanical Problem

Grant (126)* observes in his turn that the morphologically defined species is a subjective concept. He goes on: "A common practice among botanists is to recognize as a species any population exhibiting distinctive morphological characters combined with a definite geographical range. The result, of course, is that many named species are equivalent to the geographical races of a polytypic species. There are also a few botanists who adopt the so-called biological species concept." The idea that the botanical species is undefinable is "written into the Internation Code of Botanical Nomenclature which through four editions has studiously refrained from defining species." It is difficult to define a taxonomic category in words that cannot be applied either to the next higher or the next lower category of classification. In short, it is very hard for the evolutionist who sees botanical species in flux to be pinned down by any logical restriction—he merely has to alter his definitions. He is the football player who always makes a touchdown because he himself can move the touch line. Grant remarks that in some botanical groups biological species do not even exist.

Davidson (127)** has pointed out, "If we wish to argue that (botanical) species have an objective reality, we may select examples such as Ginkgo. If we wish to argue that species do not exist in Nature at all, we may select such examples as the willows". The species of willow are notoriously confused by natural hybridization, whereas this factor can scarcely affect Ginkgo biloba, which is the sole living member of its phylad.

". . . The loss of sexuality . . . simply means that true biological species do not exists in certain plant groups . . .", he adds.

Fossil Species

Among fossils there are major difficulties. Imbrie (128)*** discusses these at length: "Palaeontologists by no means agree on what a fossil species is. Burma, for example, has given thoughtful expression to the thesis that species do not have an objective reality, a view that is rejected by Simpson and others . . .

---

*Quoted by permission of the American Association for the Advancement of Science, Washington, U.S.A.
**Quoted by Permission of the American Association for the Advancement of Science, Washington, U.S.A.
***Quoted by permission of the American Association for the Advancement of Science, Washington, U.S.A.

"It is widely recognized that many anomalies arise when the genetical definition of species as actually or potentially interbreeding groups of organisms is strictly applied. Asexually reproducing organisms are left out of account, for example, as are the many instances on record in which local or temporary breakdowns occur in the genetical barrier between sympatric populations which on other evidence are classed as good species.

". . . The most obvious shortcoming of palaeontological data is that fossils normally preserve only hard sketetal parts.—

". . . Nevertheless, from general theoretical considerations on the nature of sedimentation and diagenesis, and from practical experience in portions of the geological column which have been thoroughly examined for fossils, **most palaeontologists and stratigraphers would predict that no amount of future field work will ever fill a majority of existing phyletic gaps between transient species.** (emphasis mine).

Arkell and Moy-Thomas* (129) in discussing the taxonomic problems of the palaeontologist say: "To bestow new (plant) names (specific or generic or subgeneric) simply because of a difference in stratigraphical horizons is obviously unsound. Incredible as it may seem, this has been done extensively in the past, even in large works published by reputable societies . . . It should be borne in mind that stratigraphy claims to identify the strata by the contained fossils; therefore stratigraphers who give new names to fossils because they occur in different strata are cutting away the foundations of their science."

Jones (130) tells us that many tests (shells) of Foraminifera have been given generic and specific names different from that of the adult microspheric or adult megalospheric forms. Thus three different names have been given many single Foraminiferal species. Twenhofel and Shrock (131) tell us that the same Foraminifera have been divided into 47 families by one great authority and a different 35 families by another. David Starr Jordan tells us that in American freshwater fishes each species has been described anew about three or four times. In Europe this figure rises to 6 or 8 species per single unit. The common channel catfish of North America has been described as a new species at least 25 times.

Protozoan Species and their Complexity

The problems among students of the Protozoa are very complex. Sonneborn** (132) has discussed these at length in the American symposium on species. "The so-called modern biological species concept defines a species as a group of actually or potentially interbreeding

---

*Quoted by permission of The Clarendon Press, Oxford, England.
**Quoted by permission of the American Association for the Advancement of Science, Washington, U.S.A.

populations. As the other papers in this symposium attest, this concept is widely accepted as the only valid species concept. Yet it is of admittedly limited applicability. In obligatory self-fertilizing organisms, this concept of the species contracts to include but a single individual. In exclusively asexual organisms, the concept admits of no species at all. On this concept, perhaps half or more of the species recognized by students of the Protozoa are invalid, and, in principle, cannot be modified so as to become valid. In like manner, practically every phylum of Invertebrates and all major plant groups contain numerous organisms in which species do not exists at all or in which each individual is a separate species. This greatly limits the applicability of the modern biological species concept. It has been maintained, not without some reason, that there are more species of Protozoa than of all other animals together, for each species of the higher animals is believed to be sole host to at least one species of parasitic Protozoa. If half or more of the Protozoa, and many other organisms as well, are in principle outside the domain of the modern biological species concept, it is applicable to only a minority of all organisms.

"Although this is perhaps the greatest objection to adopting this species concept as the only valid one, there are also others. In some organisms, what is now recognized as a single species on morphological grounds would be broken up into fantastically large numbers of 'biological' species. Moreover, very commonly these 'biological' species would be to an appalling degree unrecognizable and unidentifiable by routine taxonomic procedures or by any other procedures that could reasonably be expected of working biologists." Indeed on the basic of specific mating types 16 varieties of Paramoecium aurelia can now be recognized. The genes of every variety are virtually isolated from those of every other variety. The situation is even more complex than this indicates. "When the strains of the same variety are crossed, at least in some varieties, the F2 and the first backcrosses invariably yield some nonviable clones . . . this may be as high as 98 per cent after crossing certain other strains . . . The same strain crosses regularly give approximately the same results. The magnitude of the mortality seems to vary independently of the geographical proximity or remoteness of the source of strains;"

". . . Difficulties in the application of the term species arise from the attempt to make it do double duty in serving as designating an evolutionary unit, the one which shows minimal irreversible discontinuity, and as designating a readily recognizable group. For most of the last hundred years, it has been tacitly assumed that these two aspects of species coincide and that, since the evolutionary unit often represents a real level of biological organization, . . . species exist as real entities, not as human constructs made for the convenience of biologists. Modern researches, on the contrary, have shown that the evolutionary unit is not always readily recognizable . . . Moreover, by reserving species names for readily recognized groups, this procedure tactily admits that the convenience of biologists must first of all be served by the term species . . . Its (the word species) early connection with evolution theory, its wide usage, and general familiarity with it make it a great prize to capture and invest with absolute existence as a definite level of biological organization of the greatest evolutionary significance. This cannot be done without sacrifice of logic and introduction of confusion.

". . . The principle (in setting up a species) is simply minimal irreversible evolutionary divergence that yields readily recognizable difference . . ."

Summary

There is no generally acceptable definition of a species, for instance one that applies equally to sexual and asexual animal forms and to plants as well. Many seasonal forms or age groups among fish, or the two sexes of one variety, have before this been erroneously classed as different species. It is particularly hard to define a botanical species, and "good species" are rare in some families. In tiny marine forms the difficulties are enormous. The problems of the palaeontologist are unusually marked, notably because only skeletons remain, and here there is room for wide personal bias in the taxonomist. The problems of speciation in a typical protozoan, Paramoecium, have been discussed at length by Sonneborn. They are so varied as to seem practically impossible to resolve.

CHAPTER XVII

THE GREAT TRANSITIONS

O for the muscle of a humming-bird's wings
Or a bigger bird's ear for burrowing things
Under tree bark or under sod!
Subtle, indeed, are the works of God.

—Vere Jameson

PROPOSITION—In the fossil record there is a startling lack of evidence that the major types of life developed gradually out of other major types. They appear on the scene suddenly, as if by fresh creation.

Transitional Forms

A great difficulty for evolutionists has been pointed out by Merson Davies and others in the scarcity of intermediate forms. If evolution is always in process we should have more transitional and fewer terminal types—assuming we could recognize the former, of course.

Viret* (133) recently remarked in this connection that Nature reveals the **sudden** origin of the bat. He knew of no such thing as a quarter of a bat, or a third of a bat, or a half bat, but found that suddenly a new type ready for flight appeared.

Synthetic Types

Thomson mentions such annectant or synthetic types of creatures as the class Onychophora, consisting of Peripatus and allied genera. This creature resembles an annelid in having numerous regularly arranged nephridia, something not seen in insects. But it has tracheae, like simple forms of those used by insects and centipedes—something worms never have. Peripatus and its allies have a body-wall musculature like that of worms, stump-like legs and simple eyes—but resemble insects in having two pairs of appendages serving the mouth, in the heart and circulation, in salivary glands and feelers. He suggests that these creatures are connecting links between worms and insects. What he must mean is that here is a class of creatures which does not fit the tidy taxonomies of biologists, and shows how a living form can share the morphology of other lowly types **without** being related genetically—a major point scored against evolutionary theory. Not content with one puzzle, Thomson describes others, for example the Enteropneusts, with numerous gill-slits opening from the food-canal externally, a vertebrate feature never seen in other inverte-

---

*Quoted by permission of the American Association for the Advancement of Science, Washington, U.S.A.

brates. Are these vertebrate-like worms or worm-like vertebrates? Neither, of course! Just taxonomic difficulties, where life breaks out of the biologist's tidy corrals.

The Great Transitions of Classes and Orders

Dewar deals at length with some of the transformations postulated by the doctrine of evolution and should be consulted directly (chapter 7). He tells of the postulated gradual tranformation of an amphibian into a reptile, which depends on changes in the form and metabolism of the egg. "Before . . . the habit of depositing eggs in water could be changed to that of laying them on the dry land, the following alterations in the egg had to be made: the formation of a tough shell to prevent evaporation of the liquid contents of the egg and to protect it from predacious creatures; the secretion of an acid to cause the white of egg to yield its water as required; a change in the metabolism of the embryo whereby the waste products take the form of insoluble uric acid instead of soluble urea; the introduction of a quantity of yolk to enable the embryo to remain in the egg until it reached a stage when it was able to fend for itself on land; the development of two special embryonic membranes—the amnion and allantois—to protect the embryo, enable it to breathe , and act as a reservoir of the waste products resulting from its metabolism; the development of a tooth in the embryo with which to break the hard shell of the egg. Moreover, fertilization of the egg as soon as the shell evolved had to take place within the female before the shell began to harden, necessitating changes in the uro-genital organs and habits of the adult. Most, if not all, the above changes would be useless, or even harmful, until they were more or less complete; what, then, can have not only inaugurated them but caused them to continue until the transformation of an aquatic into a terrestrial egg was completed? The process, if gradual, must have taken a very long time, and how did the embryos contrive to survive during this long period of transition? It is necessary never to lose sight of the fact that, while all the transformations postulated by the doctrine of evolution were being effected, the creatures being transformed, their eggs and their young, had to live and compete with other organisms" . . .

Then the gradual transformation of a reptile into bird is predicated by evolutionists: ". . . In the case of birds the heat-regulating mechanism is not fully understood. The feathering prevents undue dissipation of the heat generated by the chemical processes of the body. The spacious air sacs, which are organs peculiar to birds, probably assist in the dissipation of surplus heat generated during periods of great activity. But these alone would not suffice to maintain a normal temperature. There seems to be a special nervous mechanism which controls the oxidation of the tissues and regulates the blood supply to every organ. It is difficult to believe that natural forces produced this mechanism just when it was required. Moreover, if the evolution doctrine be true, a temperature-regulating mechanism has been evolved at least three times over; in birds, in monotremes and in the higher mammals. Further, the eggs of warm-blooded birds have to be kept at a constant temperature. In consequence, in cold and temperate climates, birds have to incubate their eggs, and, in very hot countries to take precautions to prevent them being baked by the sun. Reptiles are under no such necessity. Incubation makes great demands on the sitting bird and exposes it to dangers to which the reptile is not subjected . . . Feathers are structures peculiar to birds. According to the evolutionist, they evolved from reptilian scales. This is not easy to believe in view of the extraordinary complexity of a feather . . . Along each side of the shaft runs a series of thin plates or lamellae, of which the broad surface is at right angles to the shaft. These lamellae are known as barbs. Along each barb runs a double row of lamellae . . . the barbules. Those on the near side of the shaft taper to a point, while those on the underside terminate in hooks. By means of these hooks the adjacent barbs are locked together and so give the feather its wonderful firmness and elasticity. Gadow estimates that some large feathers contain over a million barbules. This complicated structure is seen both in the flight feathers and those that cover the body. It is still more difficult to believe that the foreleg of a land reptile or the fore paddle of an aquatic reptile, as the result of the action of natural forces, became gradually converted into a bird's wing . . . Palaeontology lends no support to the notion that such evolution has occurred; no fossils have been found exhibiting any structure intermediate between the scale of a reptile and a fully formed feather, nor any displaying a fore limb intermediate between that of an ordinary terrestrial or aquatic animal and a wing. The feathers of the earliest-known fossil bearing them—Archaeopteryx—are as perfect as those of living birds; in the earliest-known fossils of pterodactyls and bats the wings are fully developed." . . .

If the class of Birds evolved from the class of Reptiles, bird structures must have had reptilian origins, and certain of those peculiar to birds should be studied as to their origin, for example feathers, the caecum, the oil gland, the ambiens muscle and the syrinx. Dewar does just this. The function in birds of the very variable caecum is unknown. Some birds have none, indeed. The same can be said of the oil gland, which is not needed to dress the feathers, as once thought. The ambiens muscle of the thigh or the thigh and leg is very variable or missing, but is unique when present. Birds have no vocal cords, but a syrinx instead. All but the ostriches possess it. Feathers are very complex and variable. All birds have some type of feathers, however. Many of these have an aftershaft. Some have powder-down feathers. It should be possible to rate birds on their distance from the reptilian stem by comparing them for these distinctive characters, —but, strangely enough, this is not true. Thus feathers are usually alike in any order, but yet some species may show peculiar forms, for example the feathers of the osprey, honey buzzard and a few other raptores are unique. The feather arrangement can vary, although it is usually uniform in birds of the same order, —but— there are two types of feather covering in nightjars. Cuckoos, rails and tinamous each exhibit more than one type of pterylosis (feather arrangement). The avian foot is much different from the reptile's foot, and never has more than four toes. Seven types of tendon arrangements exist. In passerines the two great tendons remain entirely separate. In the others they fuse in various degrees. In any one order or suborder the deep plantar tendons tend to be similar—but this arrangement differs in the rollers and bee-eaters, also in the kingfisher. Curiously, the type of tendon arrangement is not correlated with modes of progression. Dewar discusses this in detail, as he does skull types, showing how many types can appear in closely similar species and genera. There should be no difficulty in classifying birds morphologically on a phylogenetic plan, the evolutionist must agree. Actually, there is no correlation between skull-types, feathers, oil glands, caeca, ambiens muscles, and so forth. Powder-down feathers are found in four orders of birds, but in only eight genera! In other words, either they evolved in parallel on eight separate occasions—or the ancestral bird had them and most of his descendents lost them. In either case the logical dilemma is severe. Why did so many birds lose these feathers or how could such different forms produce identical exotic feathers, useful only as an aid to beauty?

Then there is the peculiar entepicondylo-ulnaris muscle—found only in tinamous and gallinaceous birds. Why so rare? Why at all?

Indeed, one cannot formulate a phylogenetic classification of birds that commands universal acceptance. Dewar criticizes a number of these classifications, notably that based on the presence and character of the ambiens muscle, which would thus separate the white-necked stork from the white and black stork. As has been said before, Dewar's book should be read in this general connection. Now one cannot believe that evolution has followed incomprehensible lines in making birds. The logical alternative is that birds have not evolved from reptiles or any common pro-avian ancestor. Various anatomical characters peculiar to birds are distributed among their genera almost at random.

De Beer and Swinton point out that both principal birds of the Cretaceous, Hesperornis and Ichthyornis, were held to have been toothed—until J. T. Gregory proved in 1952 that the lower jaws long attributed to Ichthyornis were really those of a young mosasaur. The upper jaw is so vague in its characters as to be indeterminate. Hence Ichthyornis offers no evidence of teeth!

Dewar goes on about that gradual (but tremendous) transformation of a reptile into a mammal—"Even if Simpson be mistaken in believing the Triconodonta and the Multituberculata to be mammals, the supposed transformation, if the doctrine of evolution be true, must have occurred on two occasions, that is, when the monotremes were

172

evolved and when the higher mammals arose.—" There are so many major differences (involved in this great transformation), notably the diaphragm, "—a fibro-muscular partition separating the thoracic and abdominal cavities. Reptiles have no diaphragm. In consequence they do not breathe as mammals do; their thorax is not a closed box; it is not alternately expanded and contracted. Sir Arthur Keith confesses his inability to comprehend how the mammalian diaphragm can have been derived from any reptile; hence, being an evolutionist, he is driven to conclude that mammals evolved directly from an amphibian (one of the Stegocephalia). The muscular coat of the alimentary canal is furnished with a layer of longitudinal muscles and one of circular muscles in reptiles, birds and mammals. In mammals the longitudinal muscles are outside the circular muscles, in the other two classes they are inside them.— Mammals are provided with mammary glands— organs entirely unknown in reptiles. In reptiles the chief nitrogenous excretory product of tissue waste is uric acid; in mammals it is urea.— Mammals have in the ear a structure not found in any reptiles. This is known as the Organ of Corti; it consists of a tunnel bounded on either side by a row of rods, having somewhat the appearance of the key- board of a piano . . . Is it credible that the longitudinal muscles of the gut of some reptile were gradually transformed into circular muscles and the circular into longitudinal? What can have made the ciliary muscle of the eye of some reptile lose its striation? Why should some reptile change the system of blood supply to its iris? What can have made the chemical processes in the body of some reptile alter so that the waste products were secreted mainly as urea instead of uric acid? . . . We have noticed that in order to convert an amphibian into a reptile its chemical metabolism must be altered in such a way that uric acid is secreted in place of urea. The transformation of a reptile into a mammal would involve a change in metabolism in the reverse direction. This would be a case of evolution retracing its steps, of reverse evolution." . . .

De Beer concedes that there are no fossil forms bridging the gaps between phyla, as, for example between the vertebrates and starfish, or between either of these and the molluscs or worms.

Keosian (134) has boldly come up with the most recent answer to the "gaps in the geological record" and the absence of annectant forms between viruses, bacteria, certain algae, sponges and so on. He postulates continuous creation (by neobiogenesis) since life began. These gaps do exist and these phyla are not related, he says. Life is continuously polyphyletic. At last an evolutionist has faced his problems squarely and decided on the only logical alternative to Creation, viz., the **continued** origin of new forms by spontaneous generation.

Still More Puzzles

Dewar raises further difficulties, too. One fundamental objection to evolution is the fact that orders rich in types (meaning flying, terrestrial , aquatic, nocturnal, wading forms such as are found among birds) should be rich in species, for surely types must have evolved **through** species. Actually the reverse is the case, and Fuchs has elaborated this fact into "law". For example, the Crustacea and Mammalia are rich in types but poor in species. Insects and Birds are poor in types but rich in species. Among plants, the Smilaceae, Rosaceae and Liliaceae are rich in types but poor in species. The Compositae, Gramineae and Leguminosae are rich in species but poor in types. Thus 13,000 species of birds show but five types, and the nearly homogeneous Coleoptera (beetles) have at least 120,000 species. The more diversified Crustacea have only 8,000 species. (These are all 1898 figures). Here is a very significant difficulty, is it not?

Tracheae as breathing organs present a major problem to evolutionists. They are found in Peripatus, the millipedes, centipedes, insects, spiders, scorpions and wood-lice (a land crustacean). There is no common ancestry claimed for all these types—and, in any case, any suggestion made here must account for the lung-books of scorpions. So convergence is called in, even when there is histological and physiological identity! Such a multiplicity of identical and complicated convergence would stagger anyone but an evolutionist! A corresponding difficulty soluble only by "convergence"—or Creation—is the nephridium of Amphioxus and the widely different Polychaete worms.

The Old World platyrrhine monkeys and the New World catarrhines belong to two different phyla—but are as similar as close genera. What a problem for evolutionists!—as is the independent origin of eyes in so many phyla, or of breasts in the three sub-classes of mammals, for example the Monotremes, Marsupials and Placentals. And yet the mammae of the Monotremes differ from the rest fundamentally, for they are branched tubular forms, not alveolar, and have no nipples. Nipples make a further difficulty for they are true or false in type, depending on their embryonic formation. And these fundamentally unlike types are distributed almost at random, for true nipples occur in all Marsupials, and in primates and rodents amongst Placentals. All other Placentals have false nipples. Thus the evolutionist must postulate that parallel evolution evolved the breast gland in the Monotremes and other mammals, then true nipples evolved in parallel in Marsupials and Placentals, or on two or three separate occasions in Placentals. Certainly the evolutionist has enormous theoretical problems, which he must not be allowed to evade merely because he rarely chooses to discuss them.

Summary

What has gone before merely serves to accentuate the difficulties about the origin of major groups, such as Phyla, Classes and Orders, in the light of evolutionary theory. One cannot logically derive one from the other, and, historically, as we shall see in a later chapter, palaeontology tells us that the Orders arose suddenly, as if in full bloom, and were **at once** characterized by a wide range of constituent species and genera.

Modern students of evolution tend to study micro-evolution only, by necessity, and then extrapolate their results, something not always logical. They rarely discuss their real difficulties, such as pre-adaptation, allometry, useless perfections, lack of transitional forms, fixity of type, the origin of tracheae or mammae, but hug the desirable problems they face that time never assuages, for example the gaps in the geological record which no amount of exploration seems to fill in. Faced with such a puzzle as a phylogenetic classification of birds designed to indicate how they evolved from reptiles, for example, the inherent puzzles of evolution come to light, and are excessive.

CHAPTER XVII

FOSSIL PLANTS

And this rich grass upon the river's brink,
How sweet to sprawl on it, and doze or think!
How strange that even our brief lend-lease of dust
Supposes flowers and fish and men a-link!

—Vere Jameson

PROPOSITION—The study of fossil plants does not indicate that the early types were simple and have gradually become more complex.

Introduction

Textbooks on Evolution usually devote much more space to animals than plants. There are obvious reasons for this. The evidence for plant evolution is very sketchy, and a hundred years of palaeontological study has filled in few of the gaps. Few authorities in the one field are competent in the other and there has been inadequate communication between the two groups, notably in palaeontology, (where their rock strata and classifications sometimes disagree) and in geography. Micro-evolution in plants all must concede (see a previous chapter). Mega-evolution is quite another matter, and will occupy attention here. Most textbook discussions on the subject lean heavily on imaginative homologies and could-have-been's which easily become translated into must-have-been's by "scientific" men already committed before the evidence has been thoroughly scanned.

Fossil Plants and their Mega-evolution

Scott points out how confused evolutionists are on some of the major features of evolutionary theory. For example, the Higher Cryptogams may be more ancient and primitive than the Bryophytes, and the latter may really be a deteriorated class. Even Bacteria may be degradations of higher organisms and not early and primitive forms. The largest flower in the world, the Sumatran Rafflesia Arnoldi, whose flower is a yard in diameter, has lost stem, leaves and roots and merely sends a spawn of threads into the host it lives on. And the Bird's Nest Orchid can live in partnership with a fungus. The Thallophytes are now broken up into several phyla, having parallel developments. The Vascular plants are now considered to be composed of several groups, developing in parallel. This sort of thing wreaks havoc with the "phylogenetic tree", of course, which postulates the linear ascent such forms do not show.

Evolutionists have long argued that Ferns came from the simpler Mosses and Liverworts (Bryophytes) or groups closely akin to these.

But the fossil record runs counter to this, for the oldest known vascular Cryptogams do not show the slightest approach to a Bryophytic fruit or sporagonium or to anything like it. Nor is there any evidence of the superior antiquity of the Bryophytic type, for the Vascular Cryptogams were highly developed in the earliest land-floras of which we have any record.

There is no clue as to the origin of the Mosses and Liverworts. Indeed, the whole class of Bryophytes may be degenerated remnants of some higher group, say evolutionists. The question, says Scott,* is "an almost hopeless one."

The Sequence of Plants

The origin of Angiosperms, which now rule the world of plants, is difficult to decipher, says Scott, for most of the fossil remains are of leaves only, and these taken by themselves can be misleading. Their sudden appearance as well-developed flowering plants in the Lower Cretaceous "is still, perhaps, the greatest difficulty in the record of evolution." Flowers are needed to attract insects. Bees and wasps date back to the Upper Oolite and Lepidoptera are of about the same age— just prior to the Flowering Plants. Scott believes that the wind-fertilized families derived from insect-fertilized flowers. How fortunate that insects of the right families arose at the right time for the Angiosperms! Was a Creator on the job?

Scott would derive Angiosperms from the Mesozoic Cycadophytes, but notes the wide differences between these families. Yet the older Cycadophytes could show resemblances, like the genus Wielandiella of Sweden, and there are simpler stamens than in most Cycads in the El Consuelo Williamsonia. Curiously, the most advanced Cycadophytes such as the Bennettiteae arose relatively early, in Mesozoic time! No similarity of appearance to Angiosperms, very complex stamen types, and no transitional forms of gynaecium have been found, he observes, nor is there any real evidence suggesting a similar mode of fertilization. Yet the embryo was dicotyledonous, and the seed exalbuminous. If the similar, complex "flowers" of the Cycadeoids actually were ancestral to those of the higher Flowering Plants, then certainly evolution since has been largely a reduction and simplification. Cycas is perhaps the most striking example of the survival to modern times of a really ancient seed-plant. The late Palaeozoic Cycadophytes are as ancient in the fossil world as any class of land-plants known.

If Dicotyledons sprang from Cycadophytes, the origin of the Monocotyledons is still more puzzling, unless they came from the Dicotyledons. Yet a typical family of Monocotyledons like the Palms is found early in Cretaceous rocks! Botanists really are uncertain at present as to the theoretical "evolution" of Monocotyledons.

---

*Quoted by permission of Holt, Rinehart and Winston, New York, U.S.A.

Scott says that evolution in plants can be traced only in the broadest outline. In the history of the seed-plants, for example, there are two evident gaps. We do not know how any postulated transition from Pteridosperms to Cycadophytes was affected. The male plants were quite unlike, for one thing. We have still less evidence on how the complex flower of the Bennettiteae arose among the flowerless Pteridosperms, notably the juxtaposition of organs to form a flower and the complex gynaecium with its reduced carpels. The other great gap is even more serious. It is the gap below the Pteridosperms. Unfortunately for the evolutionist, Pteridosperms are as early as any land plants known! The leaves and pollen-sacs are like those of modern ferns, but the seeds are highly organized and quite unlike the spore sacs of Cryptogams. It has always been assumed that homospory must have preceded heterospory. However, the latter types are found as early as the homosporous in the fossil world! Then again, all the Palaeozoic Lycopods were heterosporous, but no Ferns were,—although Ferns are a "higher" type! Moreover, Pteridosperm seeds were quite as elaborate as Cycadean seeds, and show no trace of evolution from the female sporangium to which evolutionists must trace them.

The great seed-bearing family of Cordaites is also very ancient and very complex. How can they be connected with the seed-fern stock, as evolutionists postulate? They appear too early—as far back as our fossil records go! These forms exceeded the reproductive elaborations of the Coniferae, indeed.

The very ancient Mesozoic race of ferns, the Marattiaceae, had very advanced fructifications compared to the simple spore-sacs of modern ferns. Some from Triassic and Liassic rocks belong to such recent genera as Marattia and Danoea.

The fossil Club-mosses had spores of two kinds, although evolutionists would look for homospory to appear first. The two living genera of heterosporous Lycopods, Selaginella and Isoetes, seem to have been separate types since the Palaeozoic. In the Carboniferous are Selaginella types scarcely distinguishable from the living genus, indeed with four megaspores in each sporangium as now. One Carboniferous plant of this general type, Miadesmia, went far beyond any living ally and produced "an organ closely analogous to a true seed." The finest fossils have been preserved to illustrate how little the reproductive structures of Selaginella and Isoetes have altered since the Palaeozoic!

Scott concludes that of the history of Club-mosses with spores of one kind we know "practically nothing". He adds: "We have no light of any kind on the **origin** of the Lycopods—they are too ancient for that to be possible."

He says of the Horsetails: "The evolution of the Equisetum stock, from Palaeozoic times to the present, has been on the whole a steady descent, and not an advance. The Tertiary species are generally like the larger Horsetails of the present day." The early forms seem to have had well-developed compound leaves, unlike the degenerate leaf-sheaths of the modern form, Equisetum. The Calamites of the later Palaeozoic were the most advanced types in the whole group. Scott says: "Our records do not go far enough back to throw any light on the origin of the class of Equisetales."—

A remark of Darwin's (Origin of Species) applies with special force to fossil plants: "The geological record, at all times imperfect, does not extend far enough back to show with unmistakable clearness that within the known history of the world organization has largely advanced."

Scott talks of the obvious relationships of such great groups as the Cordaiteae, Pteridosperms and Ferns, the Horsetails and Sphenophylls and adds: "Beyond this we cannot go with safety; we are left with three great races of Vascular Plants, the Ferns, the Lycopods and the joint race of the Horsetails and Sphenophylls."—"When we get back to the Devonian period, a veil falls, and all the earlier course of evolution (immensely the greater part of the whole history) remains hidden. Scientific men, however, are not always deterred from theory by the absence of facts—."

Ancient Fitness

Scott says: "If a botanist were set to examine, without prejudice, the structure of those Devonian plants which have come down to us in a fit state for such investigation it would probably never occur to him that they were any simpler than plants of the present day; he would find them different in many ways, but about on the same general level of organization." The special adaptation of Flowering Plants to Insects is probably a relatively recent advance—but we have no information on its genuine age!

Scott adds, "If the plants of later periods seem to us more perfect than their predecessors, it is because they are adapted to conditions with which we are more familiar, and which are also, in some respects, more complex. However far back we may follow the fossil records, we shall never meet with badly-adapted plants—only with plants adapted to different conditions than those of the present."

"The long, rather narrow leaves of the Cordaiteae were fitted to resist mechanical strains in the same way as monocotyledonous leaves of similar shape at the present day. In both there are parallel ribs of strong fibrous tissue running through the leaf near the upper and lower surface, that is, in the position where they afford the most resistance to bending with the least expenditure of material. In the outer cortex of the stem of Lyginodendron and many other Palaeozoic plants, there are bands of fibres united to form a network, the meshes of which are filled up with the softer cellular tissues. This formed an admirable

179

means of support, placed at the outside of the cylindrical stem, where it ought to be placed on engineering principles. The plan worked very well as long as there was not too much increase in thickness of the wood and bast inside. In some Sigillarias and Lepidodendrons, however, the growth in thickness was considerable, so as eventually to burst the outer framework, and here we find that the supporting tissues were constantly renewed from the secondary cortex as growth went on. Thus at all stages the necessary mechanical strength was provided just where it was most wanted, on the outside of the trunk . . .

"In all respects, wherever we have the means of forming an opinion, the organs of the oldest plants prove to have been just as well fitted to their work as in plants of our own times. The leaves of Sigillaria and Lepidodendron had two deep grooves on the under side, in which the stomata were sheltered; these were further protected by hairs partly closing the grooves. Quite similar devices are common in leaves of living plants which are exposed to drought . . . to check the too rapid loss of water by transpiration through the stomata or pores . . .

"The whole problem of Descent is in fact extraordinarily complex, and we are now only at the beginning of the investigation. Evolution, during the periods to which our records extend, proves to have been by no means a regular advance from the simple to the complex. Very often, indeed, the reverse has been the case."

Scott discusses the puzzled evolutionary botanist's difficulties elsewhere. He says that in the Pleistocene all the genera and most of the species are recent. "It is evident that the really early evolutionary stages of the Dicotyledons (and doubtless of the Angiosperms as a whole) must have been traversed in periods long previous to those from which their first recognizable traces have come down to us."

The late Mesozoic Cycadeoids had elaborate bisexual flowers. These seem unrelated to recent Cycads with their simple unisexual cones or still simpler stem-born carpels. Here is degenerative evolution, surely.

The stems of the ancient "seed-Ferns" attained a complexity of structure which one could seek in vain among modern plants, except in some tropical climbers, perhaps. The Palaeozoic Tree-Ferns with their elaborate anatomy, their felted roots and their often compound fructification were on quite as high a level as the most advanced living Ferns. Some of the most complicated seeds known are of Palaeozoic Age and probably referable to the Pteridosperms. Indeed, the seed may be said to have reached its zenith of complexity in Carboniferous times. The Carboniferous Horsetails, like the corresponding Club-mosses, were in every respect more highly organized than their modern successors. As the Pteridosperms and true Ferns are traced further back they do not seem to approximate. It seems that we know of no really simple Pteridosperm. The Lower Carboniferous Club-Mosses were as highly developed in their fructification as their successors. Indeed, the archegonium of Lepidostrobus Veltheimianus agrees exactly with that of heterosporous Lycopods still living.

Fossil Persistence

Scott*goes on: "We are still unable to explain completely the conducting mechanism of the wood in living plants. It is worth pointing out, however, that one of the most highly differentiated wood-structures among Gymnosperms is found in the Upper Devonian Callixylon, with its neatly localized pitted areas on the tracheid walls. It has been said that this ancient wood is as perfect as that of Pinus, though on different lines. Among more special adaptations, one may recall the pappus of the Lower Carboniferous seed Thysanotesta, the pollen-chamber and elaborate system of water-supply in Palaeozoic seeds generally, and the sheltering of the stomata in the hair-clothed furrows of a Lepidodendron leaf." In short, fossil botany does not throw much light on morphological origins. Indeed, "the infinite play of adaptation has left the ground-plan untouched from the first to last" in such items as the whorled leaves of the Articulatae, from the Middle Devonian till now. He concludes thus,—"we know a good deal about extinct plants, but not enough, as yet, to throw much light on the problems of their evolution. New discoveries constantly raise new questions and seldom solve those which were already before our minds."

Raymond** also comments on this point: "Angiosperms made a spectacular entry upon the world stage as great trees rather than as modest herbs, and palaeontologists are still ransacking the earth in search of their ancestors. The oldest known are singularly like forms now living."

Chaney (135)*** observes that "with the exception of the flower, all of the organs used in the classification of land plants had appeared before the close of the Palaeozoic era—" The earliest known angiosperms were such diverse families as the Magnoliaceae, Menispermaeceae, Lauraceae, Platanaceae and Moraceae—they must have evolved long before we know them, the faithful evolutionist must insist. What a predicament he is in! Only rarely can a developmental trend be seen in leaves since the Cretaceous plants. Fossil fruits, seeds and flowers show the same lack of change. Even Tertiary grasses like the genus Stipidium are much like the modern grass genus, Stipa.

Stebbins (136) admits the difficulty of determining rates of speciation in fossil plants. He does present data to show that herbs

---

*Quoted by permission of the MacMillan Co., New York, U.S.A.
**Quoted by permission of the MacMillan Co., New York, U.S.A.
***Quoted by permission of the Princeton University Press, Princeton, U.S.A.

and trees have changed at about the same rate since the Early Pliocene, more than 80 per cent belonging to the same **genus** still and 25 percent to modern **species**. The most complete sequence known for any herbaceous plant is in the seeds of the genus Strathiotes, beginning in the Eocene. By Upper Pliocene its seeds were quite modern. But the seeds of the modern forms have neither been collected nor studied! Moreover, little is known of the rest of the plant. Here is the best known case amongst herbs and it is wrapped in obscurity. The plant mega-evolutionist surely needs large doses of faith.

The best series of any sort is of the grass seeds of the tribe Stipeae, known from Early Miocene to its end in Middle Pliocene. Many of the latter resemble modern species of the genus Piptochaetium. All the modern forms in North America are polyploids, while the South American relatives are diploids. But the only seeds of woody plants found in North American deposits, those of the genus Celtis, are identical with modern species still found here. Hence, obviously, the herbaceous types evolved faster than the woody. But most of the herbs have failed to evolve since Middle or early Tertiary.

One of the difficulties of fossil plant classification appears in the mosses, where, as Simpson has been previously quoted, peristome characters diagnostic of **orders, families** and **genera** are said to occur in **species** living in the same way and place.

Bergen and Davis (137) suggest that each group of fungi evolved from different types of algae. But the yeasts and basidia fungi have an origin puzzling even to imaginative evolutionists. Such life habits as they have are more varied than those of any other group of spore plants. These authors say that bryophytes must have arisen from algae, but how is a mystery. No bryophytes indicate how the root system arose, it seems. They suggest that sporophytes evolved independently in such different groups as the red algae, sac fungi, brown algae and the bryophytes. Similarly, they say that the higher types of flowers have been evolved again and again independently in unrelated groups of angiosperms. How incredible such a belief is when one thinks of the convergences so involved!

Summary

Nothing is known of the origins of the great classes of fossil plants. Their oldest types are often the most complex. Relationships between the great groups cannot be postulated on any evidence in record. The initially lifeless gap is overwhelming to evolutionary theory. The persistence of ancient forms must stagger the botanical evolutionist, since it is so general. A phylogenetic taxonomy is rarely feasible, and where it has been attempted has led to ridiculous errors. The simplest forms, for example the algae and fungi, are often the most ancient. Palaeo-botany affords no firm ground for the evolutionist. Indeed, it is one of the most baffling fields he intrudes upon.

CHAPTER XIX

GAPS IN THE GEOLOGICAL RECORD

Why hope for easy answers to our plea?
Why seek for all replies in two and three?
If life were to such timid compass pent
Who would complain of it like thee and me?

—Vere Jameson

PROPOSITION—Gaps in the geological record prevent the evolutionist from proving that modern animals and plants have descended from older animals and plants by small gradations of change. There is no sign that such lacunae are due to inadequate knowledge of the rocks. They appear to be real and permanent.

Introduction

From Darwin and Huxley onward evolutionists have made much of the gaps in the geological record. Whenever some important piece of their argument is missing, whenever they cannot involve some known fossil form in a genealogy, they say with quiet assurance: "Never mind. We will find it later." But let us acknowledge that at the moment there are many huge gaps in the record. There is no evolutionary argument which can meet this objection, of course,— even if a hopeful Darwin suggests that the gap may be filled. tomorrow or 2000 years from now, and may not really be there. There is a much greater probability, if we are to introduce our own guesses under the guise of Science, that there is an original discontinuity at each particular place. The existence of such a fatal discontinuity no evolutionist dare conceive, for his theory can tolerate no such lack of proof. Hence he tries to gloss it over.

Creationists are much more apt to believe that new forms arose de novo, without discernible ancestral types. They have never yet hung themselves on genealogical trees.

Geological Gaps are Baffling — and Remain

M. Davies* says: "(The) imperfection of the geological record does not tell more strongly against the preservation of intermediate forms than it does against the preservation of finished forms . . . (Even) the most rapid form of evolution of which I can conceive or conjecture fails to account for, or even render remotely explicable, the sudden appearance among heterogeneous organisms of finished fish forms, finished bird forms, and finished mammals." Paulin* regarded

---

*Quoted by permission of Pickering and Inglis Ltd., Glasgow, Scotland.

this as "not less than miraculous" on the hypothesis of evolution, and added: "These considerations to me, a lifelong evolutionist, have proved of a highly disconcerting nature; . . . I must in all honesty confess that logically, as the matter presents itself to my mind, the argument is in favour of those who believe in the doctrine of special creations as our fathers believed in it . . . For although Darwin was at pains to explain the absence of numerous living transitional varieties between species; and the paucity of fossil remains in general; yet he never even thought of explaining why the fossil remains of a world which, on his own showing, was always full of evolving creatures should afford such a preponderance of types which must be regarded not as transitional but at terminal ones."

Simpson remarks: "The palaeontological evidence for discontinuity consists of the frequent sudden appearance of new groups in the fossil record, a suddenness common to all taxonomic levels and nearly universal at high levels. Since the record is, and must always remain, incomplete, such evidence can never **prove** the discontinuity to be original." But this is certainly strongly suggested, if we must adhere to knowledge only, and not unfounded theory. If the type of origin of new forms suggested by the known fossil record were to be named it would of necessity be called origin by "Creation"—or the neobiogenesis currently suggested by Keosian.

D. D. Davis* (138) comments in his turn on the gaps in the geological record. The sudden emergence of new types, for example families and orders, has given real trouble of late. No experimentation can apply to this problem, obviously. "A few palaeontologists even today cling to the idea that these gaps will be closed by further collecting, that is, that they are accidents of sampling, but most regard the observed discontinuities as real . . . The origin of new adaptive types, as opposed to their subsequent evolution, is the crux of the whole adaptation question . . ." Thus Davis mentions that many German morphologists in the 1930's questioned the validity of evolution, or limited its application to phyla or classes, even genera, for example Schindewolf and Goldschmidt. Davis suggests that mutational velocity can itself be a mutation! He adds: "the facts of palaeontology conform equally well with other interpretations that have been discredited by neobiological work, for example divine creation, innate developmental processes, Lamarckism, and so on, and palaeontology by itself can neither prove nor refute such ideas." Adaptation can be demonstrated in fossil material only obliquely. Davis goes on: "The crucial point in any theory of adaptation is the origin of a new adaptive type, which is an essentially discontinuous process, usually involving an abrupt change in direction . . . Practically all students of evolution agree in recognizing an element of real or seeming discontinuity in the origin of a major adaptation." Either there are bridgeless gaps or "bursts"

---

*Quoted by permission of the Princeton University Press, Princeton, U.S.A.

of evolution. Palaeontologists would concede, of course, that they must rarely get a chance to catch a new type on the make, nor would they recognize it if they did. Thus the evolution of rays from sharks may be related to the absence of a swim bladder in the latter, their flattened belly, and their habit of occasionally resting on the bottom. But try to prove such a flimsy theory! Sudden huge mutations adapted to a new environment might be a possibility here—but no such examples are known. The deep-sea decapod crustaceans must have got there from pre-adapted shallow sea forms, the pre-adaptations involving such items as reduced eyes, elongated antennae and reduced mouth parts—but all known examples of "pre-adaptations" are at the generic level or lower, and are not specialized major adaptations which could lead to monotypic families.

Romer* discounts the possibility of "saltation" in animals, for "intermediate evolutionary forms representative of this phenomenon are extremely rare (a situation bringing smug satisfaction to the anti-evolutionist) . . . Links are missing just where we most fervently desire them, and it is all too probable that many links will continue to be missing." He likes the idea of "explosive" evolution, a process particularly prominent in such invertebrate groups as the Belemnites and Terebratuloid brachiopods. But how can one ever settle in a satisfactory historical way the profound aetiological problem in palaeontology presented by the either/or dilemma of creation versus such an unprovable theory as evolutionary explosion. Moreover, there is a good deal of confusion introduced into palaeontology by parallelisms in development. "It may have been an almost universal phenomenon . . . The recognition of parallelism leads to disturbing thoughts on classification and the homology concept." Romer goes on: "It is said that the fossil record shows that generalized forms survive and specialized forms become extinct, but this is true only because extinct lines are ipso facto characterized as specialized; those which survive are labelled as generalized."

Westoll** (139) well observes: "The 'families' recognized in textbooks are of doubtful value." He goes on to contradict for the Dipnoi many of Simpson's well-known analyses of the processes and rates of mega-evolution. Simpson, as an evolutionist, has tried to establish such rates, giving only approximate figures, of course. "There is evidence that subspecies or, at least, clearly differentiated local races may evolve in less than a century but commonly require 10,000 years or so for their evolution, and may evolve for as much as 500,000 years without rising to the specific level. The evolution of a species, fully distinct genetically and morphologically, seems usually to require 50,000 years or more in nature and even in groups with fairly rapid average evolutionary rates, (such as mammals), some living species are about 1,000,000 years old . . . some living invertebrate species . . . in a few

*Quoted by permission of the Princeton University Press, Princeton, U.S.A.
**Quoted by permission of the Princeton University Press, Princeton, U.S.A.

cases seem to be as much as 30,000,000 years old . . . there are living pelecypod genera that are virtually immortal . . ."

Stebbins in discussing evolutionary rates in plants remarks that there is a low rate of evolution seen in trees. The sudden appearance of flowering plants in the Cretaceous must imply a burst of evolution then, this author believes.

Indeed these apparent breaks in the palaeontological record cannot be due to "mutations", most evolutionists believe, but to shifts of population—something no one can ever ascertain by palaeontological means, of course.

Wright (140)*, after a mathematical study of adaptation and selection, concludes: "the multiplication of species relatively rarely leads to generic differences and still more rarely to families and higher categories by a gradual cumulative process. There seems to be a large measure of truth in the contention of Willis and Goldschmidt that evolution works down from the higher categories to the lower, rather than the reverse. Nevertheless the critical event in the appearance of a higher category seems to be a major ecological opportunity rather than any sort of mutation."

Dewar comments on the "incomplete" geological record: "I submit that the figures in the table (below) show that, as regards the mammals in question, the geological record is not very incomplete; indeed it reveals to us the majority of these."

The number of genera of non-volant land mammals known to have lived at various stages of the Tertiary and in the Quarternary and the number now living in Europe and North America

Stage		Europe	North America
Basal Eocene		14	40
Lower Eocene		24	52
Middle Eocene		38	69
Upper Eocene		68	37
Lower Oligocene		80	58
Middle Oligocene		41	44
Upper Oligocene		43	57
Lower Miocene		52	51
Middle Miocene		59	35
Upper Miocene		81	52
Lower Pliocene	#	87	42
Middle Pliocene		47	18
Upper Pliocene		45	28
Pleistocene		66	84
Now Living		48	72

#Includes fossils from the Maragha beds of Iran.

---

*Quoted by permission of the Princeton University Press, Princeton, U.S.A.

It will be seen that, unless life in the past was much richer in types than contemporary Europe and North America, we can scarcely regard the fossil record as noticeably incomplete.

It would also seem (see below) that the geological record is fairly complete in the case of mammals other than bats. The latter are rarely fossilized, of course.

Type of Mammal	No. of Genera now living	Percentage known as fossils
Volant (Bats)	215	17.67
Aquatic (Whales, Sirenians, Seals, etc.)	41	70.73
Land (i.e. all mammals other than aquatic and volant)	408	57.84
Total	664	45.63

Name of Continent	No. of genera of land mammals now inhabiting it	Percentage of these known as fossils
Europe	48	100.00
Asia	134	70.15
Africa	145	49.65
North America	71	90.14
South America	86	72.09
Australia	48	45.83

The above tables provide good evidence that the fossil record is not nearly as incomplete as the palaeontologist would like us to believe. If it is nearly adequate, **the case for mega-evolution cannot be proved**.

Some Comments about Gaps in the Record

Simpson, that great evolutionary scholar, has much to say on this vital theme: "In spite of these examples it remains true, as every palaeontologist knows, that **most** new species, genera, and families and that nearly all new categories above the level of families appear in the record suddenly and are not led up to by known, gradual, completely continuous transitional sequences. When palaeontological collecting was still in its infancy and no clear examples of transitional origin had been found, most palaeontologists were anti-evolutionists. Darwin recognized the fact that palaeontology then seemed to provide evidence against rather than for evolution in general or the gradual origin of taxonomic categories in particular. Now we do have many examples of transitional sequences . . . Nevertheless, there are still a few palaeontologists, and good ones (for example, Spath, 1933; Schindewolf, 1950), who are so impressed by how much (fossil evidence) has been found that they conclude that most, at any rate, of what has not been found never existed . . . Moreover, it is a fact that discontinuities are almost always and systematically present at the origin of really high categories . . . Every year apparent discontinuities in phylogeny are filled in, and each year it becomes less logical to conclude that remaining discontinuities represent saltation. There remains, however, the point that for still higher categories discontinuity of appearance in the record is not only frequent but also systematic. Some break in continuity always occurs in categories from orders upwards, at least, although the break may not be large or appear significant to most students. It was estimated above that the mammalian orders had unknown origin sequences (assuming, for the moment, that they did not arise by saltation) that may have averaged as much as one-third as long as the recorded sequences, although probably considerably shorter . . . The earliest Proboscidea appear with large adaptive discontinuity from any probable ancestors, but probable ancestors are not known after the Paleocene and there is a lapse at least on the order of 20 million years between them and the first Proboscidea."

Simpson explains the discontinuities in the fossil record by suggesting that:— "There is time corresponding with the unrecorded sequences; the discontinuities follow time gaps. The discontinuities are not absolute; they may be very slight or almost nominal, and isolated finds of fossils of intermediate type may occur in them. Gaps comparable in length are known which certainly had occupants even though these do not appear in the fossil record. The origin-sequences are often of such length that under conditions of palaeontological sampling it is almost impossible for their record to be continuous. Chances of discovery of transitional types are often reduced by the fact that they moved between quite different ecological conditions. Relatively small populations were often involved. The rate of evolution was often relatively fast and fewer individuals occurred per structural stage than in average well-recorded sequences. The transitions were in restricted geographic regions and not always in the same region throughout any one transition . . . For instance the last known reptiles that could possibly be ancestral to birds appear in the Triassic and there is a gap of at least 15 million years before appearance of a (very reptilian) bird in the record . . . Even now it is more usual than not to assume that the animal phyla, all of which appear in the Cambrian and Ordovician as far as they have fossil records, 'must have' arisen far back in the pre-Cambrian. Pre-Cambrian life must, indeed, have been more varied than the few known fossils of that age, but there is no real reason to assume that all animal phyla arose in the pre-Cambrian, or that any except the protistans arose long (geologically speaking) before the Cambrian . . . A great many reptiles were evolving at moderate rates and more or less steadily in the direction of mammals throughout the Permian and Triassic. There is really very little difference between the last well-known therapsids and true mammals. The earliest mammals among known fossils are represented only by scraps of teeth and could well prove actual intergradation if well known. More or less 10 million years later what are certainly true mammals appear. A gap occurs, but it is not really profound and could readily be bridged by simple continuation of the sort of evolution actually recorded **before** the gap. Nor are the gaps absolute. Isolated finds have been made in what would otherwise be large gaps, and such finds always are intermediate in structure just as if transitional evolution had been going on all the time. Archaeopteryx is the most famous case in point . . . It is exactly the sort of animal we could expect from the middle Jurassic if the Aves were transitionally developing their new adaptation from toward the end of the Triassic into the late Cretaceous. It is obvious that isolated discoveries do not fill the the gap, and it is always possible to insist that the gap is still there on one side or the other (there really remains a **smaller** gap on each side, of course), but these discoveries are evidence as to what was going on during the break in the fossil record."

Most of this very able and imaginative discussion by Simpson illustrates possibilities hard to translate into probabilities, and shows us how desperately a palaeontologist believing in evolution must search for possible answers to that major flaw, the gap in the geological record. However, if there is no evidence there is no evidence, and the case falls to the ground unproven. Many of his postulates can never be authenticated, as Brough well says. Clever as they are, they are fictional until demonstrable. Certainly these defects in the evidence provide a basic attack on the whole proposal of mega-evolution.

The evolutionist's argument on the slow development of orders, classe, phyla is specious. It tells us how difficult the problem of the taxonomist is, namely that anyone can differentiate specialized and widely divergent forms, but when one attempts to trace these back to simpler "ancestors" he becomes confused in the welter of extinct forms, and finds that almost every niche in the world, ancient or modern, has been taken or is now held by living forms of vast variety on which it is hard to impose the tight harness of a taxonomical system, particularly one based on evolutionary pre-conceptions.

An evolutionist like Simpson begs the whole question of evolution when he traces existing orders or classes back to single very ancient animals showing only minimal divergence from their contemporary populations. At best he can trace them back to early populations of considerable size (if these now can be recognized as fossil entities.) He unconsciously falls into the pit digged by human genealogy, which traces to one person; and talks as if he could refer all the Equidae to one Eohippus or all camels to one Protylopus. But that is just the crux of our problem. Did all Protylopus evolve from one—or did the family type suddenly appear by quantum variation, whatever that is— it could be creation! Palaeontology can never settle such a problem. The evolutionist begs it, as he must. The evidence is only that suddenly a new type emerges, a type recognizable by several or very many specimens spread over a wide geographic area. Let us not permit the wool to be pulled over our eyes by clever theorizing. What "may have been" probably is rarely or never what actually was.

Carter points out that there can be no doubt of the differences that are seen between mega-and micro-evolution. Aristogenesis (the formation of totally new characters) (and merely a recent and slightly desperate postulate) plays a larger role in the former. It should not be assumed that one is merely an extrapolation of the other. We know less of mega-evolution because of gaps in the fossil record, especially at interesting beginnings—and yet mega-evolution, fast or slow, must have taken a long time, he concedes.

Skipping

Geological "skipping" is a great difficulty to the evolutionist. Long ago Dana wrote of land snails of the Carboniferous which then jumped to the Cretaceous and persisted, of scorpions of the Upper Silurian which next appeared in the Carboniferous along with spiders, disappeared, then reappeared in the Tertiary. Smith in 1911 spoke of the shrimp, Anaspides, found in the Carboniferous but not since, until it now appears in the streams of isolated mountains in Tasmania. Either the geological record is atrociously flawed or we have a tremendous problem here for the mega-evolutionist.

More recently, Ladd (141) has emphasized the recent finds of "living fossils", coelacanths, nine having been found by the end of 1958, a hangover from the end of the Cretaceous. In 1938 the most primitive living crustacean was found in beach sands in New England and a new order, Mystacocarida, was created for it. Then in 1953 a still more primitive Crustacean was dredged out of the mud in Long Island Sound, whose closest relative, Lepidocaris, was Middle Devonian. In 1955 a Palaeozoic mollusc, Neopilina galatheae, was found alive in the trench off the west coast of South America—a form not unlike modern shallow-water limpets. Why no evolution in these forms? Why the long stasis in their ancestral progress?

De Nouy remarks that if the islands just north of New Zealand had not been explored and the lizard, Sphenodon punctatum, had accordingly not been found there, we would have concluded that the order Rhynchocephalia had disappeared in the Jurassic. Now, however, the problem is different. For if the bones of modern or domestic animals of our day and remains of this lizard are ever found together in the dim future, palaeontologists will be puzzled when they conclude that all were contemporaneous—as they were, too. Here is a vivid example of the errors possible in palaeontological sample and inference.

Many Unknown Affinities—From Phyla to Individual Organs

Nothing is known of the ancestry of many groups, for example the spiders first seen in the Pennsylvanian. As Raymond says, this is "somewhat exasperating", and any evolutionist would echo the thought. Flies wrapped in webs and partially devoured have been found associated with spiders in the Oligocene Baltic amber, but in no older deposit.

Raymond goes on: "It is believed that vertebrates were derived from some sort of invertebrate, but the problem of their origin still baffles zoologists and palaeontologists." "Only the faintest trail" can be found. No ancestor of amphioxus has yet been found, nor any connection traceable between the first fish and amphioxus. All that connects amphioxus to the invertebrates is its ciliated larva, entirely unknown among craniates. "However, this is only a vague connecting link." Because its segmentation, gill slits and notochord are also shared by larval Tunicates, a linkage with the latter is assumed, but this really "throws no light on the problem." Perhaps the chordates came from Protochordates like Balanoglossus or Harrimania—but this also is not too helpful. Raymond remarks: "Here is a place where palaeontology should come forward with definite evidence, but it has as yet failed to do so."

"The most obvious difficulty encountered in trying to derive a vertebrate from the segmented worm is the general reversal of all parts of the body that is necessary to make the change." In the worm the ganglionic chain lies under the alimentary canal, the blood flowing forward in a dorsal vessel and backward in a ventral one below the gut. "To transform the annelid into a vertebrate it is necessary to reverse the dorsal and ventral sides, abandon the old mouth, produce a new one on the opposite side, close the old terminal anus and form another further forward, change the solid to a tubular nervous system, and develop a notochord between the central nervous system and the alimentary canal. Taken all at one time, this seems difficult of accomplishment, but we are assured that such things are physiologically possible"!

The annelid theory of vertebrate origin has no fossil backing. Annelids began as early as the Mid-Cambrian, but no fossils connect them with the ostracoderms.

The arthropod theory of origin of the vertebrates requires the manufacture of a notochord, the reversal of dorsal and ventral sides and a closing of the old mouth with the formation of a new one. But a scorpion in Ceylon was found with what seems to be a notochord. And the mouth of the vertebrate opens late in the embryo and is an ectodermal invagination, hence may really be a new structure! However, the vague arthropod theory is generally rejected because all the links in the chain are specialized, and it is generally held that simple forms of a new type do not develop from specialized forms "below" them.

Bony centra for the vertebral bodies appeared in fish much later than in amphibians and reptiles. Raymond goes on: "Few seem to realize that the trend in the evolution of fish was not toward a 'higher animal', a terrestrial creature, but toward a better adaptation to their own environment." Perhaps the notochord has been stressed too much, for the palaeontologist looking at Silurian and early Devonian cephalaspids and anaspids finds that the tripartite brain and the position of the central nervous system of the ostracoderms show no connecting links but all "led to animals with notochords." This could demand that all three came of pre-Cambrian ancestry! Amphioxus has practically no head or brain at all, so the anaspids could hardly have evolved from an animal with a poor brain and a well developed notochord. "Difficult as it is, it is easier to connect the anaspids with true fish than to trace a relationship of Amphioxus to them."

Some fish can hold on to the roots of trees with their rays, for example the climbing perch of Ceylon. But "a comparison of the fin of any modern fish with the internal supports of the leg of a terrestrial animal will show that it is impossible to derive one from the other." Even the oldest four-legged creatures, the amphibians, have the typical tetrapod bone arrangement and so no links with any aquatic form appear. The lungfish could not be ancestral to the amphibian because of their specialized fan-shaped dental plates which never could have evolved into the sharp conical teeth of amphibians. They had early lost their own teeth and could never regain them.

The origin of lungs is a major difficulty, since sharks, for example, seem never to have had even a swim bladder, and the lungfish have been ruled out as ancestors of the tetrapods. There are too many rays in fins for the pectoral fins to be ancestral to tetrapod legs, and Barrell's suggestion that fins were worn to stumps as crawlers and thus eliminated these extra rays seems incredible, surely. Scorpions, insects, diplopods, gastropods and plants of aquatic origin all adopted air-breathing at the same time as fish!

But Crossopterygian fish have an arrangement of skull bones and pineal eye, tooth distribution, and a pectoral girdle attached to the head like that of amphibia. Could this point to a genealogical relationship? Some early amphibian skulls from Greenland show very low nares openings, as in the crossopterygial fish—but the openings have different boundary bones. Some early amphibians had teeth with flutings at the base indicating similar enamel infoldings. Yet the oldest frog is from the Triassic of Madagascar and is much like the modern. Adults and tadpoles have been found in the Miocene. Obviously, the evolutionist must say: 'the group originated much earlier." Yet the modern toad or frog is structurally degenerate, lacking the size, some of the skull bones, teeth, cervical vertebrae, ribs and the tail of his Carboniferous ancestors. Raymond adds: "Unfortunately some of the so-called degenerate characteristics are distinctly different from any possessed by the ancestor."

"Absolutely nothing is known of the geological history of the 'glass snakes', the caecilians."

Eosauravus, the oldest reptile (in 1937) was recognizable as such by its only significant (?) character, the phalangeal formula of the hind foot 2, 3, 4, 5, 4! Elsewhere Raymond says: "If Diplovertebron had a phalangeal formula of 2, 3, 4, 5, 3 instead of 2, 3, 3, 3, 4 it would doubtless now be heralded as the most important of all amphibians, the ancestor of the reptiles." By what narrow margins is glory missed! Three little useless bones in the hand!—and yet all those extra rays in the pectoral fins of the crossopterygians do not really matter! They are still ancestral to amphibia! Palaeontological awards are made with curious inconsistency!

"Much has been written about the importance in the evolution of the primates of the liberation of the fore-limbs—to become the servants of the head." Yet "bipedal dinosaurs walked on their hind legs and used their anterior legs as arms and hands over a period of several million years without any great cerebral improvement."

The ichthyosaur had as many as a hundred phalanges, ignoring the reptilian formula. As many as 8 or 9 digits were found in some of them—"No other reptile, no amphibian, no bird, nor any mammal, barring such freaks as 6-toed cats, has more than 5 digits." No terrestrial ancestors of such ichthyosaurs are known. The same is true of the plesiosaurs and mosasaurs.

The oldest known pterosaurs and birds had widely spaced teeth, "indicating that reduction had been going on for some time"! What an ancestry is here implied!

Raymond continues: "The wing of the bird is more highly modified than the limb of any animal, and its other peculiarities, such as pneumatic bones, the curious vertebrae, and the synsacrum, combine to produce a skeleton much more specialized than that of the average mammal." Any parental reptilian stock is unknown; birds "are the most specialized vertebrates and on anatomical grounds may be placed at the summit of the animal kingdom."

The only Jurassic birds are two incomplete skeletons and a feather (Archaeopteryx and Archaeornis). In them the quadrate bone is movable, as in the mosasaurs and snakes. They have the single occipital condyle of reptiles, but a distinctive bone seen in no other animal but birds, namely a bar across the face formed by the quadratojugal, jugal and maxillary bones. The uncinate processes on the ribs resemble those of stegocephalian amphibians' (If we knew only the skeleton of modern birds, and not how well their legs worked, we would call their legs degenerate). Great variations in toe arrangements exist. Ichthyornis of the Upper Cretaceous had primary and secondary feathers, like modern birds, and was "about as highly specialized for flight in Upper Cretaceous times as birds are at present." Few modern birds show as great reduction of wing as in Hesperornis of the same strata! Here is a specialized form evolving, then losing a wing in extremely ancient times! What a complex evolution in an archaic type! Diatryma, the oldest ground bird, had no more wing than Hesperornis.

No ancestor to Archaeopteryx or Archaeornis has been found. Feathers are not modified scales but fundamentally different, even arising from different layers of skin cells, and are as characteristic of birds as hair is of mammals. No one has proposed an adequate theory of the origin of flight, whether it began with cursorial birds or tree climbers, Feathers are not frayed scales (the theory of Baron Nopsca). Heilman has disproved the old statement that the hind legs of the embryos of certain modern birds show lines of bristles which are the vestiges of ancestral wing feathers.

Raymond points out that "The hind limbs of Archaeornis may have borne long quill feathers, but probably were not formed into a wing. Pterosaurs were not ancestral to birds, for their vast development of the 4th finger is not matched in any bird, however ancient. Birds have no vestige of such a digit. Nor did birds come from the heavy-boned ornithischians. Nor did they come from coelurosaurs, for these had no clavicles (collar-bones), and every bird, ancient or modern, needed one (although the pterosaurs did not). In Archaeornis it seems that the quadrate bone was fixed—indeed only the Squamata among reptiles seem to have free quadrates (and not the lizards, the simplest Squamata)."

Raymond goes on to talk of Insects, and mentions that the venation of wings studied by Comstock and Needham and widely used in insect taxonomy does not coincide with the findings of palaeontologists —"merely an example of the necessity of studying the ancient representatives of a group before making generalizations"! The oldest insects are from the Upper Carboniferous, but they are already full-fledged Pterygota, telling us nothing of any ancestral arthropods. One already had a sucking mouth! Already 13 orders of cockroaches and Palaeodictyoptera are seen in this stratum. In the Permian appear advanced neuroptera, lace-wings and alder flies. In the Lower Permian the true Homoptera appear, with sucking mouths and a wing venation reduced as much as in modern forms. Mayflies are seen. In the late Permian come beetles, thrips and true stone flies. No Carboniferous insects are known to have had a complete metamorphosis, but two orders in the Lower Permian did, so the process "must have originated earlier", says the evolutionist. Where and when? One Australian insect of the Mid-Triassic had a much larger sound-producing organ on its wing than has any living type!

In the Mesozoic five modern insect orders arose, the true bugs in the Trias, the caddis flies, true flies and Hymenoptera in the Jurassic. Since the oldest Hymenoptera include some parasitic forms, this group, according to evolutionists, must be much older than the Jurassic! Where and when were these ancestors? Lepidoptera (butterflies and moths) first appear in the Eocene, but are thought to have evolved earlier! Where and when? 6 of the 8 modern subfamilies of ants are in the amber, and even then there were worker castes, aphids and plant lice and also guest beetles in their nests. 66 per cent of the genera of amber ants still live, and 8 species are practically indistinguishable from the living. The origin of bees remains as mysterious as that of the ants. The mega-evolutionist should tell us why this is so. The creationist could.

The first mammals, the Multituberculata, had already lost their canines and had peculiar large molars—therefore they were already specialized and ancient, says the evolutionist. Yet they are from the Upper Triassic! Where are their predecessors? Opossums like modern types are seen in the late Cretaceous. Marsupials are more specialized than placentals because the milk dentition is so reduced that only one tooth on either side is shed! The marsupials show a sort of rudimentary placenta in one modern group!

Bats arose early in the Tertiary. They share with the baleen whales the honour of being the most specialized mammal—but are not quite at the top as they have not yet managed to lose their teeth! Isn't evolutionary thought an amusing thing?

The Edentates, even when they first appear in the Palaeocene, are very specialized in respect to tooth loss. Where are their ancestors?

No pedigree of the true cats is known .They appear first in the Lower Miocene.

The pigs appear in the Oligocene and have no known ancestry as yet! The hoofed mammals have been thought to evolve from the creodonts, but there are no definite connecting links.

Giraffes are not traced beyond the Pliocene. The relation of the antelope to other mammals is unsolved. The large Pleistocene Camelops had more loss of teeth and so was more specialized in this respect than the camel that has survived, curiously enough. The swift Miocene Stenomylus, the gazelle camel, was better adapted for speed than any other member of the camel group that ever lived—but he is extinct!

Neither the tree sloths nor the hairy anteaters can trace their ancestry.

Raymond points out: "Only 2 of the 10 Ordovician 'immortals' have well-supported claims to their titles. One is the geologically famous brachiopod, Lingula. Fossils have been found which show the mold of the fleshy pedicle, and others which retain imprints of all the numerous muscles of the modern form. The other is the worm-tube, Spirorbis—the size, form, direction, and rate of coiling are so nearly identical in Ordovician and recent specimens that there is no way of distinguishing between them.—Spirorbis is just as common on the late Palaeozoic plants of the coal swamps as it is on the brown seaweeds of the present day."

More Forms with Unknown Affinities

No intermediate forms connect the whales with their ancestral (?) Cretaceous placentals. They appear in the early Tertiary fully adapted. They must have had great preliminary changes, evolutionists admit; therefore these must have gone on at a high evolutionary rate.

The platyrrhine monkeys of South America appear suddenly in the Miocene of Patagonia, as do the Hystricoidea (porcupines, guinea pigs, chinchillas, and so on) whose origin is equally sudden and puzzling. The characins are a puzzle, too, for their origin is obscure and they are found only in Central and South America and Africa. There is no evidence that they ever lived elsewhere!

The Darwin finches of the Galapagos Isles have no known affinity.

Merson-Davies points out "the most striking forms—fishes, ichthyosours, pleiosaurs, pterodactyls, birds, mammals, bats, whales—the forms which represent the most striking departures or specializations of structures come in the most abruptly. The links are ever the fewest just where they are the most wanted; it is almost always just where evolution must be supposed to have travelled furthest that we have least evidence that it has travelled at all." Evolutionists need links badly. They are generally **essential** to the theory, indeed.

Allee* (142) notes that "at the beginning of the Cambrian—such profusion of types existed that it is generally concluded that more than half of the total evolution of invertebrates had taken place before the beginning of the Cambrian". And this despite the fact that there is small or no evidence for such a process, so overwhelmingly essential to the evolutionist! And in the same symposium Romer points that little or no fossil record is available to tell of the origin and early stages of the vertebrates, the evidence deriving from comparative anatomy and embryology. It is not surprising, therefore, that "at one time or another almost every important group of invertebrates has been suggested as the ancestral type from which the vertebrates have sprung."

Summary

No matter how long or how intensive the search, the palaeontologist still finds in the record of life disconcerting geological gaps in great number and of vast duration. No matter how he tries to argue his way out of this dilemma, he is more and more surely forced to believe in "bursts" of evolution, the only alternative to creation.

---

*Quoted by permission of the University of Chicago Press, Chicago, U.S.A.

Everyone must now decide which idea fits the evidence best—or if these concepts are different views of the same act.

The great transitions from fish to amphibian, from amphibian to reptile or reptile to bird, when discussed critically, indicate that extraordinary difficulties for the evolutionist at once arise.

The great number of forms, such as insects or rabbits, which seem to have no ancestors, should be stressed. The evolutionist must find their grandfathers. He still cannot. Why? Perhaps they had no ancestors?

CHAPTER XX

TROUBLE WITH FOSSILS

We peer through eye-holes on the masking years
And touch a gaping skull whose battered face
Glimpsed the first mammoth and the sabre-tooth,
Or handle an abraded, splintered bone
That sketched red bisons on a fire-lit wall
And in its turn was split by cannibals.

—Vere Jameson

PROPOSITION—The genealogical tree of the horse is but the story of change inside one family, something we may concede, however hard it is to believe when examined in detail. Taxonomy is always difficult, especially when attacked intensively, and is only in its infancy, unfortunately, in a theory which subsumes all living things.

Introduction

The long suit of the palaeontologist who supports evolution is the fossil pedigree, the family tree of the horse, camel, rhinoceros or certain shelled invertebrates. Here is the visual proof of evolution, surely. Let us now examine the best known of these pedigrees in detail.

The Horse

The pedigree of the horse is not by any means what it was when first arranged by Marsh and Cope about 70 years ago. Simpson draws up a family "tree" that is so different it would scarcely be recognized as applying to the same family Of course, this is just evolution inside a family, something to which the author assents. Fundamentally he has no quarrel with the general thesis, only with some of its details and, most of all, with the extrapolations therefrom. Evolution inside a family is not evolution of phyla or orders or classes, but a much simpler thing, and perhaps is occasionally demonstrable—although mega-evolution is not.

The earliest member of the family is said to be the American Hyracotherium. Schindewolf has pointed to its sudden appearance as proof of the sudden development of this family. From this animal to Equus (the contemporary horse) there may have been 15 million generations, or at least 1500 billion individuals. Now let us look at teeth as an index of evolutionary change. If each tooth character were controlled by one gene mutation per 10^7 individuals, probably a low rate for small mutations, then in that period of time at least 150,000 mutations could have occurred at that site (error in Simpson's figures?) If one-fifth were favourable, there would have been at least

30,000 favourable mutations. If only a thousandth of those represented new steps there were 30 such. Divided into 30 steps changes in any character become small. In ectoloph (mean molar size) length, for example, the maximum change was from about 8 to about 40 mm. and therefore each of 30 steps would be no greater than 1 mm. In the smallest species the intragroup range for this character was about 3mm. From such conjectural calculus is can be estimated that mutations may just account for the development of categories lower than the family.

We usually think of horse evolution as progressing since its beginnings toward increase in size. But smaller forms arose in the pedigree twice, when the late Miohippus produced Archaeohippus, and when the small Nannippus followed Merychippus.

We speak of the evolution of hypsodont (grazing) from brachyodont (browsing) teeth, carelessly forgetting that this change must have meant correlated change in the whole digestive tract. On this latter we have no information at all, of course. That prairie grass first became plentiful in the Miocene and so conditioned this change in horses is made questionable by the fact that grazing mammals of other groups had appeared much earlier elsewhere, for example in the Eocene and Oligocene.

Simpson remarks: Another "sort of survival of the more specialized is largely nominal transformation of an ancestral group into its more advanced descendants, as of Hyracotherium into Epihippus and so on. This is not a sequence involving lower and higher zones but evolution of and in a single, changing zone."

The development of the horse is not by "orthogenesis", (in a straight line) says Simpson. And he quotes Jepsen: "There is a tendency to put the cart before the horse." It is not a single line of gradual transformation, as college texts so often indicate. Its botanical analogue is not a tree but a bush. Many so-called genera in this bush are not genera at all, but structural changes. For example, there were many different kinds of horses in the Eocene, not convenient to designate as genera. Most Miocene horses had a peculiar pre-orbital pit that Equus lacks. Modern Equus has simpler tooth patterns than some Pleistocene species. The lower to upper limb ration has fluctuated widely, and indeed is less in Equus than in the early Pliohippus. A corresponding variation and then decrease is seen in the forelimb.

There was no trend to gradual reduction of the side toes. Such an idea, says Simpson, "is flatly fictitious." Many types of feet developed and varied widely. "Eocene horses all had digitograde, padded, doglike feet, with 4 functional toes in front and 3 behind. In a rapid transition (not actually represented by fossils) early Oligocene horses lost one functional front toe and concentrated the weight a little more on the middle hoof as a step-off point, but retained a padded, unspringing foot. This type persisted without essential change in all browsing horses. The Parahippus-Merychippus lineages in a rapid but general transition (which is represented by fossils) lost the pad as a functional element and became truly unguligrade, developed a complex springing mechanism in the middle toe, which normally carried all the weight, and reduced the side toes which were, however, retained and functional as buffers and stops. This type of foot was retained, again without essential change or evident trends, in all lineages derived from Parahippus through Merychippus except Pliohippus. In early Pliohippus another rapid transition (also known from fossils) involved loss of the side-toes, strengthening and simplification of the springing mechanism, and development of check ligaments. This type persisted . . ."

Simpson goes on: "The Equidae had no trends that continued throughout the history of the family in any line, affected all lines at any one time, occurred in all lines at some time in their history, or were even approximately constant in direction and rate in any line for periods longer than on the order of 15 to 20 million years at most (usually much less)."

Thus "ancestral" forms lived beside their descendants (?) for millions of years, neither form displaying any obvious advantage over the other. Was there any? Thus Clark tells us that Parahippus survived into the Upper Miocene, although this genus had already given rise to the next equid by the Middle Miocene! Bather suggested that if all written records were lost, perhaps we could reconstruct English history from coins. However, this would be apt to make James, the First, the son of Elizabeth. Perhaps palaeontologists often do such things.

Originally Kowalevsky devised a European pedigree for the horse. Now Marsh's and Cope's alternative American ancestral tree is preferred. The Hyracotherium common to both Europe and America gave rise, apparently, to different lines, which by migrations back and forth have altered still further, but the real ancestry of modern equus was American, evolutionists say nowadays.

Watson* (143) says: "Freed from the palaeotheres, the Equidae begin in Europe and North America in the form Hyracotherium, small with three and four-toed feet, with cheek teeth extremely brachyodont and of simple sex-tubercle pattern. It passes on through Orohippus, Epihippus, Mesohippus, Miohippus, Pliohippus, Plesippus to Equus, and from Merychippus direct to Hipparion. With the partial exception of the very few known specimens of Epihippus, this series shows a steady increase in size through the whole history, although at various times dwarf members occur. (Archaeohippus is a dwarf Parahippus, Nannippus is a dwarf Hipparion, the Shetland pony is a dwarf Equus and the dwarfs in a very curious way retain the characters of the

---

*Quoted by permission of the Princeton University Press, Princeton, U.S.A.

normal sized horses from which they were derived). Throughout the series of horses, from its beginning to its termination in Equus and Hipparion, we find a tendency to increase the area of the grinding dentition of the two jaws by an increase in size and by further elaboration of the pre-molars, and we find concurrently an increase in the depth of the teeth to the extreme presented by the African Pleistocene Hipparion. These changes proceed steadily in the normal horses but in the side branch, Anchitherium, Hypohippus, and so on, in which there is a very marked increase in size, although the premolars increase in size relatively to the molars, and in complexity, their relative height does not increase. The same series of animals shows an increase in the transverse sectional area, and ultimately in the length of the third metapodial, in comparison with its neighbours on either side. The process in Equus is carried to the stage at which the lateral metapodials are only about two-thirds the length of the median bone with which they lie in contact . . . It is evident and has long been realized that the effect of these changes is to secure an improvement in mechanical efficiency. The horses are now galloping animals; when moving at the highest speed of which they are capable—somewhat of the order of 40 miles per hour—they gallop, all the feet at a certain stage of the stride being off the ground at the same time, the whole weight of the animal very little later being received on one hind foot, the leg flexing to take up the shock. The magnitude of the impulsive forces acting, in the case of a large horse, is very great indeed and it is clear that only extremely good design in an engineering sense enables the whole structure of the leg to take up the initial shock and to control the subsequent movement of the horse . . ."

All this ignores the efficiency of such runners (although lighter creatures) as the antelope (on 2 toes), the cheetah and the dog and wolf (5 toes before and 4 behind). It seems very doubtful that a one-toed horse could outstrip such a 2-toed or 5-toed animal in a race. And one recalls the extraordinary frequency of "splinting" in the young horses of all racing stables. Is the one-toed foot really an advantage in running? However, Watson says that he has found healed fractures in the lateral toes of Mesohippus, whose lateral toes made contact with the ground.

Davis calls attention to the fact that teeth develop as part of the whole nutritive apparatus, and cannot be arbitrarily isolated. The palaeontologist cannot reconstruct all from a part, because there are such examples as the extinct chalicotheres which combined ungulate dentition with clawed feet, a hitherto unknown combination.

Shortly after the Origin of Species appeared Rutimyer found that the milk pre-molars of Equus resembled the permanent pre-molars of Hipparion and called this a "recapitulation". Unfortunately for such a conclusion it now has been concluded that Hipparion was not ancestral to Equus! The resemblance was purely "fortuitous", say de Beer and Swinton, for in most horses the milk pre-molars of the earlier types resemble the permanent teeth of the descendants. This may merely mean, of course, that adult types tend to simplify their embryonic forms, which is often true, or that the embryonic form is a more generalized type from which many mature types, even simpler types, can diverge.

Dewar points out that the horse embryo never shows any trace of lateral toes, and, indeed, that the first limb remnant is longer than broad, not broader than long as in five-toed animals. There are three metapodial bones in the embryo, but no toe rays appear on their ends. Does the embryo forget that the evolutionist is watching it?

Lucas (144) reminds us that the horses drawn on cave walls by primitive man were low, heavy, large-headed, Shetland pony types. Julius Caesar had a true polydactyl horse, and others have been shown in our day in sideshows. This fact, of course, no more means that ancestral horses were polydactyl than that six-fingered men remind us of an ancestral type.

Gadow reminds us that "Creatures intermediate between these 3-toed animals (like Hipparion) and the genus Equus . . . are unknown."

Perhaps the series should really begin with Orohippus rather than Hyacotherium—for the latter is such a general type it could be ancestral to the rhinoceros just as easily, it is said.

If the contemporary widely variant kangaroos were only to be found as fossils they undoubtedly could be arranged to show that a creature with 4 legs of equal length developed into one having the unequally long hind legs of the great grey kangaroo. Perhaps, says Graebner, as much could be done with antelopes, which differ in size (by great amounts), in colour and marking, in size, shape and angle of the horns, in length of tail, shape of teeth, of eyes, of nostrils, notably in hooves. Some hooves are large, some small, some have an extra set of laterals, some have very long limbs, some have peculiar fore legs. The anteater of South America is another form which has very divergent species. One can see how tricky pedigrees can be from such pseudo-examples as are here cited.

Marsh's collection of horse fossils at Yale convinced T. H. Huxley of the irrefutable truth of evolution. Darwin planned to visit it but his health did not permit it. As Lull* says, he died "without having seen such a culminating proof of the theory of evolution."

General Remarks on Taxonomic Difficulties

Colman (145)** remarks that: "There are many instances where the limits of genera, families and even orders seem almost matters of

---

*Quoted by permission of the MacMillan Co., New York, U.S.A.
**Quoted by permission of the Clarendon Press, Oxford, England

individual opinion." He goes on: "The analogy with the 'family trees' used to express human pedigrees is misleading since the latter are based in the arbitrary fiction of unilateral—mostly patrilineal— descent." And further:: "It is unlikely that we shall ever arrive at any degree of certainty regarding the origin of the great phyla, partly because palaeontology fails us and partly because their origin takes us back to organisms so widely different from any now living that speculation as to their structure and mode of life becomes unprofitable. On the other hand, the species within a genera, and often the genera within a family, are distinguished by characters so few in number and so trivial in morphologic significance that any attempt to assign phylogenetic meaning to them is mere guess-work. We can be fairly confident about the origin of mammals, but not about the beginnings of vertebrates or the interrelations of the species of mice. It is of great interest to note that our botanical colleagues seem, on the whole, to be less confident than the zoologists in ascribing a phylogenetic meaning to their classification—perhaps this being due to more hybridization."

Smart (146) adds a novel approach to the problem. He points out the burden of systematic studies on any museum or cabinet naturalist, particularly in entomology. He mentions the 30 years of intensive study of the mosquito from Theobald to Edwards which multiplied the known species from 450 to 1400, and points out how few insects have been studied as thoroughly. He records that it took 3½ years to produce a paper on the Palearctic races of one butterfly, **Papilio machaon.** The Nearctic forms were not dealt with at that time! If we know so little about common insect forms, what generalizations dare we make about other plants and animals?

Coulter* (147) tells us that the construction of a family tree is troublesome because of the missing links. "Botanists construct as best they can an imaginary picture of the missing links, so as to complete the sequence of steps in the evolution of the plant kingdom. Obviously such a practice is mainly guesswork, but, like many such hypotheses, has been very useful in organizing subject matter and stimulating research." What an admission on genealogical "trees"! He goes on: "the record of the rocks reveals practically nothing of the earlier chapters in the evolution of the plant kingdom. For these, therefore, we must rely upon the types of plants still in existence, plus a liberal measure of scientific imagination."

Tucker (148)** remarks in respect to birds: "It is only exceptionally that the fossil record of any group is complete enough to allow a direct reconstruction of the critical stages of its evolution in structural terms . ." The theory of Pycraft that feathers develop from frayed scales he criticizes on the ground that no explanation can be offered of "the transformation of a scale into so strikingly different

*Quoted by permission of the University of Chicago Press,Chicago, U.S.A.
**Quoted by permission of the Clarendon Press, Oxford, England

a structure as a feather." Moreover "frayed-out scales would have been useless as supports without the complex interlocking mechanism which distinguishes the feather and which hardly could have been developed all at once." Moreover, adaptation is scarcely the cause of the backwardly developed barbs on the overturned edges of the proximal barbules, which prevent the hamuli from slipping, and which are only effective against pressure from beneath the feather. These barbs appear not only on flight feathers but body feathers, where the pressure can be only from above! A feather is useless without interlocking mechanisms, and can hardly have arisen by gradual adaptation. All ancient birds had wing quills well developed and therefore must have been arboreal.

It has been pointed out by Simpson that speciation is the only mode of evolution that is open to experimental study, although it is not the most important to the evolutionist. Phyletic evolution, which is the crucial point, is a peculiarly palaeontological problem. Here is the great dilemma of the evolutionist and goes back to the major distinction to be made between micro- and mega-evolution. I believe they are two completely unlike processes, the one demonstrable and the other purely fictitious.

A generation ago morphologists thought in terms of the transformation of one adult structure into another adult structure in another organism. They entirely ignored the concomitant alteration of physiological and biochemical processes such change would demand. D. D. Davis says: "The assumptions demanded by such an interpretation often strained credulity beyond the breaking point." It still does. Now we think that adjacent teeth alter together by moeosis, just as Washburn showed that the epiphyses of a region like the shoulder react or develop in harmony, not as isolated units.

Raymond goes on: "Most chroniclers of the history of life begin or end with a 'family tree', with roots in the protozoans, a trunk of invertebrates, and a series of modern animals ornamenting the branches. I have only an elementary knowledge of botany, but I doubt if there ever was such a plant."

Lunn (149)* once said: "Faith is the substance of fossils hoped for, the evidence of links unseen."

Summary

The genealogy of the horse is critically examined. It suggests that there have been many variant forms inside this family, early (?) types existing shoulder to shoulder with their improved (?) descendants (?) for millions of years. Was the emergence of one-toed forms an

---

*Quoted by permission of Eyre and Sportisewoode (Publishers) Ltd., London, England.

advantage? The transitions in toe structure are scarcely authenticated by fossils, it must be said.

The whole idea of a phyletic tree in any larger grouping than

the zoological family at once raises the most formidable difficulties. The taxonomist has only begun his work, in any case, and may not be ready to propose a theory of the relationship of living things for at least another century. Darwin came too soon.

CHAPTER XXI

ANCIENT MAN

Here was the mirror of God's laughless mirth!
Here was the sorrow foundering the skies!
Here their intemperate hope and long surprise!

—Vere Jameson*

PROPOSITION—There is now and has long been a great variety of human and anthropoid forms on the earth. Brutal types of man are very ancient, but contemporary types were coeval with them. There is thus no evidence here for the evolution of modern civilized man. He appeared suddenly in the Near East about 9000 years ago.

Introduction

This is a very difficult topic to discuss at the moment, since radiocarbon and fluorine datings are altering the age of so many remains. Moreover, there is a plethora of skeletal material already discovered but not yet described, and more is being recovered every year. Only tentative conclusions are possible, and the results of tomorrow's digging may upset those. On all counts this chapter is much harder to write than it would have been 30 or even 20 years ago, but at least it can now discuss the antiquity of modern types of man.

Quantity of Remains

In 1927 Osborn could say that between 1823 and 1925 the remains of fully 116 persons of the Palaeolithic or Old Stone Age had been found in Europe. Andrews says that (by 1945) the remains of 40 individuals of the Pekin group had been unearthed, including fragment of 14 skulls, 4 of these being fairly complete. Pieces of 7 Pekin thigh bones have been found. There were perhaps 80 Pekin individuals, of very diverse type. The second skull was larger than the first one described, for example, and had a more convex forehead. Brain capacity varied between 900 and 1200 cc. In 1955 Clark could record 8 Pithecanthropus fragments, besides a large number of teeth not yet described. Along the Solo River in Java Oppenoorth found parts of 11 human skulls and 2 lower leg bones near Ngandong. At Mount Carmel skeletons of 18 individuals were found, 5 practically undisturbed. When the first Cro-Magnon men were found in 1852 at Aurignac there were 17 skeletons, all later re-buried and now lost to us. When he was rediscovered in 1868 at Les Eyzies parts of 5 skeletons were found. By 1902 fully 15 individuals had been recovered

---

*Quoted by permission of the Ryerson Press, Toronto, Canada

at Grimaldi. Indeed more than 100 individuals of this race have now been recovered. In 1894 Mosha found a tomb in Moravia containing 20 burials. At Vestonice Absolon found 20 more skeletons of the Predmost culture.

In 1937 von Koenigswald found fragments of the skull of 2 more individuals of Pithecanthropus erectus in Sangiran, the latter of the two having a brain volume of about 775 cc. and a definite Mid-Pleistocene dating.

Much of von-Koenigswald's extensive skeletal material from Java had not been described by 1948. Great quantities of South and East African material are not yet published.

It may be noted here that all the Sinanthropus speciments (Pekin man) were lost during the second World War,—although casts of the earlier fossils have been preserved.

A Modern Perspective on Fossil Man

No attempt will be made here to review in detail the various fossil finds of the last century, because any book, such as Hooton's or Clark's (150) or Andrews' (151) or Wendt's (152), will provide more data than there is room for here.

Suffice it to indicate very briefly here what the major items are, and their provenance:

Olduvai (Zinjanthropus)	- Lower Pleistocene
Pithecanthropus of Java	- Middle and Lower Pleistocene
Pithecanthropus of Pekin (Sinanthropus)	- Middle and Lower Pleistocene (late Mindel)
Heidelberg	- Interval between 1st and 2nd phases of second or Mindel glaciation.
Swanscombe Steinheim } Homo sapiens	- 2nd interglacial or Mindel-Riss
Fontéchevade Ehringsdorf Quinzano } Homo sapiens	- Riss-Wurm interglacial
Krapina	- last interglacial
Saccopastore	- last interglacial
Mount Carmel	- 3rd interglacial
Florisbad Boskop Springbok } Homo sapiens	- Mid-Pleistocene

Solo Man of Java	- Upper Pleistocene
Neanderthal	- last interglacial or glacial (4th)
Rhodesian Man	- Upper Pleistocene?? or "undatable'
Cro-Magnon (Homo sapiens)	- last glacial
Upper Choukoutien	- late Pleistocene
Shanidar one	- 45,000 years ago (radiocarbon)

Then comes a long list of skeletal remains which various authorities have classified among old types, but dubious geological backgrounds or the newer fluorine datings render such views less tenable. Sometimes, as in the Punin or Cohuna skulls, all that is wrong is that the remains are too modern in type to fit the conception evolutionists have of the form of early man. Some may later br "proven" to be very old.

These may be listed here for convenience thus:

Eyasi man of Tanganyika	- discredited by insufficient fragments
1st Oldoway (Olduvai) man of East Africa	- discredited by fluorine - perhaps Upper Pleistocene (Aurignacian C)
Wadjak man of Java	- discredited by vague geology
Keilor man of Australia	- discredited by radiocarbon
Talgai man of Australia	- discredited by vague geology
Cohuna man of Australia	- discredited by vague geology
Aitape man of New Guinea	- discredited by ?
Galley Hill man of England	- discredited by fluorine
London man of England	- discredited by vague geology
Bury St. Edmunds man of England	- discredited by vague geology
Foxhall man of England	- lost
Kanam man of East Africa	- discredited (?) by geology and fluorine
Elmenteita of East Africa	- discredited by geology and fluorine
Minnesota man of Central U.S.A.	- discredited by recent form
Punin man of Ecuador	- discredited by recent form
Lagoa Santa and Confins man of Brazil	- discredited by recent form
Calaveras man of U.S.A.	- discredited by recent form

Analysis of the Rejecta

Most of the skeletal remains of the last table have had good sponsors, and there were good reasons for their consideration as very ancient types. For convenience these are listed here.

Site	Sponsor	Evidence for	Reasons suspect	Reasons rejected
Eyasi	Weinert	restoration	modern teeth, geology	fluorine
1st Oldoway (Olduvai)	Leakey	geology and Chellean implements	burial, filed lower incisors, good chin, modern teeth	fluorine
Wadjak	Dubois	brow ridges, low foreheads, geology, largest palate, jaw like Heidelberg	geology, teeth, chin, nose	geology
Keilor	Keith	"irrefutable Pleistocene age"	large skull, reduced 3rd molars, modern teeth, open metopic suture	radiocarbon
Talgai	Mahoney	Appearance, very prognathous, large palate, large canines	unknown geology, modern type	vague geology
Cohuna	Keith	very prognathous, heavy brow ridges, largest canines, palate large as male apes, thick skull	vague geology	vague geology
Aitape	Australian Geological Survey	geology	modern type	vague geology
Galley Hill	Keith and Hooton	very fossilized, thick skull, heavy brow ridges	modern type	fluorine
London	Keith	geology, characters of occipital region and bone	vague geology	vague geology fluorine
Bury St. Edmunds	Keith	geology, vault was broad and flat	vague geology	vague geology fluorine

Site	Sponsor	Evidence for	Reasons suspect	Reasons rejected
Foxhall	?	geology	jaw only	modern type **vague geology** jaw has long been lost
Kanam and Kanjera	Leakey	geology	vague geology,(?) modern type	vague geology modern type
Elmenteita	Leakey	geology	vague geology modern type	vague geology modern type
Minnesota	Jenks and Hooton	geology, prognathism, largest molars with crowns wrinkled and 3rd molar is larger than 2nd, upper incisors shovelled.	modern type	modern type
Punin	?	geology, large teeth, low vault, retreating forehead.	geology	geology
Lagoa Santa and Confins	Lund. Acad. Sci. Minas Geraes	geology, brow ridges, keeled vaults	geology modern type	geology modern type
Calaveras		geology, brow ridges	modern type (Hrdlcka)	modern type (Hrdlcka)
Other American Finds	(see Wormington) (156)	geology, fluorine dating, and so on	modern types	modern types

It will be seen from the above that many a skeleton has been discarded because it did not fit evolutionary schemes that were vigorously held by such debaters as Hrdlcka. Yet many of these forms had fairly good geological evidence behind them. Some of those with the best geological and anatomical evidence have been discredited by fluorine studies. Facts like these should give one pause in any conclusions as to the antiquity or recency of various physical types of man.

Moreover, as Campbell (153) has pointed out, the excessive multiplication of genera and species in any study of fossil hominids bedevils the whole field of study. Some 60 per cent of the specific names proposed for them are invalid by the international rules of zoological nomenclature.

General Analysis of the Accepted Remains

Perhaps the single outstanding item is the group of Homo sapiens skulls found at Swanscombe, Fontéchevade, Ehringsdorf, Steinheim and Quinzano. On the basis of such evidence modern man is undoubtedly old. The age of the Swanscombe finds has been corroborated by the fluorine method, too. In other words, men like us were anciently nearly contemporary with brutal forms like Pekin man, Java man and Olduvai man half a world away. Man seen in horizontal section at any one time in the ancient world must have presented very diverse forms indeed—as he does now, for that matter.

Another point that is noteworthy is the variability of various skeletons in each ancient group. For example, the four Pekin skulls studied by Weidenreich differed considerably in size—in fact could be divided into two groups thus, perhaps male and female. Weinert said that some Pekin men were like Pithecanthropus, some like Neanderthals, and some like moderns. The limb bones were those of modern man, as were two belonging to Pithecanthropus erectus also. Sinanthropus teeth showed no increase in size from the 1st to the 3rd molar and no simian gap.

Krogman* says: "The unique importance of the Sinanthropus material lies in its tremendous range of variation." Hooton observed: "If these specimens had been recorded in half a dozen widely separated parts of the earth and had been described by as many anatomists, the latter would probably have created as many new species or even genera of man."

The infantile P. erectus skull called Homo Modjokertensis had a steep forehead and no brow ridges. P. erectus 1 had 150 cc. more brain capacity than P. erectus 2. P. erectus 4 has the simian diastema or gap (the first time it was found in these skulls), but it has a larger

---

*Quoted by permission of Ciba Pharmaceuticals, Summit, N.J., U.S.A.

mastoid process and the foramen magnum well forward, adapted to the upright posture of man.

Mount Carmel man was extremely variable, it seems. Two types of men were found in adjacent caves there, Skuhl and Tabun, the latter being the older, probably, (but the stone tools were alike). Classed by Hooton as Neanderthals of different breeds, all had modern legs. The almost complete Tabun woman had Neanderthal features, but the most ape-like pelvis yet recorded; she had a much more modern foot than had the classic Neanderthal type. Her hand was Neanderthal. Some of those Mount Carmelites had chins and some had none. All had big brow-ridges. The skulls varied greatly, and the cranial capacity varied. The Tabun 2 mandible is larger than the Heidelberg mandible in some measurements, but had a chin and some features even more modern than other Tabun jaws. McCown and Keith remark that without exaggeration one could say that if these skeletons had been found in different sites at different times and if each had been described by a different anthropologist, we probably would have had an equal number of races of fossil man erected.

One need not emphasize the wide variation among Neanderthal finds. The best way in which to point this up is to remind ourselves that the largest and smallest Neanderthal skulls were found on the large island of Gibralter.

Two skeletons in one grave at Obercassel (Magdalenian) would have been assigned to separate races if found apart, says Weidenreich. Chancelade man has been called an Eskimo and Grimaldi man a negro.

Finally, the Upper Cave at Choukoutien has yielded the most bizarre family of all. The old man here had one wife resembling an Ainu or Melanesian, and one an Eskimo. This suggests that our racial types are older than the Upper Palaeolithic, says Hooton.

Size of Brain

As skulls or their fragments are often the only or at least the best recognized skeletal material found where fossil man is uncovered, and certainly provide the greatest variety of differentiable features either now or in ancient times, much has been made of skull size insofar as it may reflect brain size and the presumed development of the brain.

Here one is at once impressed by the large cranial capacity of many ancient forms of man whose skulls, however, may be of different shape than those of modern man. I have listed some of these here:

Largest gorilla	- 650 c.c.
Primitive Australians	- low as 900 c.c.
1st Olduvai man	- not estimated yet

Pithecanthropus 1	- 900 to 914 c.c.
Pithecanthropus 2	- 750 c.c.
Sinanthropus	- 850 - 1300 c.c.
Rhodesian man	- 1300 c.c.
Ehringsdorf	- 1480 c.c.
Solo man	- 1035 - 1255 c.c.
Swanscombe	- 1325 - 1470 c.c.
Boskop	- 1630 c.c.
Fontéchevade	- 1550 c.c.
Neanderthal	
Gibraltar woman	- 1300 c.c.
Neanderthal type	- 1480 c.c.
La Chappelle	- 1625 c.c.
Mount Carmel - man	- 1518 - 1587 c.c.
woman	- 1271 - 1350 c.c.
Upper Choukoutien	- 1500 c.c.
Cro-Magnon	- 1472 - 1660 c.c.
Modern man	- 910 - 2100 c.c.

- Wedda   910 c.c.
- Australian 1250-c.c.
- Eskimo   1480 c.c.
- European 1320 c.c.

Enough is recorded here to indicate that primitive man had skulls of considerable capacity, often exceeding that of modern European types. If volume alone were the criterion modern man would rank low in the list. Weidenreich (154) remarks that one can safely say that any expansion of the human brain case beyond the volume attained in the Neanderthal era cannot be shown. And Clark* adds: "—the information to be obtained from endocranial casts regarding brain functions is strictly limited . . . but they have mostly been based on a serious misconception of functional localization in the cerebral cortex and also on the false assumption that certain of the structural areas of the cortex (as defined microscopically) have rather constant relationships to sulci and convolutions. In the past, many inferences have been made regarding the acquisition of articulate speech, the degree of manual skill, the ability to learn from experience, and other mental faculties in fossil hominids; these must now be discontinued. This applies equally to the assumption that right- or left-handedness can be inferred from a consideration of the assymmetry of the cerebral hemispheres. There is no doubt, also, that some previous authorities

---

*Quoted by permission of the University of Chicago Press, Chicago, U.S.A.

213

have seriously exaggerated the extent to which the fissural pattern of the brain can be delineated from endocranial casts. In lower mammals the convolutions of the brain are often outlined with great precision on such casts; but, unfortunately, in hominids and the large anthropoid apes the sulci usually do not impress themselves clearly on the endocranial aspect of the skull except near the frontal and occipital poles of the brain and in the lower temporal region . . . The results of these studies are expressed entirely in morphological terms . . . and rightly so, for even the study of the gross anatomy of the normal human brain itself has so far not demonstrated any feature by which the intellectual abilities of the individual during life can be deduced."

Teeth

Often teeth are the only remains found. Indeed, the genus Sinanthropus was "erected" on one tooth by the Canadian, Davidson Black. What of teeth?

Hooton says: "Early human types may have some teeth that are indistinguishable from those of apes and vice versa. Dentitions that would have been assigned confidently to early apelike forms of man have been discovered implanted in crania of veritable apes." . . . On the basis of teeth alone, it might have been claimed that Australopithecus was human. However, we must admit that teeth do not make the man . . ."

The Heidelberg jaw had ordinary sized human teeth set in that huge mandible. Von Koenigswald's giant man, Meganthropus, has teeth "definitely human in conformation", however large.

The litle Taungs ape child possessed an absolutely human set of milk teeth, with the exception of a single permanent molar.

There may be a negative correlation between total stature and size of the mandible, says Clark, who finds the evidence for the large size of Meganthropus dubious. The orangutang has larger teeth than man. But Leakey, who has recently found a giant child's tooth of Chellean date among the remains of giant extinct animals believes that Olduvai men were giants too.

Other Skeletal Features

The Predmost skull had great development of the supraorbital ridge, but this was divided into supracilliary and supraorbital elements. The young Neanderthal skulls from Gibraltar, La Quina, Mount Carmel and Uzbekistan, the young Pithecanthropus skull from Modjokerto and the young Australopithecus skull lacked brow-ridges. The Ehringsdorf skull, with a thinner table than any Neanderthal, had the heaviest brow-ridges. In the late Mousterian (Neanderthal) man there was a continuous, uninterrupted supraorbital torus. All Mount Carmel skulls had heavy brow-ridges. The Steinheim skull had massive brow-ridges but the occiput of modern man. On the other hand, the contemporary type of Fontéchevade man had no brow ridges. No ape but a gorilla could match the great supraorbital bar of the Rhodesian man; its forehead is lower and narrower than any Neanderthal type and is little more vaulted than Pithecanthropus. But the eye orbits are large, the nasal root is depressed, the speech area is well developed, the legs are modern, the palate is enormous, the teeth are modern, with a reduced 3rd molar, and **dental caries**. The most recent Olduvai skull has tremendous malar arches, large orbital fossae and great interorbital width.

The 12th century Gardar man left a skull (and jaw particularly) which resembles that of Palaeolithic man, Keith records. Indeed, the jaw is larger than that of Heidelberg. Had it been found alone it would have forced a revision of our ideas as to the site and duration of the evolution of man.

Some Sinanthropus jaws are more primitive thant the jaw of Heidelberg and some resemble those of modern Mongols, says Wendt.

The walls of the Swanscombe and Fontéchevade skulls were remarkably thick.

Cave (155) told the International Congress of Zoology in 1958 that Neanderthal man did not stoop. Boule, who originally reconstructed his skeleton, did not allow for the fact that he was dealing with an old man with arthritis. The man of Neanderthal probably really walked as erect as modern man, it is now believed.

Fluorine studies of the Pithecanthropus femurs confirm their antiquity, but they are "indistinguishable from that of Homo sapiens," says Clark. The Sinanthropus femora are also modern.

The Neanderthal foot had a separated great toe and a small heel, but Hooton says: "Such a foot could probably be fitted in a modern shoe shop."

Hooton concludes: "You can, with equal facility, model on a Neanderthaloid skull the features of a chimpanzee or the lineaments of a philosopher. These alleged restorations of ancient types of man have very little, if any ,scientific value and are likely only to mislead the public." Yet they are kept in the Hall of Man in museums and textbooks. Is this not of dubious integrity?

American Finds

Hooton remarked in this connection that "none of these 'fossil' Americans showed craniological or metric features that could not be duplicated in the skeletons of recent Indians, and in no single case were the geological, palaeontological and stratigraphic associations such as establish indubitably the Pleistocene age of the finds." . . . "It may be presumed that some of these finds were, in fact, geologically ancient . . . To my satisfaction, at any rate, the reality of late Pleistocene man in North America is attested by the find of Minnesota man." In this case the geological evidence was excellent. It was not an interment. The endocranial silt was sterile on pollen culture. The molars are much larger than those of Heidelberg, Ehringsdorf, Spy, Krapina, and the Aurignacian man of Combe Capelle. The 3rd molars are larger than the seconds and the molar enamels are wrinkled as in orangs and only rarely in man. The upper middle incisors are shovel-shaped. Wormington (156) agrees that it was probably an ancient skeleton.

Man in America may or may not be ancient, but at least there is evidence from his language that he has long been here. For example N. C. Nelson is quoted by Macgowan (157)* as saying that the American Indian developed about 160 linguistic stocks, with 1200 or more dialect subdivisions. North and South America seem to possess more native language families than all the rest of the world. None of these languages but Eskimo seem to have an identification with Old World languages. By 1492 the Indian was adapted to 8 different climates, from Arctic to tropic, from arid to humid, from sea-level to 14,000 foot heights in Peru.—"He developed agriculture, and invented or perfected the arts and crafts of pottery, weaving, dyeing, metallurgy, sculpture, poetry, painting, architecture, city planning. In his agriculture he utilized irrigation, discovered fertilizers, and developed twenty exclusively American plants which now supply more than half of the world's provender. He was the first to write numbers through the use of zero and numerical position. He practised trepanning—the removal of a piece of skull to relieve pressure on the brain—and he discovered how to use certain medicines and narcotics. In his textiles he employed all the weaves known to us today. He contrived efficient methods of government. He proliferated into 368 major tribal groups and developed fifteen culture centres of distinct individuality. In the United States he left 100,000 mounds as the product of one of his cultures; in Middle America, 4,000 ceremonial cities of stone . . . Of Indian culture traits Clark Wissler remarks that 'the range in variety and individuality seems even greater in aboriginal America than in the primitive Old World' " . . .

Critics like Hrdlcka once upon a recent time so furiously attacked all evidence of prehistoric man in America that, as Macgowan says: "no scientist desirous of a successful career dared intimate that he had discovered indications of a respectable antiquity for the Indian"—"As Hooton puts it, the glacial antiquity of a New World skeleton cannot be disproved by "the modernity of its anatomical characters alone. Homo sapiens was full-fledged in the Old World before the end of the Glacial period. Late Glacial entrants into the Americas need not prove their age by an array of archaic and simian physical features.

*Quoted by permission of the MacMillan Co., New York.

The acid test of their antiquity must be geological". Roberts points out that opponents of early man in America always demand a more primitive physical type as evidence for the same antiquity in the New World as was credited to forms living in the Old at a comparable time.—Even Hrdlcka (158) had weakened so far, by 1937, as to concede that there were recent American skulls that were practically replicas of the Magdalenian and even of some of the upper Aurignacian skulls of the Old World; indeed, occasional skulls remind one even of the Neanderthals in certain characters. Thus a skull of an early American may resemble a skull of an historic Indian as well as a skull from the Old World of glacial age.

Recently discovered Tepexpan man had many primitive features, heavy brow ridges, a Neanderthal-like torus on the occiput. This skull has been dated at 11,000 to 12,000 years old by radiocarbon.

Many finds proving the contemporaneity of man, mammoth and mastodon have been made, such as Spillman's find at Quito. Macgowan remarks anent this: "This problem of when the mammoth died should puzzle the Old World as well as the New and cause us to question the dating of Neanderthal and Cro-Magnon quite as much as Folsom man. Oddly enough, it does nothing of the kind. In Europe the mammoth is accepted as diagnostic of the glacial period. The fact that Magdalenian man of Southern France sketched a mammoth on the wall of a cave proves that the man existed in the Great Ice Age. But in America, if a spear point turns up with the bones of a mammoth, too many anthropologists accept it as proof that the animal died after the ice fields had melted. The mammoth proves the antiquity of man in Europe; man prove the modernity of the mammoth in America. The only shred of evidence to support such reasoning is the questionable pottery and coal that lay beside the mastodon bones in Ecuador." . . .

Wendt tells of a cave in Patagonia containing bones of the long extinct giant sloth, Grypotherium, split open by human agency. Charred bits of hide were found. A wall had been built across the cave as if to separate part of it off as a stable, and behind it were bales of hay and a thick layer of sloth dung. Perhaps man had once domesticated the giant sloth here.

Krogman (159) reviewed the American finds up to 1941, and discarded all that had been found up to that time: "None of these earlier finds are acceptable as demonstrating any very great antiquity In all instances the type is modern; that is, it can be duplicated among living groups; in no instances is a real geological antiquity demonstrable for these finds." His report should be consulted by those interested.

Keith (160) thinks that the Punin skull found in 1923 in Ecuador is old. It lay with extinct fossil animals. As he remarks candidly, if it had been the skull of any other creature than man, its age would not have been questioned. It is Australoid in its affinities. Its cranial capacity was small. Its wisdom teeth were never formed!

Hrdlcka says: "Extensive experience with human remains in the Old World teaches that whenever such remains approach or are of geological antiquity . . . they show, at least in some respects, more primitive features . . . On the basis of this the physical anthropologist is justified to expect that American specimens of presumed geological antiquity should behave similarly. Such a demand might possibly be thwarted by a rare individual example, but certainly not repeatedly or even invariably."

The famous Calaveras skull of 1866 was found 130 feet below the surface in a mine, was fossilized and covered with adhering conglomerate, (containing water-worn pebbles of much altered volcanic rock), but it is modern and "was placed where it was found as a hoax"! This hoax was never proven, however. The well-known Lansing, Kansas skeletons of 1902 were found in loess 20 feet below the surface, but Krogman dismisses them thus: "Geological age is uncertain; type is modern." The famous Vero, Florida, finds of 1915-1926 are either late Pleistocene or early post-Pleistocene, for extinct fossil remains are found in bed two along with the human bones. But here again it is modern man that was found!

Howells found four skulls in 1935 in Wyoming of much the same type as the Minnesota girl. In 1934 Bell and Hrdlcka found a "Neanderthaloid" skull at Cedar Creek, Nebraska (but of late Mississippi Mound-Builder culture!). A skeleton found in 1937 near Folsom, New Mexico, and one found in 1933 by Jenks in Brown's Valley, Minnesota, were also modern. In 1936 "heavily mineralized" bones were found near Bradwell, Saskatchewan, of the age of the Kewatin Ice sheet (late Pleistocene). But all these are modern finds! Similarly the human remains found in association with those of extinct animals in 1830 in Bishop's Cave, near Las Cruces, New Mexico, and in Gypsum Cave near Las Vegas, Nevada, must be intrusive, although the cave deposits are Pleistocene! "The Utah lake skull approaches the upper range of Neanderthal possibilities." There is a report of the incredulity about the Folsom finds of scientists trained to accept current views of man's evolution—even after they had examined them themselves!!!

The Midland skull from Texas has been dated at about 10,000 years by radiocarbon. Indeed radiocarbon dating indicates that men using stone-tipped spears were hunting mammoth, bison, horse and tapir in Arizona at least by 10,000 B.C., were living in Illinois in the Modoc Rock Shelter by 8,000 B.C., and had reached the tip of South America by 6700 B.C. After recent excavations at Lewisville, near Dallas, Texas, "hearths" older than 37,000 years were found. A

Clovis point found here is usually regarded as 10,000 to 15,000 years old, however.

All these American data are very conflicting. They mean, really, that skeletal remains have frequently been found on these continents that would be regarded as satisfactorily dated and very old if they had been found in Europe or Asia, but the modernity of the skeletons here has upset evolutionists so much that even radiocarbon dates can scarcely reconcile them to the "American plan" of making Homo sapiens. As a result, most of these have been and still are ignored. Radiocarbon datings may force a reassessment of the whole situation and may carry modern man back as far in the Americas as in Europe.

The subject has been reviewed recently by Wormington and her book should be consulted by students of the subject, especially page 226 et seq. (156)

Modern Dating

Accurate chemical methods of dating have altered many of the conclusions derived from previous geological studies and "stone age culture" theories.

Cesare Emiliani's studies of marine cores and the oxygen-16 and oxygen-18 found in the contained shells depends on the fact that Foraminifera shells take up a smaller proportion of oxygen-18 when the climate is warm than when it is cold. His curves of world temperature oscillations closely parallel the glaciation inferences already drawn by geologists. He has decided that the earliest glacial advances occurred about 300,000 years ago in place of 1,000,000 years ago, and that the beginning of the last recession of the ice should be placed at 20,000 years. This dates most human fossils at less than 200,000 years, Swanscombe man at about 120,000 years, and Fontéchevade man at about 70,000 years old.

Fluorine dates have confirmed the antiquity of the Swanscombe skull. They also have made the Australopithecus of Taungs and Makapan Kageran in age, like the adjacent late Pleistocene breccia. Sterkfontein is slightly younger and Swartkrans still younger, and Kromdrai, Kamasian and Eyasi are about the same age as Sterkfontein. Thus really there are two groups of East African remains, Australopithecus Africanus in the second part of the Kageran and A. Robustus (Paranthropus) coming later, in the beginning of the Olduvai or Kamasian.

Radiocarbon dating is still in its infancy. It began about 1949 (Dr .W. F. Libby). The American methods carry dates back only 35,000 to 40,000 years, but at Groningen the method has been extended to about 70,000 years. It probably has reached its rearward limit here. We know that the Ice Age ended barely 10,000 years ago, only half as far back as scientists used to believe. Dates are now coming in in profusion every few months in journals like Science. What do they show? The dates given here are the older relevant figures that have appeared:

Peat from Florisbad skull	- more than 44,000
Lewisville, Texas	- 37,000 years ago?
Peat near Brussels resting on Mousterian layer, Levalloisian flakes	- over 36,000
Charcoal from San Diego (California)	- over 35,000
Neanderthal man (Shanidar Cave of Iraq)	- more than 34,000 years old
Charcoal in Salzofen Cave (Austria)	- 34,000 years old
Hearth - true Mousteroid - Havea Heah Cave, Cyrenaica	- 34,000
Charcoal, Mount Carmel - Upper Levalloiso - Mousterian	- 33,000
Charcoal in Niah Caves (British Borneo)	- 41,500 to 19,600 years old
Charred mammoth bone (same site)	- 30,000
Charcoal from "Mousterian" level of Hazar Mord Cave in Iraq	- more than 25,000
Hearth from Dordogne cave - Perigordian 4	- about 24,000
Charcoal on Santa Rosa Island (California)	- 17,000 years ago
Hearth at Magdalenian layer at La Garenne, France	- 11,100 and 15,900
Carbonized wood in gravel underlying Lupembian stone blade at Mufo, Angola	- 14,500
Arizona hunters	- 12,000 years ago
Charcoal from Late Magdalenian Grotte de Vache (France)	- 11,650
Modoc rock shelter	- 10,000 years ago
Charcoal, late Magdalenian (Hamburg, Germany)	- 10,500
Loess from Magdalenian culture Baden - Wurttemberg	- 10,200
Magdalenian cave at Baden - Wurttemberg	- 10,200
Land snails higher than Folsom layer (Lubbock, Texas)	- 10,000
Sandals from Fort Rock Cave, Oregon - oldest artifact in Americas	- 9,050
Russell Cave	- 9,000 years ago
Jarmo village (Iraq)	- 9,000
Man reached Straits of Magellan	- 8,700 years ago

Burned bone of sloth, horse, guanaco and human bones - Palliaike Cave, Chile	- 8,600
Keilor terrace near Keilor skull	- about 8,500
Charcoal in Lascaux Cave (France)	- 8,200
Maize in New Mexico	- 6,000 years ago

Unfortunately, as has been mentioned already, a radiocarbon dating carried out by the techniques used very recently can take us back only 35,000 years or so, which does not help us to date Mid-Pleistocene finds. It does, however, date Neanderthal and Cro-Magnon man, as well as the end of the Ice Age, and puts these very much closer to the present than was suspected on geological grounds, even 10 years ago. Mid-Pleistocene man also comes much closer to the present with the oxygen-16 dates, his antiquity being roughly halved. It is to be hoped that new dating techniques will be introduced soon which will add much more to these tantalizing beginnings.

Wormington is dubious of the accuracy of carbon 14 dates and does not hesitate to discard them where geology and good judgment suggest they are incorrect. Others share her doubts, especially since Jarmo has shown a radiocarbon spread of 6,000 years when archeologists feel that it was occupied for only 500 years, (161).

Incongruities and Puzzles

Many of these have been touched on above, for example the relative recency of Taungs and other Australopithicene remains despite their primitive type skeletons, the relative recency of the end of the Pleistocene, the decreased antiquity of Mid-Pleistocene man, the relative recency of the Keilor and Galley Hill skulls, the variability of Sinanthropus and Java man, the modernity of all ancient bones apart from the skulls, the puzzles created by teeth, notably by the giant teeth recently found in Java, China and Kenya, and lastly, the puzzling modernity of American finds of credible geological antiquity. But there are others.

For example, can one equate cultural remains and intelligence? Were the men who left only stone tools of low mentality, or did it take more courage and wit to kill cave bears and mammoths and men with such weapons than with machine guns? Is the modern Eskimo, a Neolithic man, not as intelligent as the other Canadian who mans the Dew Line which traverses their mutual territory? At the moment Trans-Canada Airlines has a full-blooded Eskimo stewardess, several Eskimos are being trained as miners, and it is generally remarked by those who know that the untaught Eskimo can be the more efficient mechanic when engines stall in the white man's motorboats. In 1959 Time carried an item describing true Stone Age Men in south-eastern Brazil, living with bows and stones axes only a few score miles from Western civilization. It is of interest that one of the boys of this tribe so recently brought to light plans to be a taxi driver! It has long been held, of course, that the art of late Pleistocene man would do credit to any 20th century artist, and these men were not only masters of colour and pigment but of form. They had developed unfading colours, indeed, that we cannot yet duplicate. Neanderthal and Cro-Magnon men buried their dead, sometimes with necklaces and other ornaments. Glacial man may have been the cannibal that the Choukoutien cave suggests or that is proven by the knife cuts on the bones of Predmost —but modern Aztecs and Papuans have had the same taste in meat. At Vestonice, Absolon discovered an organized village where certain areas had been set aside for living quarters, with fireplaces near and refuse pits farther away, stacked mammoth bones, a statuette factory. There were ornaments, tools, weapons, even spoons and a two-pronged bone fork, says Andrews. A half skull served as a lamp or drinking tankard—as was the case in European concentration camps less than 20 years ago. Perhaps Predmost man was not so primitive as stone and bone tools might suggest. In his early diggings in East Africa Leakey made African Aurignacian contemporary with European Mousterian, and the former included pottery—never found in Europe before Neolithic times. The artist of Font-de-Gaume sent a copy of his bull bison drawn on a piece of slate at least 200 miles across France, perhaps as an advertisement of what he could do on request.

Now a note on the variety of physical type in ancient man. Remarks have often been made on the variation in skeletal remains of the people of Mount Carmel, or the Upper Cave at Choukoutien, or the Predmost people, or even of Sinanthropus and Pithecanthropus themselves. Imagine how much they differed from a possible contemporary of theirs like Swanscombe man! Coon (162) has remarked on the same sort of thing in recent excavations in Asia. In Formosa there were three distinct types of skulls found in excavations at An Yang—a north Chinese, a heavy mongoloid and a north European (with shovel incisors). Indus Valley skulls he saw in Calcutta might have come from Sumeria or Denmark or the Mediterranean. One was obviously Australoid, and one was a typical Mongoloid. It would seem that ancient man had major racial and even local variants too. One has only to recall the "negroid" Grimaldi skull to see where such variation leads us. Ancient Scandinavian rock drawings show ships and perhaps an elephant and a giraffe. These men travelled far before the days of the Vikings, it seems.

When did village man appear? Was it at Vestonice? Or was it at Jarmo in Iraq, the earliest agricultural village so far dated by radiocarbon—about 9,000 years ago? These old Iraquis grew barley and two kinds of wheat, reaped with flint sickles, cracked grain on milling tones and parched it in ovens. They had domesticated the goat, perhaps also sheep, pigs, dogs, cattle and horses. They have left a variety of bracelets, stone bowls and figurines. Radiocarbon also creates its own riddles!

Braidwood (163)* has reviewed the evidence recently. He suspects that "the general Near Eastern area was the focus of differentiation and eventual spread of anatomically modern man and of his earliest characteristic habits in the preparation of flint tools . . . The whole range of human existence, from the biological . . . through the cultural . . . bands of the spectrum took on completely new dimensions (here).

"The earliest appearance of urban civilization (is) first in alluvial Mesopotamia, about 5,500 years ago, and only slightly later in Egypt."

. . . "Really early traces of Pleistocene man, such as have been found in southern and northwestern Africa, have not yet been noted in the near East."

. . . "On both sides of the Suez there were fluctuations in utilization of various types of tools . . . The first is the tentative occurrence of the blade-tool traditions, in the Tabun cave on Mount Carmel, in contexts which include Acheulian corebiface tools; blades also appear in the Yabrud cave near Damascus soon thereafter. The second is the appearance, in just-subsequent Levalloiso-Mousterian levels on Mount Carmel and in nearby caves, of fossil men who show a trend toward anatomically modern morphology. The third is the apparent long persistence, in Egypt and its environs, of the Levaloiso-Mousterian industries, after—at the end of the earlier subphase of the upper Pleistocene—the blade-tool tradition had taken over in southwestern Asia. If the geochronology is as we expect, the early appearance in southwestern Asia of blade-tools and of human beings with anatomical tendencies toward modern man (at a time when 'classic' Neanderthal man was flourishing in western Europe) makes this area a focus of some interest. There is not, of course, complete agreement that either the blade tools or anatomically modern man did first appear in the area". . .

An open village site at Zawi Chemi, of radiocarbon dating 8,900 B.C., and a parallel Natufian site in Palestine may mark the transition from cave to open plain living.

When and where did fire originate? Obviously Sinanthropus used it. Leakey concludes that Acheulian man did not have it. But Oakley says evidence of the use of fire was found in the Early Acheulian camp at Torralba in Spain.

Wechler (164) believes that Neanderthal man developed in north-eastern Asia and Homo sapiens south and west of that. They may have hybridized at Mount Carmel. Leakey (165) insists, of course, that Lower Aurignacian stone techniques in Africa preceded those in Europe. At least the Homo sapiens character of the Heidelberg dentition rules out the Asiatic Pithecanthropoid as an ancestor of Homo

*Quoted by permission of the American Association for the Advancement of Science, Washington, U.S.A.

sapiens, Wechler holds. He cites authorities as concluding generally that Rhodesian man is not Neanderthaloid but an early type of Homo sapiens, Perhaps he is "undatable", as Zeuner believes. Florisbad and Boskop are Homo sapiens, probably. Wechler believes that Homo sapiens and Neanderthal man had a long, independent evolution.

The "Evolution" of Man

Where and when did pre-hominid ape-like creatures become hominids or man? Did this change really occur? This is the crux of our study, of human evolution at least.

Obviously a great variety of ape-like creatures once lived that were not too similar to modern anthropoids. There were such creatures as the giant ape of Kwangsi, described by Pei Wen-Chung, which was roughly contemporaneous with Pekin man. There was Australopithecus, which has made such an impression on Clark, a creature having a brain of 450 to 700 c.c. volume (cf. largest gorilla at 685 c.c.), no diastema, reduced canines, a tooth eruption of the Homo sapiens type never found in apes ,teeth in the upper jaw like those of Pithecanthropus, and molarization of the first milk molar. However, he was contemporaneous with Pithecanthropus, Clark concedes . . . and this has been stressed more recently in Science by "H.L.S. Jr." Teilhard de Chardin flatly denies that there is any valid evidence that Australopithecus used fire, Professor Dart to the contrary.

In 1950 Mayr (166) put forward a new classification, the half-brained and full-brained men. The former included Pithecanthropus and Sinanthropus. The full-brained men included Heidelberg, Neanderthal, Rhodesian and Solo man, also ourselves, of course. Coon points out: "according to Mayr's methodology, an evolutionary change in brain size or brain shape implies no greater genetic shift than a change in skin colour or in hair form." Coon goes on to postulate that perhaps "unlike his descendants of the Age of Gunpowder, Homo sapiens of the Middle and Late Pleistocene period killed off his more archaic rivals for ecological lebensraum utterly and without trace. Yet . . . the cultural difference between a hunter armed with blade tools and one armed with flake tools must have been infinitely less than between Englishmen armed with rifles and Australian aborigines. Neither cultural difference nor repugnance at the grotesque elf-like faces of the aborigines prevented the English from doing what wandering men have been doing with foreign women throughout recorded history."

Dobzhansky (167)* asks: "Where did modern man come from? Where did he first arise? The problem is very complex, speculation concerning it rife, and no convincing solution is yet in sight. Some students have conjectured that modern man developed in Africa, others that he came to Europe from Asia, and destroyed the Neander-

---

*Quoted by permission of John Wiley and Sons, Inc., New York.

thalian natives. According to some authorities, Europe had some human inhabitants who resembled modern men during the second interglacial period (35,000 or more years ago), before the appearance of the Neanderthalians. Very few remains of this hypothetical race have been found, and those which have come to light are fragments not easily interpretable. The skull fragments found at Fontéchevade in France, at Swanscombe in England and at Steinheim and at Ehringsdorf in Germany may have been rather sapiens-like, despite their great age. It looks as though there lived in Europe during the middle of the Ice Age a race rather like ourselves and yet not ancestral to us. Some experts, in a kind of desperation, regard all fossil hominoids, except the Cro-Magnons and more recent races, as collateral branches of the human family tree, which became extinct without contributing to the direct ancestry of modern man. This makes the origin of modern man more puzzling than ever . . . Coon and other anthropologists are probably right that some modern European populations show persistence of genes derived from the Neanderthalians. In like fashion, within the last few centuries the white race has displaced the red-skinned men in the Americas and the blackfellows in Australia. It is possible that the Neanderthalians themselves had, at a much earlier time, displaced the Swanscombe and similar populations which had inhabited Europe before them . . . To ask where Homo sapiens first appeared is therefore meaningless. Races and local populations are evolutionary trial parties which explore the various possibilities of adaptation. The gene pool of the mankind now living contains genetic elements which were present in many and perhaps in all major populations of the past."

Krogman raised a problem for the thorough-going evolutionist to consider: "There is, according to Osborn, a very real problem inherent in the fact that in the New World Monkeys, the Old World Apes and the Anthropoids the thumb is rudimentary and, in some forms, even absent. It is inconceivable to him that Man, with his highly developed thumb, could have passed through a stage in which the thumb was under-developed or lost. A true ancestor—says Osborn—must be sufficiently generalized that it possess 100 per cent of the characters and potentialities of its descendants . . . A more pertinent observation by Osborn is that primitive man (Neanderthal) has the brain and the intermembral proportions of Man, not Ape or even Ape-Man; furthermore, the Red Crag implements, probably 1,2500,000 years in age, 'demonstrate the possession of a perfectly formed hand with a well-formed grasping thumb, with deft fingers guided by a clever and designing mind lodged only in a large forebrain.' "

Weidenreich (186) graphically compares the variations in skull size and shape in early man with the corresponding variations among dog breeds. The data are very striking (see pp. 44, 45 of "Apes, Giants and Man"), and suggest that the vast differences in size and shape in different breeds of dogs skulls could be exactly paralleled by alterations in size and shape of skull in what would then be corresponding strains or varieties of man.

Finally, Oliver and Howells* (168) have provided very good evidence of the failure of micro-evolution to develop under nearly ideal laboratory conditions on the southern half of the island of Bougainville in the Pacific:

"Our data from two closely related major populations on the island of Bouganville furnish unusually good controls for the purpose: the populations appear to have common origin but have been separate for more than two centuries; they are of comparable size and are subdivided into a similar number of subpopulations which act to a considerable degree as actual breeding populations; their cultural mating patterns differ enough to cause a significantly greater degree of intermarriage across subarea lines in one population (Siuai) than in the other (Nagovisi) . . .

"The situation might be expected to permit a greater between-group differentiation in Nagovisi than in Siuai, due to such factors as isolation, drift (though the populations involved are not especially small), and action of local environmental influences, but this is not found. Between-group differentiation exists to a highly significant degree in the same number of traits in both populations. Neither genetic theory nor previous anthropometric information explain some of the findings: (a) Differentiation among the subpopulations of Siuai and Nagovisi shows no correspondence with differentiation between the two main populations. (b) The tendency toward local differentiation differs somewhat between Siuai and Nagovisi: both exhibit the tendency in head and face breadths: Siuai shows it in trunk diameters especially; Nagovisi shows it in face heights."

Few such opportunities to study human micro-evolution can ever present themselves, and it is highly significant that the Bougainville data do not support evolutionary theory. Here is practice, not mere theory.

Wormington's remarks on the problem of the origin of American man are worth reading, (p 254 et seq.) She says that students of the subject must sometimes feel that prehistoric Indians lack historical roots and are afloat in time.

Summary

Man is as ancient in the world as Mid-Pleistocene. From his beginnings he has always varied greatly in skull size and type, but has been alike in torso and legs. He had as large a brain at first as now— often larger. He was anciently contemporaneous with different anthro-

---

*Quoted by permission of the American Anthropologist U. of Arizona, Tucson, U.S.A., and the Authors.

226

poids than at present. These latter were always similar to and yet very unlike man, as now. Man always was composed of various physically different races or varieties. These probably hybridized at any points of contact. He was spread over the greater part of three continents, Europe, Asia and Africa,—and perhaps another three.

After thousands of years of existence in which his populations were scattered and scanty, often living under very arduous glacial conditions, he may have been replaced rather completely and suddenly by a modern type culture which started village life in the near East. This transition occurred about 9,000 years ago and quickly developed into the historic civilization of that area and of all the lands we know since. With this episode "modern life" began. Perhaps "Adam" was the first of these men, starting life anew on the terms we now know, living for reasons and objectives akin to ours, with our hopes and fears and troubles. His children may have intermarried with remnants of their older, more savage neighbours, and we may be the descendants of all the "men" who ever were. At least this could explain the history of our activities in this brutal century.

CHAPTER XXII

IN CONCLUSION

The iron years still throw their sparks, it seems,
Against the carborundum of my dreams.

—Vere Jameson*

When the theory of evolution was broached 100 years ago by Darwin, Wallace, Huxley and others, those brave scientists met a storm of abuse, ridicule and vilification, much of which Huxley's sharp wit and comprehensive scientific knowledge were able to rebound on the head of the attackers. The proponents of Special Creation have fought a losing battle with the evolutionists ever since, partly because they were so poorly grounded in science, partly because they relied mainly on authority and prestige and prejudice while these factors worked for them, and partly because their arguments were flimsy and often dealt with half-truths only. Therefore they steadily lost the support of fair-minded and educated men.

The Puritans who fled from Great Britain to secure religious freedom were quick to persecute those who in their turn dissented from them. A mirror image of this has developed in our day. For in its turn Evolution has become the intolerant religion of nearly all educated western men. It dominates their thinking, their speech and the hopes of their civilization. The indefinite self-perfectibility of man has become sound doctrine in a day when men search in vain for a comprehensive ethic which can rescue the world before the current disintegration of international character, the reorientation of the power-balance between the white and other races, and the progress of nuclear physics reduce all ethical and other human problems to the history of a little dust. As Weizsacker** (169) has recently said:

"—Science today is the only thing in which men as a whole believe: it is the only universal religion of our time . . . The scientist has thus got himself into an ambiguous position: he is a priest of this new religion, possessing its secrets and marvels; for what to others is puzzling, strange or secret is plain to him. It is suddenly clear in many countries that the future of a nation, of a continent, of a view of life depends on producing enough scientists. Is this immoderate faith in the power of science justified? The scientist worthy of the name, who is therefore concerned to know the truth, must realize that what he knows is only a fraction of what he needs to know if he is really

---

*Quoted by permission of the Ryerson Press, Toronto, Canada.
**Quoted by permission J. R. Geigy A. G., Basel Switzerland.

to be fit to carry responsibility for the lives of men. The situation of the scientist is well illustrated by the following story. A man was seen in the street one night, looking for something on the ground by the light of the street lamp. 'What are you looking for?' 'My door key'. 'Have you lost it?' 'Yes.' 'Is this where you lost it?' 'I don't know' 'Then why are you looking here?' 'Because here I can see.' Science looks where it can see. That is legitimate; but there are many things it does not see, and what should its attitude be towards them? Ought it to wait until it has explored them, perhaps in ten, perhaps in a hundred years? There are many things science does not see, and above all it does not see man himself scientifically, in all the ramifications of his status."

At the same meeting, Nissen* (170) of Basle observed that a notion existed nowadays that—"there is an unassailable precision and completeness, some inexorable logic, about the theories and practical achievements of science. Fortunately this is not so. It is indeed a reassuring thought that even in mathematics, physics and chemistry it remains a condition of progress that principles assumed to be soundly based are constantly being assailed and overturned. There is something particularly human, perhaps one might saye humane, about this: it implies the right to be mistaken . . . it may be useful to stress this element of **insecurity** which is inherent in all our efforts and inferences and which opens the way to new considerations and perhaps to new aims . . ."

The argument from majority opinion has never impressed me. Had it been effective a century ago Evolution could never have raised its head. It is no more valid now. Were it good, Communism would rule our world and none should resist it. Were it applicable to the religion that is Evolution it would still suppress the latter, for Buddhism and Mohammedism have more adherents, as has Roman Catholicism. Evolutionists, like all scientists, should never think of themselves as members of "the one tolerated party", but should merely consider the facts in dispute, because by definition Science is interested only in truth, not in its adherents or their prestige. Moreover. not all scientists are evolutionists (171), although evolutionists often claim this in an off-handed manner, as if that rendered further criticism futile and reflected on the mental actuity of any dissenter. Names could be given, but are probably not worth recording, for the recitation of authorities is not really a mode of argument. For example, there is many an eminent botanist whose unbelief, rarely naively explicit, can be gleaned from his printed pages.

One writer, Acworth, in his book on Butterflies, remarks, apropos of all this: "a layman equipped with all the relevant facts of any problem is quite as capable of forming sound, and sometimes sounder, conclusions on facts as is a specialist who tackles his subject from a

---

*Quoted by permission of J. R. Geigy A. G., Basel, Switzerland.

special angle. If this were not so, few men would accept the awful responsibility of a judge who may have to sentence a man to death on circumstantial evidence derived, perhaps, from medical or anatomical technicalities of which he had no self-acquired knowledge of his own. Not only so, but a judge's decision is seldom, if ever, questioned on such a ground."

My critics are sure to criticise my competence to discuss the problems at issue, since books on this topic are usually written by zoologists, palaeontologists, geneticists or other like biological specialists. But obviously the problem long ago transcended all these fields, singly or combined, and all these are out of their depth, too, in any far-ranging discussion of the features of evolution. Where all have lost any firm footing, what does it matter if another swimmer bobs up beside them, one more interested in bacteriology, entomology, surgical anatomy, nutrition and teratology than many of them may be? The writer readily admits his lack of competence. He as cheerfully challenges their. But where all that is to be read must pass through one reader's mind, there are some obvious advantages in having had it already predigested in one other mind. Hence the attempt of one author, in a day when few of like mind are academically independent as he, to deploy his thin armies over so broad a battlefield, where so many titans have long marched and countermarched and so many paladins lie in their tumuli.

Few opinions of men are sacrosanct, and Evolution is merely one view of how the world of Nature reached its present status. The loud and persistent attestations that it is not theory but "fact" merely serve to indicate how shaky some of its foundations are.

The great reason why the theory of evolution has made such headway among reasonable men is that it is simple yet comprehensive, leaves out the supra-human and therefore deals only in readily apprehended motives and terms, and, as anyone must admit in fairness, contains a great deal of demonstrable truth. But the same arguments can be used to justify Communism, Fascism, Existentialism and many another current "ism". No truth is so dangerous as a half truth, or one that has been stretched to shadow more land than any one hide can cover.

Thomson has proclaimed that the fact of evolution stands more firmly than ever, but adds that uncertainties in respect to its modus operandi are immense. For example, he asks who has clearly understood the origin of any single species.

The test of simplicity is used as a measure of the validity of scientific theories—perhaps by Occam's razor. But Goodman (172) discusses at length "What is the test of simplicity?"—for truth is not simple and not axiomatic. His article should be read by many an evolutionist intent on the inclusive and easy answer.

Our whole experience of life is that it is not simple, not readily comprehensible, not to be added up by 2's and 3's, full of unexpected complications like the paradoxical freezing of water or the physics of quanta, and characterized by equilibria rather than by one-way reactions. It would be curious if such phenomena were not to be found in the manifold manifestations of living things also, plants, animals and the vague in-between's, such as slime-moulds or viruses.

Carter* says: "the theory that the whole structure of later animals is inherent, but unexpressed, in all their ancestors—is absurd; it is impossible to believe that an early metazoan, or even an early fish, had inherent within it all the organization of a mammal. If the pre-formation theory is discarded, the only alternative is that new **pattern** has arisen in evolution."—Yet what is this but the doctrine of special Creation or something very like?

I can do no better than quote Carter's last two paragraphs at this juncture. Here the great zoologist puts his cards fairly on the table at the end of a fine presentation of the evolutionary theory he believes in:

"If the objections that can be brought against our theory of evolution fail, we must conclude that the theory is in all probability on the right lines. This does not mean that it is complete; it is by no means so. Nor would it be true to say that it is accepted by all contemporary zoologists that our present theory in all respects is sound in its outlook on the problems of evolution. It is probably healthy that this should be so, for progress results from disagreement and discussion —there is little spur to further investigation when all are agreed. Each zoologist will have his own reasons for dissatisfaction, but perhaps one of the commonest is that the theory of evolution that results from modern work is too mechanical, that, at least when dealing with the higher animals, it takes too little account of their higher functions and especially of their behaviour and powers of choice. Animals choose their environments; they modify their behaviour to some extent, and so are able to exert some control over the action of the environment upon them, and ultimately over their evolution. It seems to some zoologists that recent work treats animals far too much as if they were entirely at the mercy of the environment, that it deals with them too much as chemical and physical systems and too little as living and behaving organisms. These objections may be vague, but they are a real criticism, and indicate a direction in which future work may advance the theory. They show us some of the gaps in our theory; they do not give any good reason for discarding it. There can be no doubt that wider knowledge of animal behaviour would greatly help our interpretation of evolution.

"The incompleteness of the theory is another point at which it is open to criticism. No one can look at the immensely complicated

---

*Quoted by permission of Sidgewick and Jackson, Ltd., London, England.

organization of an insect or a vertebrate without doubting that our relatively simple theories can completely explain the origin of such complexity. The belief is unavoidable that there is much in evolution of which we have no knowledge. If it is the whole life and activities of an animal that evolves, our interpretation cannot be complete until we have complete knowledge of the animal's life, and we are very far from that knowledge of an animal. One feels this insufficiency very forcibly when we consider the course of evolution in the life-history. The life-history evolves at least in part by change in the organization that controls its general course in the individual. But we have hardly any knowledge of this control. We know that organs may cause the differentiation of neighbouring organs by evocation, and that genes may modify the progress of differentiation in the life-history by their action on enzymes. But we have no general knowledge of the organization upon which they act, the system that causes the appearance of a set pattern in the development of each species and controls the growth of the parts so that the body keeps to the specific form. That organization is at present outside our knowledge, and it is therefore inevitable that our theory of its evolution is incomplete. We are never able to give more than a summarized and superficial account of phenomena of life in an animal. Evolution is a general and fundamental biological phenomenon, and our account of it is necessarily superficial. But if we are right in thinking that the modern theory of evolution gives a consistent account of the range of fact, already wide, provided by our present knowledge of many biological sciences, we may at least conclude that the theory is sound so far as it goes. However much it needs modification in the future, it is not likely that it will be shown to be wholly false."

We chase the great Designer down a long, dim alley, only to find that He has darted through a secret door or turned an unexpected corner. He acts as if He were a wit as well as an engineer, subtle as well as simple, infinite in resource as well as in dimension, and not too chummy except by His own choosing.

What I have sought to do in these pages is to throw further illumination on certain recesses of the problem of life not well lit in college biology textbooks. Their biassed presentation of the facts of Nature would be reprehensible in any theologian, and is quite as evil in scientists ostensibly devoted to objective truth, let the chips fall where they may. It is wicked to teach the Biogenetic Law as law when its flaws are so obvious that few top-flight embryologists give it credence, and when the whole world of botany lends it such scanty support. It is bad to make no attempt to sculpture the real Pithecanthropus when finally his remains came out of hiding after decades of rest in Dr. Dubois' cabinet. It is unwise to hide the facts about bacteria and fungi because they do not fit evolutionary theory, or to fail to stress the great hiati in the world of plants. It is bad to publish theories of origins as if they were facts, to postulate ancestors for which there is no evidence, to adduce theories of the origin of feathers and flight that a kindergarten child would jeer at, to ignore the profound bio-chemical changes demanded in altering blood pigments from those carrying a copper ion to those carrying an iron radicle, and so on. I have tried, as I said above, to bring some of these hidden data into the light again.

Waddington has pointed to the way in which wild animals remain uniform, to the consistent development of the different types of cells in the body with no intermediate types. It's as if development was "canalized". All is not change, in short. Fixity of type is the principal feature of all living forms and fractions of living forms that we know.

Muller has pertinent remarks to make on the continuance of living forms. The normal phenotype has a superior stability over mutant phenotypes. He feels that "the organism cannot be considered as infinitely plastic and certainly is not equally plastic in all directions. Certain types of mutants are much more apt to arise than others, and are often restricted to certain small groups. Certain muta-tions, like Haldane's porcupine boy, are almost too rare to recur. He says that even the change in degree of a given character, due to natural selection, cannot be as simple and easy a process as is sometimes supposed.

Where does the flux that is life come to a standstill in face of the stasis that is also life? I believe at what taxonomists have arbitrarily designated as the "family" level. Little changes fill out the picture of fluid life—but large changes reside only in the imagination of zoolo-gists, I suspect. What we call for our convenience kingdoms, phyla, classes and orders were created by God Almighty, when He made "creatures after their kind." From there on each kind has made kinds by means of micro-evolutionary processes.

May I conclude with the words of Professor Vialleton* (173):

"There is, then, when one considers evolution in the light of the real evidence, both great doubt and also exaggeration of its value, resulting in an idea which is very anthropomorphic, namely, that everything has always begun very humbly and later has developed into very complex and lofty forms. Once again one must say that this is not the picture presented by nature. One scarcely sees, throughout the geological ages, a gradual slow multiplication of types of organization. One does not find at first, a unicellular being, then simple colonies of cells, then Coelenterates, etc. On the contrary, Louis Agassiz re-marked a long time ago (1859) that in the first known fossils one finds side by side representatives of all the great groups except the vertebrates, which seems to prove that the living world from its origin has been composed of diverse types, perfectly distinct one from the

---

*Quoted by permission of Gaston Doin Co., Paris, France.

other, which have divided amongst them the various functions of life and the available space on the surface of the globe . . .

"Evolution has not begun from forms truly simple in order to pass over into more complicated forms; the types of organization one finds have always displayed their essential character initially. Genuine evolution, therefore, as one ascends the geological column, from the first to last representative of any type of organization, is trivial in sum, and scarcely permits one to believe in its overweening power to effect biological transformations."

CREATION

Vere Jameson

The Old Professor told us—
And he was gowned in learning and degrees—
That life began unnumbered aeons since
At edge of an utterly, awesomely lonely sea
In a seeming-miraculous, purely chance collision
Of wandering carbon with casual bits of mist
In an ambitious cell. Even more wonderful still
Not one life only pulsed inside that membrane
But all life lay there—shadowy still, but there—
In it both jaw of shark and dauntless Churchill;
There curled the lateral line and feline whisker
Lying beside the surgeon's cultured touch
Able to sew the arteries in a wound;
There was the eye of the squid and Admiral Halsey;
There crouched the schemes of python and Nobel prizeman;
There lay the panther and Jesus for anyone
Who could train his excited transit over this protoplasm
On the faint hair-lines of the future.

Now this may be true, and I would not say he lied.
But I fear his collegiate, not too sensible mind
May have been gripped in the fierce, relentless claws
Of a siren, soulless, predatory theory
Flying far over facts and all the love we know.
For credulous as I am, I can not believe
That the life of my mother or child was thing of chance.
Knowing a little of chemical reactions
I must admit I am coerced to doubt
That an undirected, uncontained explosion
Should develop the current that since has sneered at time,
Which moved the plesiosaur and Moses' pen;
Nor can I conjure up that gendering cell,
So ultimately rich in variation,
So grandly spawning all the layered rocks,
In which I must imagine Auden's lines
Snuggled beside the ova of a tapeworm,
And Einstein's fertile, roving calculus
Predicated in the pterodactyl's thumb.

As I remember it he then went on
Demanding unlimited ,multi-millioned time
For life upon its desperate, tottering ladder
From which whole monstrous races fell forever
Into the plastic, photographic rock.

235

"However small the changes that we see
But give us time," he cried.
Time, time, that sleepy, crawling, twisting time,
Time of the subtle, slow-dissolving views,
Time, the dark forest, 'mong whose myriad trees
Hosts upon tired hosts have bumped the years.
Time, that old ocean bottomless to man
—If any floor to that abyss was laid—
Time, maddened time, which dragged that cell to bloom
In Paul and Moses, Plato, Tamerlane,
The Japanese opium policy in China,
The incinerators for screaming women in Poland.
"All this is noble if by Natural Law,
And clarifies the prowess of the years,
Proving how feckless they who still uphold
That church-worn and contentious credo
An immanent, answering, helpful God!"
Although such climbing of the tree of life
Is not accredited by history —
The brief span none but theorists ignore —
And if life, undirected, by itself
Can end so doubtfully as in our day
Much guidance do we need and should have had
From that dim God forgetful I must scorn.

However —
I am persuaded that the good old man
Had grown myopic nosing through his books
And so ignored plain lessons of his years
And all the age of man. Strange he should be
More sure of rocks than his own eyes and ears,
More sure of Darwin than his radio,
Aware of them, yet unaware of life.
He died the other day, and now I hope
Knows more of how a man may be evolved
Into a spirit, and much less, **much** less
Of how we spurned that first, fantastic cell
Bulging with genes centrifugal and wise
And climbed to where we now stand webbed in war.

A Classification of Plants and Animals

(adapted from Stirton (174*)

Kingdom - Plantae

	Schizomycetes	- Bacteria
Phylum - Thallophyta	Chlorophyceae	- Green algae
	Myxophyceae	- Blue-green algae
	Phaeophyceae	- Brown algae
	Chrysophyta	- Golden-brown algae and diatoms
	Eumycophyta	- Fungi
	Myxomycetes	- Slime Molds
	Pyrrhophyta	- Dinoflagellates
	Euglenoidia	- Euglenas
	Chloromonadina	
	Cryptomonadina	
	Euflagellata	
	Rhodephyceae	- Red algae

Phylum - Bryophyta
Phylum - Tracheophyta
Subphylum - Psilopsida
Subphylum - Lycopsida - Club mosses, Scale trees
Subphylum - Sphenopsida - Horsetails
Subphylum - Pteropsida
  Class - Filicineae - true Ferns
  Class - Gymnospermae
    Subclass - Pteridospermae - Seed ferns
    Subclass - Cycadophytae
      Order - Cycadeoidales
      Order - Cycadales
    Subclass - Ginkophytae
    Subclass - Cordaitae
    Subclass - Coniferae
  Class - Angiospermae
    Subclass - Dicotyledonae
    Subclass - Monocotyledonae

Kingdom - Animalia

  Phylum - Protozoa - flagellates, trypansomes, amoeba, foraminifera, radiolaria

---

*Quoted by the courtesy of John Wiley and Sons, Inc., New York, U.S.A.

Phylum - Porifera - sponges
Phylum - Coelenterata - hydroids, man-of-war, jellyfish, sea ane-
    mones, ctenophores
  Class - Anthozoa - corals
  Class - Graptolithina - graptolites
Phylum Platyhelminthes - planarians, flukes, tapeworms and ribbon
    worms
Phylum Nemathelminthes - roundworms, perhaps the Gordian
    worms and Acanthocephala and marine worms
Phylum Trochelminthes - rotifers
Phylum Bryozoa
Phylum Brachiopoda
  Class - Inarticulata
  Class - Articulata
Phylum - Mollusca - molluscs or lamellibranchs
  Class - Amphineura
  Class - Gastropoda - snails, slug, turritellas, whelks, limpets,
    abalones
  Class - Cephalopoda - squids, nautilus, belemnites and ammonites
  Class - Pelecypoda - clams, oysters
  Class - Scaphopoda - tooth shells
  Class - Onychophora - sea spiders, linguatulids
  Class - Crustacea - lobsters, crabs, ostracods, barnacles
  Class - Trilobita - trilobites
  Class - Chilopoda - centipedes
  Class - Diplopoda - millipedes
  Class - Arachnoidea - spiders, mites, ticks, scorpions, king crabs,
    eurypterids
  Class - Insecta - insects
Phylum - Echinodermata
  Subphylum - Pelmatazoa - sessile types
  Class - Cystoidea
  Class - Blastoidea
  Class - Crinoidea - sea lilies and feather stars
  Subphylum - Eleutherozoa - free-swimming types
  Class - Holothuroidea - sea-cucumber
  Class - Asteroidea - starfish and brittle stars
  Class - Echinoidea - sea urchins, heart urchins, sand dollars
Phylum - Chordata
Subphylum - Acrania - pterobranchs, acorn worms, tunicates and
    lancelets
Subphylum - Craniata - vertebrates
  Class - Cyclostomata - lampreys and hagfish - extinct ostracoderms
  Class - Pisces - fish

Class - Amphibia - frogs, toads, salamanders, legless caecilians and extinct labyrinthodonts

Class - Reptila - lizards, snakes, turtles, crocodiles, tuatera, dinosaurs, plesiosaurs, icthyosaurs, pterosaurs, etc.

Class - Aves - birds

Class - Mammalia - mammals

The Rock Strata as Recently Classified

(after Raymond) (slightly modified)

Caenozoic Era
{
Recent - began about 15,000 years ago.
Pleistocene - began about 1,500,000 years ago.

Tertiary
{
Pliocene - began about 15,000,00 years ago.
Miocene - began about 30,000,000 years ago.
Oligocene - began about 40,000,000 years ago
Eocene - began about 50,000,000 years ago.
Palaeocene - began about 60,000,000 years ago.
}
}

Mesozoic Era
{
Upper Cretaceous - began about 105,000,000 years ago.
Lower Cretaceous - began about 120,000,000 years ago.
Jurassic - began about 150,000,000 years ago
Triassic - began about 180,000,000 years ago
}

Palaeozoic Era
{
Permian - began about 225,000,000 years ago
Pennsylvanian (Upper Carboniferous) - began about 270,000,000 years ago.
Mississippian (Lower Carboniferous) - began about 300,000,000 years ago.
Devonian - began about 345,000,000 years ago.
Silurian - began about 375,000,000 years ago.
Ordovician - began about 435,000,000 years ago.
Cambrian - began about 600,000,00 years ago.
}

Proterozoic Era — Began about 1,000,000,000 years ago.

Archaeozoic Era — Began about 1,500,000,000 years ago.

GLOSSARY

of Scientific Terms found in this Book

Acanthocephala—parasitic, gutless, nematode-like worms that carry on their anterior end a retractible rostrum crowned with hooks.

Acanthodia—an order of elasmobranch fishes.

Acarine—pertaining to the mites (arthropods).

Agaricaeae—mushrooms and toadstools.

Agglutinogen—an antigen that produces agglutinin.

Agoseris—perennial herbs of the Cichoriaceae.

Agrobacterium—a soil organism, a plant pathogen, a genus of the Rhizobiaceae family.

Akene—the product of a single, uniovulate carpel, the pericarp being tough.

Allometry—change in proportions as size increases.

Alpheus—a Macruran crustacean.

Amoeba—a microscopic animal perpetually changing shape.

Amino-acid—the simplest unit building block out of which polypeptides and hence proteins can be assembled.

Ammonite—a genus of extinct cephalopods, curled like a ram's horn.

Amphibian—living on both land and water, as do frogs, toads, salamanders and such.

Anapsid—the skull wholly roofed over and imperforate.

Ancon sheep—a race of sheep with long bodies, short legs, and crooked forelegs.

Ancylostomum—a group of nematodes.

Angiosperm—a plant whose seeds are enclosed in a true ovary.

Ankylosis—the internal fixation of a joint.

Annelida—the true worms.

Anopheles—the mosquito which is a vector for malaria.

Anthropometric—having to do with the measurements of anthropoids (monkey, ape, man).

Antigen—a substance introduced into the blood which can stimulate the latter to produce antibodies.

Aorta—the great dorsal bloodvessel of the body.

Aphid—a plant-louse tended by ants for its honey-dew.

Apterous—without wings.

Aquilegia—a group of the Anemonoideae.

Arboreal—pertaining to life in trees.

Archaeopteryx—the earliest bird yet found.

Arginine—an amino-acid, one of the hexone bases.

Aristogenesis—the formation of totally new characters in any form of life.

Arthropod—a phylum of creatures having jointed legs, and including Crustacea, Myriapoda, Insecta, and Arachnoidea.

Artiodactyl—animals having an even number of digits.

Ascidia—the sea-squirts.

Atavism—a reversion to an ancestral type.

Autolytus—a marine worm resembling a centipede but asexual.

Axolotl—a reptile like a salamander found in Mexican lakes, remaining immature because of thyroid deficiency.

B. coli—the bacilli predominating in the large bowel.

Bacteriophage—a virus preying on bacteria.

Bacterium—a microscopic organism capable of producing infection. It it stopped by porcelain filters. It may be bacillus (rod) or coccus (tiny sphere).

Bandicoot—an insectivorous marsupial.

Bastard-wing—the alula or three quill-feathers on the first digit of the bird's wing.

Batrachian—frog.

Batrachoid—like a frog.

Belemnites—an extinct genus of Belemnoidea (molluscs).

Beluga—sturgeons and whales.

Benthonic—flora and fauna found at sea bottom.

Biotype—all the individuals of like genotype.

Blastem—the primordium of an organ.

Blastula—a hollow ball of embryonic cells.

Brachiation—the ability to travel about by use of the arms, as in apes.

Brachyodont—browsing.

Brachiopod—a phylum of animals possessing an arm and foot and resembling a mussel, but having dorsoventral valves.

Braconidae—a group of entomophagous insects (Hymenoptera).

Branchial—having to do with gills.

Buccal—pertaining to the mouth.

Byblis—a carnivorous plant of the Lentibularaceae.

Caecum—the first portion of the large bowel.

Caenogenesis—embryonic characters which become adult characters prematurely by acceleration of maturation of the embryo.

Calamostachys—one of a class of fossil Equisitales of the Calamarieae.

Callianassa—a member of the Rhizocephala parasitizing Galathea and Porcellana.

Callopterus—a ganoid fish of the Eugnathidae.

Caper—an herb family which includes the spider plant.

Carabidae—ground-beetles.

Carbohydrate—one of the three basic constituents of food, together with fats and proteins. It is composed of atoms of carbon, oxygen, and hydrogen.

Caries—decay of teeth.

Carotin—a yellow pigment which is a precursor of vitamin A.

Carettochelys—a family of turtles with no bony shield, the shell covered with soft skin and the neck not retractile.

Catalyst—an agent capable of accelerating a chemical reaction without being itself involved in that process.

Catarrhine—monkeys with nostrils close together, oblique and directed downwards. They have opposable thumbs on all 4 limbs.

242

Caytoniales—subangiosperms from the English Jurassic—perhaps really gymnosperms.

Ceanothus—the California lilac.

Cephalopod—an order of molluscs including the octapus, and squid, having a head with tentacles.

Cerambyx—a type of beetle whose larvae bore in wood.

Ceratodus—a Sirenoid lungfish, with one lung, found in Queensland.

Cestode—a flatworm of the tapeworm type.

Cetacea—whales.

Characin—a type of sea fish.

Chelate—claw-like.

Chelonea—turtles.

Chevrotain—a small musk deer.

Chiroptera—bats.

Chlorophyll—the green pigment of green plants.

Chordate—creatures having a notochord.

Chromatophore—a pigment cell or group of cells which, under sympathetic control, can produce a colour change.

Chromosome—a rod or thread of the nuclear chromatin.

Chrysalis—the resting phase of an insect, between the larval and the adult form.

Cichlid—a teleost fish family which shelters the eggs and young in the mouth.

Ciliary muscle—surrounds the iris of the eye at its margin and controls the sphericity of the lens.

Ciliate—having cilia, hair-like vibrating organs, usually assisting in locomotion.

Cirripedes—a class of marine animals of the Annulosa, including the barnacles and acorn-shells.

Cloaca—the common exit of the bowel and bladder in birds and reptiles.

Clostridium—a genus of bacilli which are usually anaerobic and form clostridial or plectridial spore forms.

Coccyx—small fused vertebrae at the lower end of the spine.

Coelacanth—a fish, no longer held to be extinct, having a hollow spine

Coelenterata—sponges.

Coelom—the cavity of the ovum just after fertilization, formed by separation of the entoderm.

Coelurosaur—an extinct dinosaur with hollow bones.

Coenocyte—a tiny plant organism, not divided into separate cells by cell walls.

Coleoptera—the beetles.

Colubrine—serpentine.

Commensal—living at the same table.

Communalism—living together to the disadvantage of none.

Compositae—a family of Asterales, often with crowded florets.

Copepod—forked-tail animals of the Class Crustacea found in both fresh and salt water.

Crepis—a group of the Compositae (plants).

Crinoid—a class of sea animals, the sea lilies.

Crossopterygian—an extinct order of fish.

Cryptic species—a genetically separate species whose physical differences are not obvious.

Cruciferae—plants having flowers with four petals.

Cryptopsophis—an amphibian of the Family Coeciliidae with only one series of teeth in the lower jaw.

Cryptoniscidae—parasitic arthropods, found on Rhizocephala, whose adult female has no trace of crustacean affinity.

Cucujo—a bupestrid beetle.

Culex—a genus of mosquitoes.

Cyanophyceae—the blue algae.

Cyclops—having no heart.

Cyclostome—a class of Vertebrates with a circular mouth, including the lamprey and hagfish.

Cynipidae—insects that are entomophagus or gall-forming, the latter type attacking oaks particularly.

Cyperaceae—a family of grass-like herbs, usually growing in marshy places.

Cyprinodont—a teleost fish bearing live offspring.

Cysticercus—the larval form of certain tapeworms.

Daphnia—the laurels.

Datura—the cactuses.

Dicotyledon—a type of plant having two seed-leaves.

Digitograde—walking on the toes.

Dinoflagellate—a tiny tailed alga, invisible to the naked eye.

Diplacus—a genus of Dipsacaseae, including the teasel.

Diptera—two-winged flies.

D N A—desoxyribonucleic acid.

Drepanophycus—a Lower Devonian plant whose stem only is known. It has a protostele.

Drosophila—a fruit-fly widely used in mutation studies.

Echeveria—a genus of flowering plants with the corolla strongly five-angled.

Echinoid—referring to a class of animals containing the sea-urchins and sand dollars.

Ecology—the study of the habits of living forms in relation to their environment.

Ectoderm—the outside layer of the three primitive germ layers found just after fertilization of the ovum.

Ectoloph—the mean size of a molar tooth.

Edentate—a mammalian order with no teeth in the front part of the mouth, and what teeth there are have no enamel.

Elasmobranch—sharks or dogfish. These fish have a cartilagenous skeleton, placoid scales and a heterocercal tail.

Elver—a young eel.

Enterovirus—a bowel-inhabiting virus.

Entoderm—the innermost layer of the three primitive germ layers formed just after fertilization of the ovum.

Entomophagous—creatures which eat insects.

Enzyme—a protein catalyst formed by living cells but able to act apart from them.

Ependyma—the layer of cells lining the canals of the brain and spinal cord.

Epicaridae—parasitic arthropods with separate sexes, the dwarf males living attached to the females.

Epiglottis—a cartilage at the root of the tongue designed to cover the glottis while swallowing.

Epiphylluma—belongs to the epiphyllous algae and lichens.

Epilobium—a genus of Oenotheraceae.

Eschericheae—bacteria in the bowel of normal animals and man which ferment carbohydrates but do not produce acetyl-methyl-carbinol.

Euphorbiaceae—a plant genus found in the Mauritius, India, Portugal, etc.

F$_2$—the second generation of hybrid forms after a cross.

Faeces—bowel excreta.

Filaria—a genus of threadworms responsible for lymphatic obstruction and thus for elephantiasis.

Fistula—an abnormal opening from one body cavity to another or to the outside.

Flagellum—the tail on such small creatures as bacteria or protozoa.

Foetus—an embryo.

Foraminifera—belonging to the class Rhizopoda or Sarcodina of the Protozoa. Usually marine, with pseudopodia and shell.

Foramen magnum—the opening at the base of the skull through which the spinal cord connects with the brain.

Fovea—a small pit in the thinnest part of the macula of the eye, which has no rods but only long and slender cones.

Fungus—parasitic or saprophytic cryptogams having no chlorophyll, such as mushrooms or molds.

Gall—an excrescence on trees, especially on oaks, produced by insects.

Gallinaceous—pertaining to fowl or hens.

Gallinula—the moorhen.

Gallus—the genus of fowls.

Gametophyte—the gamete-forming phase in the alternation of plant generations—the sexual phase.

Ganoid—the scaled fishes.

Gasterosiphon—a close relative of Mucronalia which attacks holothurians.

Gastraea—a postulated primitive sac-like animal having only the ectodermal and entodermal cell layers.

Gastropoda—a Class of Mollusca having a stomach and foot, such as snails.

Gecko—a species of house lizard.

Gene—a factor in the germ cell existing in pairs, one half derived from each parent, and thus constituting the unit of heredity.

Genlisea—a tropical American-African genus of Leutibulariacea.

Genotype—the genetic constitution of the individual.

Gilia—a genus of the Polemoniaceae (plants).

Gingko—the gingko trees.

Glomerulus—a capillary network in the kidney, contained in Bowman's capsule.

Gnathidae—a suborder of the Isopoda, parasitic on fish for a part of their life cycles, later living free in colonies.

Goby—a small fish whose ventral fins form a disk or sucker.

Gonococcus—the bacterium responsible for gonorrhoea.

Gordian worms—long, thin worms similar to Filariae, without a mouth or anterior intestine, and with a muscular system unlike that of nematodes.

Gramineae—the grasses.

Greensand—a layer of sandstone composed largely of glauconite and related to the gault under the Chalk.

Gregarine—pertaining to sporozoa which are usually parasitic on insects, crabs, etc.

Guanine—a leucomain which is a decomposition product of nucleins.

Gymnosperms—plants whose seeds are not enclosed in a true ovary. Naked seeded.

Haemocera—a genus of Monstrillidae (copepods) which is a parasite on Salmacina.

Haemoglobin—the red pigment in mammalian blood.

Haemolytic—able to decompose red blood cells.

Haplochitonidae—Pike-like fishes representing the salmonoids in the southern hemisphere.

Hebes—southern species of the Rhinanthoideae.

Heliamphora—a genus of South American pitcher plants.

Helix—a genus which includes the common snail.

Hemiptera—the true bugs, where the base of the sucking beak is far forward on the head.

Hermaphrodite—a bisexual creature.

Holothurian—a Class of Echinoderms, the sea cucumbers.

Homo—the genus man.

Homology—tissues or organs having the same relation, particularly when the primary embryonic layers are used as the reference.

Homoplasy—convergence of structures.

Hutchinsonella—a cephalocarid—trilobitoid crustacean of vast age.

Hydrozoa—a class of fresh water Coelenterates.

Hyla—a tree frog.

Hymenolepis—a genus of the Hymenolepidae worms, parasitic on mammals and birds.

Hymenoptera—an order of insects having four membranous wings.

Hyoid bone—a small bone in the front of the neck on which the tongue is based.

Hypericuna—St. John's wort—in the Family Hypericaceae.

Hypha—the thread-like filament of fungal mycelium.

Hypertely—the overdevelopment of adaptational features.

Hypocereal—having the notochord terminating in the lower lobe of the caudal fin.

Hypsodont—grazing.

Hystricomorph—the porcupines.

Ichneumon fly—a small parasitic hymenopterous insect which lays eggs in or on larvae.

Ichthyophys—a vermiform amphibian without legs, with cycloid scales in the skin and distinct or concealed eyes.

Insectivore—an order of insect-eating vertebrates.

Invertebrate—an animal without a backbone.

Isopod—an order of crustaceans whose feet are of equal length and move in the same direction, e.g. the wood-louse.

Jumping Blenny—a teleost fish found near the shores of temperate and tropical seas.

Killifish—a carnivorous teleost fish.

Lacertila—the lizards.

Lamarckian—the view sponsored by the French zoologist, Lamarck, that acquired characters are heritable.

Lamellibranchiata—the molluscs having gills, including oysters, mussels etc.

Lamelliform—pertaining to plates or layers piled one on the other.

Lanugo—the fine, fuzzy hair on the skin of the newborn human.

Lastroea—a genus of the wood-ferns (Dryopteris).

Leguminosae—plants bearing pods, such as peas and beans.

Leishman body—a stage through which the Leishmania trypanosome passes in its insect host.

Lemur—a nocturnal anthropoid animal related to the monkey—principally seen in Madagascar.

Lentibulariaceae—a family of carnivorous plants with only five genera.

Leptocephalus—an eel with a transparent body and colourless blood.

Leptothrix—an iron-metabolizing bacterium.

Lepus—the hares.

Leucosoleniidae—a genus of homocoelous sponges.

Liliaceae—the lilies.

Lingual tonsil—lymphoid tissue on the base of the tongue.

Linum—a genus of the Linaceae, the flax.

Lipid—heterogeneous compounds soluble in fats and their solvents, and including fats, waxes, sterols, etc.

Longicornes—beetles having very long antennae.

Lycopsid—a group of cryptograms consisting of Lycopodiales and Equisetales.

Madia—the tarweeds.

Mallophaga—a parasitic group of apodous insects which devour wool, hair, feathers, etc.

Malpighian corpuscle—a nodule of lymphoid tissue in the spleen about the smaller arteries. Also used for a renal structure.

Mammal—a vertebrate with breasts for suckling its young.

Mandible—the lower jaw.

Mantis—an orthopterous insect which preys on other insects.

Marsupial—mammals carying their young in a pouch.

Mastigina—protozoa of the class Mastigophora.

Mastoid process—the bony process just behind the ear.

Mauchamp sheep—a sport of the Merino breed.

Medusa—the jelly-fishes.

Melanism—the tendency to darken colour to black or near-black.

Meninges—the membranes covering the brain and spinal cord.

Mesoderm—the medial layer of the three primitive germ layers found just after fertilization of the ovum.

Metapodial—the portion of the foot between the toes and tarsus.

Metazoa—the many celled animals—excluding only the Protozoa.

Miyiasis—lesions caused by parasitic dipterous larvae, whether on the skin or in the bowel.

Mollusc—one of the Mollusca, soft-bodied, hard-shelled invertebrates, like snails, oysters, etc.

Monocotyledon—a plant group characterized by one cotyledon or embryo-lobe.

Monophyletic—all derived from one primal stock.

Monotremata—an order of mammals which lays eggs, such as the duck-bills.

Monotropa—the Indian Pipe plant.

Monster—a congenitally deformed creature.

Mouflon—a wild sheep of the mountains of southern Europe.

Mucronalia—a parasitic gastropod of the Eulinidae attacking sea urchins, starfish and holothurians.

Multituberculata—the suborder Allotheria, all fossil.

Mutation—a sudden sport or alteration which is transmitted genetically thereafter.

Mycetocyte—one of the follicle cells at the posterior pole of the oocyte through which the aphid egg is infected by symbionts.

Myriapoda—a class of the Arthropoda.

Myrmecophilous—favourable to ants.

Myrus—an eel having nostrils in the upper lip.

Myxobacteria—an order of Schizomycetes comprising the slime molds.

Myxomycetes—the slime-molds.

Myxosporidia—an order of Neosporidia, living principally in fishes.

Nascent—being born or created—in process of development.

Nauplius—the earliest larval stage of some shrimps and entomostracan crustaceans.

Nautilus—a small cephalopod whose female has a thin shell and webbed, sail-like arms.

Nematocyst—a stinging cell.

Nematodes—threadworms.

Nemertina—the flat-worms.

Neolithic—the new stone or polished stone age.

Neoteny—the premature maturity of immature forms.

Nereid—a round, segmented worm of the Chaetopoda. Marine.

Neurospora—a pink mold which is a haploid ascomycete.

Nictitating membrane—the third eyelid in birds and some reptiles, etc.—it moves from side to side.

Notochord—the cartilagenous band forming the basis of the spinal column.

Notoungulate—a group of hooved herbivores that flourished in South America.

Nucleoprotein—a constituent of cell nuclei composed of a compound of protein and nuclei acid.

Occipital condyle—the articulation of the base of the skull on the upper end of the spine.

Occipital torus—a rounded edge on the occipital bone near the superior curved line.

Oenothera—the primroses.

Oestrid—the warble flies.

Ontogeny—the development of the individual.

Oolite—a concretion in limestone of small, rounded granules—a geological stratum between the Chalk and the Lias.

Ophidia—the snakes.

Opisthocoelous vertebrate—the different segments of the bony spine have concavities facing backward.

Organ of Rosenmuller—the epoophoron.

Ornithine—diamino-valeric acid, found in bird excreta.

Ornithischia—one of the two great divisions of dinosaurs, those having no teeth in the front of the jaw and having "bird-hips".

Orthogenesis—evolution along straight lines.

Ostracoderm—fossil only—the first vertebrates—jawless.

Ovigerous frena—the egg-carrying folds of cirripedes or barnacles.

Paedomorphosis—embryonic characters appearing in the adult.

Pagurid—a crab.

Palaeolithic—the age of the use of chipped flints.

Palaeontology—the study of fossils.

Palatine tonsil—lymphoid tissue on either side of the throat, usually referred to as "the tonsil".

Pangolin—the scaly ant-eater.

Panniculus—a superficial fascia.

Papilio—the swallowtail butterflies.

Paramoecium—a very common single-celled protozoan found in our ponds.

Parathyroid gland—a set of small glands perched on the thyroid gland, having to do with calcium metabolism.

Passerine—an order of perching and song birds.

Peperomia—a wild pepper-like plant found only in Florida.

249

Pergomorphi—a small fish used commercially for an oil rich in vitamin D.

Peripatus—a velvet worm of the Class Onychophora.

Peristome—the toothed opening of the spore case in the true Mosses.

Petiole—the leaf-stalk.

Phalanx—a single bony segment of an extremity, such as the finger or toe.

Phenotype—the characters of an organism due to the response of genotypic characters to the environment.

Photosynthesis—the capacity of light to build up certain organic substances in plants, usually in the presence of chlorophyll, a green pigment.

Phycocyanin—the blue pigment found in the Cyanophyceae.

Phycomyces—the molds.

Phylogeny—the development of a phylum in the world of living things.

Pieris—the "white" butterflies, usually feeding on the Cruciferae.

Pineal gland—an endocrine gland in the centre of the head, near the pituitary gland.

Pinna—the ear lobe.

Pinus—the pines

Pistil—the female organ of the flower, comprising stigma, style and ovary.

Placenta—the after-birth.

Placoid—plate-like, such as hard scales or dermal teeth.

Plantigrade—walking on the sole.

Plasmodium—a mass of naked protoplasm formed by the aggregation of amoeboid bodies without nuclear fusion.

Platyhelminthes—the flat-worms.

Platypus—the Australian duck-mole or ornithorhynchus.

Platyrrhine monkeys—monkeys whose nostrils are far apart and directed forward or sideways.

Plethodont—a salamander subfamily with amphicoelous vertebrae and 4 or 5 toes.

Pneumococcus—the bacterium responsible for lobar pneumonia.

Poeciliidae—teleost fish of the family Cyprinodontidae.

Polarity—the property of any body which has two ends of opposite qualities.

Polemonium—a family of the Tubiflorae (plants).

Polychaeta—worms with bristle-like feet, of class Chaetopoda.

Polycirrus—an annelid.

Polydactyl—having many digits.

Polygordius—a marine worm of the class Archiannelidae.

Polyphyletic—having more than one origin from different major divisions of the animal or plant kingdom.

Polyploidy—where the chromosome number is reduplicated and has several times the normal haploid gametic number.

Polysaccharide—a carbohydrate series having more than three molecules of saccharides, comprising starches, dextrins, glycogen, gums, cellulose, etc.

Polystomum—a monogenetic fluke found in the urinary bladder of the frog—belongs to the trematodes.

Porifera—a phylum of porous animals to which sponges belong.

Porphyrin—one of a group of iron-free or magnesium-free pyrrole derivatives forming the base of the respiratory pigment of plants and animals.

Potto—the West-African lemur or kinkajou.

Precipitin—a specific antibody in immune serum which forms a precipitate with its proper antigen.

Primate—the highest order of mammals, including apes and man.

Prognathism—protrusion of the lower jaw.

Prostatic vesicula—the sinus pocularis.

Proteae—a type of straight rod bacteria in the bowel.

Protein—one of the three basic food constitients, together with fats and carbohydrates. It is made of many and very complex molecules, composed of chains of various amino-acids.

Pseudomonas—a genus of bacteria which is saprophytic and pigment-producing.

Psilophyton—a group of prairie plants.

Pterosaur—the pterodactyls or flying reptiles of the Mesozoic.

Pterylosis—the feather arrangement.

Puccinia—the rusts (Basidiomycetes).

Pupate—the act of entering the pupa or chrysalis—a phase in the metamorphosis of moths and butterflies.

Pylorus—the sphincter at the distal end of the stomach.

Quercus—the oaks.

Quadrate bone—the bone with which the lower jaw articulates in birds, reptiles, amphibians and fishes.

Rana—a genus of frogs.

Raptores—an order of birds of prey including the eagle, hawk, owl, etc.

Ratites—the flightless birds like the ostrich, emu, etc. having a breast bone that has no keel.

Refraction—the bending of light at the boundary between media of different densities.

Retina—the vascular, pigmented membrane at the back of the cavity in the eyeball.

Rickettsiae—a group of bacteria-like microorganisms parasitic on arthropods and difficult to culture apart from their hosts.

R N A—ribonucleic acid.

Rodent— a vertebrate of the order Rodentia with strong incisor teeth but no canines.

Rosaceae—the roses.

Rubisceae—a family of Caprifoliales, annual and perennial herbs, shrubs and trees.

Rotifera—a phylum of wheel animals.

Salmo—the trout, salmon and char fishes.

Salmonella—a bacterium found in acute inflammations of the bowel.

Scarabidae—the chafer-beetles.

Scorpionidae—the scorpion family.

Scrophularia—a family of plants of the order Polemoniales.

Selachian—pertaining to the shark or dogfish family.

Sepal—a leaf of the calyx at the base of the flower.

Sepia—the cuttle-fish.

Sibling—offspring of the same parents—but not at the same birth.

Simian diastema or gap—the gap seen in monkeys and apes between the canine tooth and the first premolar.

Siphonales—algae.

Sirenia—sea-cows or manatees.

Sitaris—a European genus of blister beetle or oil beetle. It preys on solitary bees.

Solenocyte—slender club-shaped tubular flagellated cells connected with the nephridia of some Polychaetes, Trochelminthes and Amphioxus.

Solenodon—the tuatera.

Spiracle—a breathing-hole in animals. The blow-hole of cetaceans.

Spirochaete—a spiral-shaped or corkscrew-like bacterium.

Sporophyte—the diploid spore-producing phase in the alternation of plant generations.

Stamen—the male organ of flowering plants and therefore the organ giving pollen.

Staphylinidae—beetles ranging from carnivorous to phytophagous forms, having an exposed abdomen.

Staphylococcus—a bacterium occurring as Gram-positive spheres, arranged in irregular groups or short chains, commonly found in abscesses, etc.

Stigma—the top of the pistil or female organ of flowers.

Stipule—a small leaf-like appendage at the base of a leaf-stem.

Stolon—the runner of such a plant as the strawberry.

Stoma—a breathing pore on the under side of leaves.

Stomodaeum—the ectoderm-lined portion of the alimentary canal.

Streptomycin—an antibiotic isolated from soil, with broad-spectrum qualities.

Strobilus—a cone.

Stromatolites—fossils probably produced by stone algae.

Suctorian—a cyclostomous, sucking-mouthed fish.

Sulci—fissures on the surface of the brain.

Supraorbital ridge—a ridge of bone over the eye orbits.

Sus—the pigs.

Symbiosis—living together in mutual benefit.

Syrinx—the lower larnyx or song-organ of birds.

Tachinid—pertaining to flies of the order Diptera which are parasitic on other insects.

Talpa—the moles.

Taxonomy—biological classification.

Tegmen—pertaining to the skin.

Tenrec—a tailless, hedgehog-like insectivore of Madagascar.

Terebratuloids—Brachiopods or lamp-shells which have hinges and a blind gut.

Termitophile—friendly to termites.

Test— the shell or hard covering of an animal.

Thompsonia—a gregarious parasite of the Rhizocephala, usually attacking corals and Alpheidae.

Thymus gland—a ductless gland near the base of the neck.

Thyroid gland—an endocrine gland in the front of the neck near the larnyx, controlling the metabolic rate of the body.

Tinamou—a South American game bird resembling our quail.

Trachea—a breathing-tube.

Trematode—a flatworm type which includes the flukes.

Trichosurus—a genus of phalangers.

Triconodonta—animals having a 3-cusped tooth with the cusps all in one plane.

Trilobite—an extinct Palaeozoic crustacean having its body divided into three lobes.

Trypanosome—a blood parasite responsible for such disease as sleeping sickness.

Tuatera—Sphenodon, the only living representative of the order Rhyncocephalia—found only in New Zealand.

Tunicate—the sea-squirts or other forms of Urochorda.

Turacin—a red pigment from the feathers of an African bird, the turakoo.

Uncinate process—the hook-like process on the ribs.

Ungulata—mammals with hooves.

Urea—a soluble nitrogenous excretory product found in urine.

Uric acid—the end-product of nucleic acid breakdown in mammals.

Urodeles—amphibians keeping their tails as adults.

Vermiform appendix—what everyone calls his "appendix". It looks worm-like and therefore is "vermiform".

Veronica—the Speedwells of the Family Schrophulariaeceae.

Vertebrate—having a spinal column.

Virus—the tiniest discrete form of living matter. It is not stopped by a porcelain filter, as is a bacterium.

Viverridae—civets and genets.

Xenocoeloma—a parasite of polycirrus; the only hermaphroditic copepod.

Xiphophorus—a small fish with a peculiar sword-like tail.

Zea-Tripsacum—the maize family.

REFERENCES

(1) Simpson, G. G.—The Major Features of Evolution, Columbia University Press, New York, 1953.

  see also - Chapter in Genetics, Palaeontology and Evolution, ed. by G. L. Jepsen, E. Mayr, G. G. Simpson, Princeton University Press, Princeton, N.J., 1949, p. 205 et seq.

  and - Evolution and Geography, Condon Lectures, U. of Oregon, 1953.

(2) Gregory, W. K.—Chapter in Studies on Fossil Vertebrates, ed. by T. S. Westoll, University of London, Athlone Press, 1958, p. 59.

(3) Carter, G. S.—Animal Evolution, Sidgwick and Jackson, Ltd., London, 1951.

(4) Sonneborn, T. M.—The Species Problem, ed. by E. Mayr, Pub. #50 of the A.A.A.S., Washington, D.C., p. 155, 1957.

(5) Paulin, R.—Nature 184:1387, 1959.

(6) Keene, W. W.—I Believe in God and Evolution, 4th ed. Rev., J.B. Lippincott Co., Phila., 1925.

(7) Kelly, H. B.—A Scientific Man and the Bible, Harper Bros. Ltd., New York, 1925.

(8) Glaessner, M. F.—Nature 183:1472, 1959.

(8) Axelrod, D.—Science 128:7, 1958.

(10) Brough, J.—Chapter in Studies on Fossil Vertebrates, ed. by T. S. Westoll, University of London, The Athlone Press, 1958, p. 16 et seq.

(11) Smith, H. W.—From Fish to Philosopher, Little, Brown and Co., Boston, 1953.

(12) Dewar, D.—Difficulties of the Evolution Theory, London, Edward Arnold and Co. 1931.

  see also - Journal of Trans, Victoria Institute 64:120, 1932.

(13) Wood, A. E.—Evolution 11:417, 1957.

(14) Seward, A. C.—Plant Life through the Ages, Cambridge, the University Press, 1931.

(15) Darrah, W. C.—Textbook on Palaeobotany, D. Appleton-Century Co., New York and London, 1939.

(16) Wald, G.—Scientific American 191:45, 1954.

(17) Miller, S. L. and Urey, H. C.—Science 130:245, 1959.

(18) Crick, F. H. C.—Chapter in the Biological Replication of Macromolecules, Symposia of the Society for Experimental Biology #12, Cambridge, The University Press, 1958, p. 138.

(19) Bendich, A.; Pahl, H. B.; Rosenkranz, H.S.; and Rosoff, M.—Chapter in the Biological Replication of Macromolecules, Symposia of the Society for Experimental Biology #12, Cambridge, The University Press, 1958.

(20) Beadle, G. W.—Science 129:1715, 1959.

(21) de Nouy, L.—Human Destiny, Longmans, Green and Co., New York, London, Toronto, 1947.

(22) Muller, H. J.—Chapter in Genetics, Palaeontology and Evolution, ed. by G. L. Jepsen, E. Mayr and G. G. Simpson, 1949, Princeton University Press, Princeton New Jersey, p. 421 et seq.

(23) Cameron, T. W. M.—Parasites and Parsitism, London: Methuen and Co., New York: John Wiley and Sons, 1956.

(24) Stanley, W. M.—Science 128:906, 1958.
see also - Virus Symposium, Mod. Medicine of Canada 13:27, 1958.

(25) Thimann, K. W.—The Life of Bacteria, MacMillan Co., New York, 1955.

(26) Nicol, H.—Microbes by the Million, Penguin Books, Middlesex, England and New York, 3rd Ed. Rev., 1945.

(27) Oginsky, E. L. and Umbreit, W. W.—Introduction to Bacterial Physiology, W. H. Freeman, San Francisco, 1954.

(28) Fenner, F.—Brit. Med. Bull. 15:240, 1959.

(29) Jarwetz, E.; Melnick, I. L. and Adelberg, E. A.—Review of Medical Microbiology, Lange Med. Pub., Los Altos, Calif. 1954.

(30) Lamb, I. M.—Scientific American 201:144, 1959.

(31) Baron, L. S; Spilman, W. M. and Carey, W. F.—Science 130:566, 1959.

(32) Braun, W.—Bacterial Genetics, W. B. Saunders Co., Philadelphia and London, 1953.

(33) Burkholder, P. R.—Science 129:1457, 1959.

(34) Cannon, H. G.—The Evolution of Living Beings, Thomas, Springfield, Ill., 1958.

(35) De Beer, G. R. and Swinton, W. E.—Chapter in Studies on Fossil Vertebrates, ed. T. S. Westoll, University of London, The Athlone Press, 1958, p. 1 et seq.

(36) Sinnott, E. W. and Wilson, K. S.—Botany, Princples and Problems, 5th ed. 1955, McGraw-Hill Book Co., New York, Toronto, London.

(37) Stone, B. S. and Yamaki, T.—Science 129:807, 1959.

(38) De Beer, G. R.—Embryos and Ancestors, Rev. Ed., Oxford, Clarendon Press, 1951.

(39) Smith, J. M. —The Theory of Evolution, Penguin Books, 1958.

(40) Arey, L. B.—Development Anatomy. Sixth Ed., W. B. Saunders Co., Philadelphia and London, 1954.

(41) Ballantyne, N. W.—Manual of Antenatal Pathology and Hygiene Wm. Green and Sons, Edinburgh, 1904, vol. 2, pp. 98-100

(42) Bill, A. H.—J. Am. Med. Assoc. 166:1429, 1958.

(43) Brain, R.—Lancet 2:857, 1957.

(44) Allee, W. C.—Chapter in The Nature of the World and of Man, ed. by H. H. Newman, Garden City Publishing Co., Garden City, New York, 1927, p. 260 et seq.

(45) Wald, G.—Science 128:1401, 1958.
see also - Chapter in Modern Ideas on Spontaneous Generation, Annals N.Y. Acad. Sci. 69:352, 1957.

(46) Packard, G. H.—Creation by Evolution, ed. by Francis Mason, New York, The MacMillan Co., 1928, p. 34 et seq.

(47) Millot, J. and Anthony, J.—Review of Anatomie de Latimeria Chalumnae (1958) in Nature 183:566, 1959.

(48) Thomson, J. A.—Concerning Evolution, Yale U. Press, New Haven, U.S.A. 1925.

(49) Davis, D.D.—Chapter in Genetics, Palaeontology and Evolution, ed. by G. L. Jepsen, E. Mayr, G. G. Simpson, Princeton University Press, Princeton, N.J., 1949, p. 64 et seq.

(50) Scott, W. B. —Chapter in Creation by Evolution, ed. by F. Mason, New York, The MacMillan Co., 1928, p. 8 et seq.

(51) Wallace, A. R.—The Geographical Distribution of Animals, 2 vols., New York, Harper and Bros., 1876.

(52) Wigglesworth, V. B.—Scientific American 200:100, February, 1959.

(53) Quay, W. B.—Science News Letter, May 11, 1957.

(54) Ruud, J. T.—Nature 173.848, 1954.

(55) Pycraft, W. P.—Camouflage in Nature, 2nd Rev. Ed., Hutchinson and Co., London, 1925.

(56) Poulton, E.B.—Chapter in Creation by Evolution, ed. by Francis Mason, New York, The MacMillan Co., 1928, p. 174 et seq.
   see also - The Colours of Animals, New York, D. Appleton and Co., 1890.

(57) Dobzhansky, T.—Am. Scientist 45:381, 1957.

(58) Lull, P. S.—Organic Evolution, New York, The MacMillan Co., 1917.

(59) Kershaw, W. E.; Wright, C. A. and Mattingly, P. F.—participants in Symposium on Evolution of Host-Parasite Relationships at B.A.A.S.—see Nature 184:760, 1959.

(60) Caullery, J.—Parasitism and Symbiosis, transl. by M. Lysaght, Sidgwick and Jackson, Ltd., London, 1952.

(61) Wheeler, W. M.—Social Life among the Insects, Constable and Co., London, Bombay, Sydney, 1922.

(62) Wheeler, W .M.—Chapter on Ants in Creation by Evolution, ed. Francis Mason, New York, MacMillan Co., 1928, p. 210 et seq.

(63) Crompton, J.—The Hunting Wasp, Collins, London, 1948.

(64) Fabre, J. H.—The Wonders of Instinct, T. Fisher Unwin Ltd., London, 1918.
   see also - Book of Insects, Hodder and Stoughton, London, n.d.

(65) Muesbeck, C. F. W.—Science 127:434, 1958.

(66) Gates, R.R.—Human Ancestry, Harvard University Press, Cambridge, Mass., 1948.

(67) Hooton, E. A.—Apes, Men and Morons, New York, G. P. Putnam's Sons, 1937.
   see also - Up from the Ape, The MacMillan Co., New York, Rev. Ed. 1946.

(68) Weitz, B.—J. Hygiene 50:275, 1952.
(69) Mourant, A. E.—The Distribution of the Human Blood Groups, C. C. Thomas, Springfield, Illinois, 1954.
(70) Bird, G. W. G.—Nature 184:109, 1959.
(71) Witschi, E.—Science 130:372, 1959.
(72) Kaplan, N. O.; Ciotti, M. M.; Hamolsky, M. and Bieber, R. E.—Science 131.392, 1960.
(73) Burton, M.—Illustrated London News, August 12, 1954, p. 302.
- Ibid, November 1, 1958, p. 760, June 23, 1956, p. 786.
- Ibid, March 8, 1958, p. 392.
- Ibid, January 11, 1958, p. 64; May 17, 1958, p. 832; January 4, 1958, p. 28; November 9, 1958, p. 952.
(74) Roberts, M.—The Serpent's Fang, London, Eveleigh Nash and Grayson, 1930.
(75) Hingston, R. W. G.—The Meaning of Animal Colour and Adornment, London, Edward Arnold and Company, 1933
(76) Cott, H. B.—Adaptive Colouration in Animals, Methuen and Co., London, 1957.
(77) Allen, G.—The Colour-Sense, Houghton, Osgood and Co., Boston, 1879.
(78) Leppik, E. E.—Evolution 10:421, 1956.
(79) Acworth, B.—Butterfly Miracles and Mysteries, Eyre and Spottiswoode, London, 1947.
(80) Crompton, J.—The Spider, Collins, London, 1950.
(81) Haskins, C. P.—Of Ants and Men, Geo. Allen and Unwin Ltd., London, 1947.
(82) Donisthorpe, H. St. J. K.—British Ants: their Life-History and Classification, London, 2nd Ed. Rev., 1927.
(83) Jordan, D. S. and Kellogg, V. L.—Evolution and Animal Life, New York, D. Appleton and Company, 1908.
(84) Dice, L. R.—Natural Communities, U. of Michigan Press, Ann Arbor, Michigan, 1952.
(85) von Frisch, K.—Bees, Cornell University Press, Ithaca, New York, 1950.
(86) Shipley, A. E.—Chapter in Creation by Evolution, ed. by F. Mason, New York, MacMillan Co., 1928, p. 186 et seq.
(87) Graebner, T.—Evolution, 2nd Rev. Ed., Northwestern Publishing House, Milwaukee, 1922.
(88) Tinbergen, N.—The Study of Instinct, Oxford, The Clarendon Press, 1951.
(89) Hess, E. H.—Science 130:133, 1959.
(90) Woodbury, A. M.—Principles of General Ecology, New York, Toronto, The Blakiston Co., Inc. 1954.
(91) Verwey, J.—quoted by Tinbergen, p. 155 (see #88 above).
(92) Bostock, M.—Evolution 10:421, 1956.
(93) Kettlewell, H. B. D.—Nature 183:918, 1959.
see also - Scientific American 200:48, March, 1959.
(94) Huxley, J.—Life, June 30, 1952, p. 67.

(95) Gager, C. S.—Chapter in Creation by Evolution, ed. by F. Mason, New York, MacMillan Co., 1928, p. 37 et seq.

(96) De Laubenfels, O. J.—Science 130:97, 1959.

(97) Clausen, J.—Stages in the Evolution of Plants Species, Cornell University Press, Ithaca, New York, 1951.

(98) Sprague, T. A.—Chapter in The New Systematics, ed. by J. Huxley, Oxford, Clarendon Press, 1940, p. 435.

(99) Allan, H. H.—Idem, p. 515.

(100) Crane, M.B.—Idem., p. 529.

(101 Kellogg, V. L.—American Insects, 3rd Ed. Rev., New York, Henry Holt and Co., 1908.

(102) Darwin, C.—Insectivorous Plants, London, John Murray, 1875.

(103) Lloyd, F. E.—The Carnivorous Plants, Chronica Botanica Co., Waltham, Mass., 1942.

(104) Wood Jones, F. W.—Unscientific Excursions, London, Edward Arnold and Co., 1934.

(105) Merson Davies, L.—The Bible and Modern Science, 3rd Ed., Pickering and Inglis, London, Glasgow and Edinburgh, n.d. (after 1925).

(106) O'Toole, G. B.—The Case against Evolution, New York, The MacMillan Co., 1925.

(107) Lunn, A. H. and Haldane, J. B. S.—Science and the Supernatural, Copyright 1935, Sheed and Ward, Inc., New York, N.Y.

(108) Walls, G. L.—The History of the Human Eye, Ciba Symposia 5:1586, November 1943.

(109) Shute, E. V.—Nature 143:161, 1939.

(110) Wald, G.—Life and Light, Scientific American 201:92, 1959 (October)

(111) Smith, A. V.—Biol. Rev. 33:197, 1958.

(112) Griffin, D. R. and Grinnell, A. D.—Science 128:145, 1958.

(114) de Beaufort, L. F.—Zoology of the Land and Inland Waters, Sidgwick and Jackson Ltd., London, 1951.

(114) Gadow, H. F.—The Wanderings of Animals, The Cambridge University Press, England, 1913.

(115) Willey, J.—Convergence in Evolution, London, John Murray, 1911.

(116) Kellogg, W. N.—Science 128:982, 1958.

(117) Romer, A. S.—Chapter in Genetics, Palaeontology and Evolution, ed. by G. L. Jepsen, E. Mayr and G. G. Simpson, 1949, Princeton University Press, Princeton, New Jersey, 103 et seq.

see also - Chapter in The Nature of the World and of Man, ed. by H. H. Newman, Garden City Publishing Co., Garden City, New York, 1927, p. 304 et seq.

(118) Geiling, E. M. K.—Note in Med. Alumni Bull., U. of Chicago, 1958.

(119) Raymond, P. E.—Prehistoric Life, Cambridge, U.S.A., The Harvard University Press, 1958.

(120) Miller, H. J.—Chapter in Genetics, Palaeontology and Evolution ed. by G. L. Jepsen, E. Mayr and G. G. Simpson, 1949, Princeton University Press, Princeton, New Jersey, p. 421 et seq.

(121) Scott, W. B.—Chapter in Creation by Evolution, ed. by F. Mason, New York, The MacMillan Co., 1928, p. 81 et seq

(122) Bateson, W.—Science 55:55 and 373, 1922.

(123) Voss, G.; Phillips, C. and Stewart, S. A.—Solving Life Secret of the Sailfish, Nat. Geographic 109:859, 1956.

(124) Carson, R. L.—see Chapter in The Species Problem, ed. by E. Mayr, Pub. #50 of the A.A.A.S., Wash., D.C. p. 23 et seq., 1957.

(125) Darlington, C. D.—Chapter in The New Systematics, ed. by J. Huxley, Oxford, Clarendon Press, 1940, p. 137.

(126) Grant, V.—The Species Problem, ed. by E. Mayr, Pub. #50 of the A.A.A.S., Washington, D.C., p. 39, 1957.

(127) Davidson—see article by Grant above - p. 65.

(128) Imbrie, I.—Ibid, p. 125.

(129) Arkell, W. J. and Moy-Thomas—Chapter in the New Systematics, ed. by J. Huxley, Oxford, The Clarendon Press, 1940, p. 395.
   see also - Evolution 6:449, 1952.

(130) Jones, D. J.—Introduction to Microfossils, Harper and Bros., New York, 1956.

(131) Twenhofel, W. H. and Shrock, R. R.—Invertebrate Palaeontology, McGraw-Hill Book Co., New York and London, 1935.

(132) Sonneborn, T. M.—The Species Problem, ed. by E. Mayr, Pub. #50 of the A.A.A.S., Washington, D.C. p. 155, 1957.

(133) Viret—quoted by G. G. Simpson from notes on a Symposium on Evolution held in Spain, Evolution 10:333, 1956.

(134) Keosian, J.—Science 131:479, 1960.

(135) Chaney, R. W.—Chapter in Genetics, Palaeontology and Evolution, ed. by G. L. Jepsen, E. Mayr and G. G. Simpson, 1949, Princeton University Press, Princeton, New Jersey, p. 190.

(136) Stebbins, G. L.—Idem, p. 229.

(137) Bergen, J. Y. and Davis, B. M.—Principles of Botany, Ginn and Co., Boston, Mass., 1906.

(138) Davis, D. D.—Chapter in Genetics, Palaeontology and Evolution ed. by G. L. Jepsen, E. Mayr, G. G. Simpson, Princeton University Press, Princeton, New Jersey, 1949, p. 64 et seq.

(139) Westoll, T. S.—Idem, p. 121 et seq.

259

(140) Wright, S.—Idem, p. 365 et seq.

(141) Ladd, H. S.—Science 129.69, 1959.

(142) Allee, W. C.—Chapter in the Nature of the World and of Man, ed. by H. H. Newman, Garden City Publishing Co., Garden City, New York, 1927, p. 260 et seq.

(143) Watson, D. M .S.—Chapter in Genetics, Palaeontology and Evolution, ed. by G. L. Jepsen, E. Mayr, G. G. Simpson, Princeton University Press, Princeton, New Jersey, 1949, p. 45 et seq.

(144) Lucas, F. A.—Animals of the Past, Am. Museum of Natural History, Handbook Series #4, 6th Ed. Rev., New York, 1922.

(145) Colman, W. T.—Chapter in New Systematics, ed. by J. Huxley, Oxford, the Clarendon Press, 1938, p. 321, et seq.

(146) Smart, J.—Idem, p. 475, et seq.

(147) Coulter, M. C.—The Nature of the World and of Man, ed. by H. H. Newman, Garden City, New York, p. 216 et seq.

(148) Tucker, B. W.—Chapter in Evolution, ed. by G. R. de Beer, Oxford, the Clarendon Press, 1938, p. 321, et seq.

(149) Lunn, A.—The Flight from Reason, Eyre and Spottiswoode, Ltd. London, 1931.

(150) Clark, W. E.—The Fossil Evidence for Human Evolution, U. of Chicago Press, 1955.

(151) Andrew, R. C.—Meet Your Ancestors, Viking Press, New York, 1945.

(152) Wendt, H.—I Looked for Adam, Weidenfeld and Nicholson, London, England, 1955.

(153) Campbell, B. G.—see Editorial in Brit. Med. J., 2:487, 1959.

(154) Weidenreich, F.—Apes, Giants and Man, U. of Chicago Press, Chicago, 1945.
see also - Some Problems dealing with Ancient Man, Am. Anthropologist 42:375, 1940.

(155) Cave, A. J. E.—Quoted in Time, July 28, 1958, p. 46.

(156) Wormington, H. M.—Ancient Man in North America, 4th Ed. Rev., The Denver Museum of Natural History, Pop. Series #4, 1957, pp. 18, 19, 25, 58, 89 and 196, 246 and 226 et seq.

(157) Macgowan, K.—Early Man in the New World, The MacMillan Co., New York, 1953.

(158) Hrdlcka, A.—Am. J. Physical Anthropology 22:175, 1937.

(159) Krogman, W. M.—Ancient Man, Ciba Symposia 3:790, 1941 and 3:804, 1941.

(160) Keith, A.—New Discoveries Relating to the Antiquity of Man, W. W. Norton and Co., New York, 1929.

(161) Reed, C. A.—Science 130:1629, 1959.

(162) Coon, C. C.—Am. Naturalist 89:257, 1955.

    see also - Paper at the Wenner-Gren Supper Conference, U. of Michigan, April 12, 1957—see memoir #86 of American Anthropologist.

(163) Braidwood, R. J.—Science 127:1419, 1958.

(164) Wechler, J. E.—Am. Anthropologist 56:1003,1954.

(165) Leakey, L. S. B.—Adam's Ancestors, Methuen and Co., London, 1934.

    see also - Illustrated London News, June 28, 1958, p. 1104, and July 5, 1958.

(166) Mayr, E.—The Species Problem, ed. by E. Mayr, Pub. #50 of the A.A.A.S., Washington, D.C., p. iii and pp. 1, 371, 1957.

(167) Dobzhansky, T.—Evolution, Genetics and Man, John Wiley and Sons, New York, and Chapman and Hall Ltd., London, 1955.

    see also - Am. Scientist 45:381, 1957.

(168) Oliver, D. L. and Howell, W. W.—Am. Anthropologist 12:9, 1954.

(169) Weizsacker, C. F.—Reports of Geigy Bicentenary Scientific Day, Basle, Switzerland, June 3, 1958.

(170) Nissen, R.—Idem.

(171) Dobzhansky, T.—Science 127:1091, 1958.

(172) Goodman, N.—Idem, 128:1064, 1958.

(173) Vialleton, L.—Membres et Ceintures des Vertebres Tetrapodes, Paris, Librairie Octave Doin, 1924 (8 Place de l'Odeon)

(174) Stirton, R. A.—Time, Life and Man—New York, John Wiley and Sons, Inc., 1959.

INDEX OF PROPER NAMES

265

272

273

moeosis 204
mold 26, 29, 30, 31
mold (slime) 111
mole 144
molecule 19, 20, 21, 22, 23, 24, 111
mollusc 153, 159, 160, 173, 190
Mollusca 5, 7, 8, 9, 11, 15, 35, 88, 109, 128, 129, 137, 140, 141, 144
Molluscoidea 7, 8
Moloch 143
Monarch butterfly 97
Monema flavescens 135
Monias 154
monkey 11, 43, 57, 68, 78, 79, 131, 142, 152, 153, 157, 159, 225
monkey (catarrhine) 174
monkey (platyrrhine) 174, 196
Monocentras japonicus 68
Monocotyledon 16, 112, 177, 179
Monotremata 154, 159, 171, 172, 174
monotreme 12, 79
Monotropa 90
monster 50
Moraceae 181
mosasaur 172, 193
mosquito 30, 63, 203
mosquito (culex) 63
moss 11, 115, 176, 177
moth 35, 54, 56, 85, 87, 88, 95, 102, 103, 104, 105, 107, 118, 122, 124, 125, 135, 195
moult 125
mouse 53, 103, 143, 203
mouth 59
mucus 63
mudfish 50, 87, 132, 157
Mugil olivaceus 141
Mugilidae 140
mullet 98, 99
Mullerornis 154
Multituberculata 172, 195
muscle 19, 21
mushroom 94
mussel 159
mutation 28, 29, 30, 31, 32, 56, 57, 58, 59, 64, 65, 72, 95, 100, 111, 114, 120, 126, 184, 185, 186, 199, 233
Mutelidae 159
Mutillid wasp 107
mycetocyte 69
Mycorrhiza 68
Mynah 107, 133
Myriapoda 7
Myrmica 74
Myrus 65
Mystococarida 190
Myxostomaria 62

N

Nannippus 199, 200
nascent organ 49, 50, 51, 55, 60
natural selection 8
nauplius 35, 37, 63, 66
Nautilus 8, 36, 90, 128, 141
Neanderthal 208, 211, 212, 213, 214, 215, 217, 218, 221, 222, 223, 224, 225
Nearctic 203
negro 80
nematocyst 64, 134, 144
nematode 68, 119, 134, 144
Nemertina 35
nemin 119
Neolithic 221
Neopilina galatheae 190
Nesocepalus macrolepidotus 86
neoteny 43
nephridium 169, 174
Neptis nemetes 108
nerve 135
Nesomyidae 154
neural tube 58, 59
neuroptera 194
newt 11, 46, 59, 157
niche (ecologic) 161
nictitating membrane 51, 57
nightingale 99
nightjar 106, 172
nightjar (common) 106
nightjar (South American) 160
nipple 55, 126, 174
non-adaptation 136
nostril 56
Nothofagus 161
notochord 41, 51, 58, 191, 192
Nototrema 142
Nubecularia 45
nucleic acid 21, 22, 27
Nucula 8
Nyctibius 106
Nyctimantis 154

O

oak 96
Oberohe 119
Obolella 45
octopus 81
Odynerus 76
oestrid fly 65
Ogodon 155
oil (beetle) 157
oil-bird 53, 135
oil (gland) 171, 172
Olduvai man 207, 208, 211
olfactory nerve 56

279